Iowa's Heritage of Pioneer Family Farms

Family Owned Farms Settled from 1834 to 1864

by Herb Plambeck

For
JERRY BRITT
with My Best Wishes
For Good Health, Good
Fortune, and Good Farming
Herb Plambeck
Sept. 25, 1996
Farm Progress Show

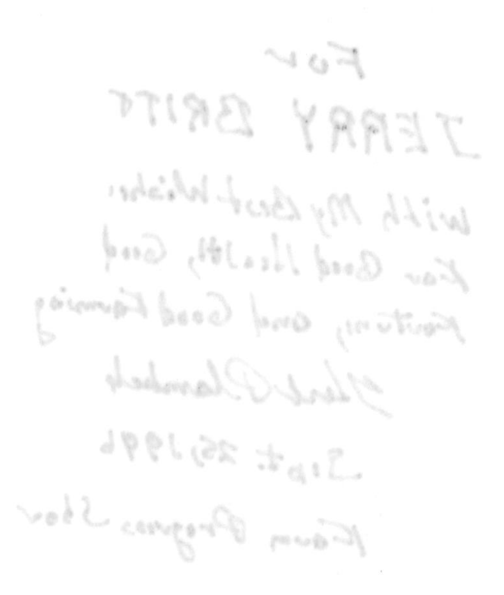

Published by
Sigler Printing & Publishing, Inc.
Ames, Iowa 50010-0887

Library of Congress Catalog Card Number: Applied for
ISBN Number: 1-888223-06-5

This book is dedicated to the memory of Iowa's intrepid pioneer farm families who conquered the prairies and established Iowa's rich rural heritage.

It is also a tribute to those who have followed the pioneers to maintain the family farm and assure the continuation of Iowa's agricultural superiority.

Herb Plambeck

Herb Plambeck

PREFACE

This book was written in 1996 with the hope it would serve as a contribution to the Iowa Sesquicentennial when the entire state celebrated its 150th birthday anniversary.

It is a volume centered on the trials, tribulations, and triumphs of some of Iowa's earliest farm pioneers. They were the intrepid men and women who braved, and ultimately conquered, almost insurmountable odds to establish homes and farms as early as 1834 through 1846, when statehood was achieved, and on into the trying period of the Civil War.

A second volume has also been written featuring the experiences and accomplishments of early settlers across the entire state during the period 1865 through 1895 -- all farms more than 100 years in the same farm family's hands.

Prompted by the Sesquicentennial Commission's search for Iowa's oldest farms and farm families, these books are the result of countless hours of research and writing. They are the end product of visits, calls, correspondence, questionnaires, family albums, and other materials from families whose farm tenure extends to as many as 164 years.

At the conclusion of the statewide search, more than 300 such farms, and their families, with up to a century and a half or more of ownership have been chronicled with 200 farm summaries and more than 90 pictures found in this volume.

Many of Iowa's oldest family farms were established by European natives who had endured long, difficult ocean voyages to reach America-- "The Land of Their Dreams".

Iowa's other early settlers came from many other states east of the Mississippi River as far away as Maine, New York, and Pennsylvania.

Whatever way they came to our state -- by ship, prairie schooner, covered wagon, ox cart, horseback, or even trudging many miles on foot -- all had one goal in mind. That goal and that purpose was to own a parcel of rich Iowa soil and start a new life on the American frontier.

The first settlers to arrive found Indians still roaming the countryside, often begging for food, and on rare occasions, kidnapping a white baby.

The pioneers found the prairie soil and timberlands untouched, clear blue streams with countless fish, and with deer, fox, wolves and other wild game on every side.

Challenges and hardships were encountered at every turn. Guns, axes, hoes, spades, scythes, and other hand tools were a "must". Log, sod, or stone homes had to be built, and woodlands needed to be cleared.

Oxen-drawn breaker plows were first used to turn the prairie ground and unlock the riches of the soil.

Market places for delivering grains, grinding wheat for flour, and buying necessities for the household or the farm were often many miles away.

There were no schools, churches, or doctors' offices. Clothing was often made on a home-spinning wheel.

While hardships were many and challenges great, those dauntless pioneers listed in these books set the stage for Iowa's future national Agricultural dominance. To them, and their descendants, many of us owe a collective debt of sincere gratitude.

ACKNOWLEDGMENTS

No undertaking involving the production of two large books, historical in nature, and about several hundred of Iowa's pioneer farms and their owners, could possibly be done alone.

Without the cooperation of some 325 of those families, there would simply be no way to author the books.

The same is true of Iowa Sesquicentennial officials and those in the Iowa Department of Agriculture and Land Stewardship. Without their support, there could be no books.

To acknowledge all officials on the Sesquicentennial Commission and the Department of Agriculture is out of the question. However, the names of Robert Ray, former Iowa Governor and now the Commission Chairman, and Scott Raecker, the Executive Director, and of Secretary of Agriculture Dale Cochran and two of his associates, Linda Roose and Helen Peterson, must be recognized. Their help and encouragement was most valuable.

Similarly, two folks at Sigler Printing and Publishing of Ames must be singled out. They are Ron McMillen, the president, and Dave Popelka, special projects director, who has shepherded both books through the organizing and publishing process from page 1 to their back covers.

My most heartfelt gratitude, however, must go to the two ladies pictured on this page.

One is my long-suffering wife, Laura, who has not only stood by me every minute through these months of endless challenges, but has also proof read every word, handled countless phone calls, checked sentence structure often, also finding the "right" word, as well as serving as business manager.

The other lady is my longtime secretary "extraordinaire", Ruth Schultz, who has now lived through helping produce a half dozen of my books, masterminding every word on the computer or word processor, catching my occasional errors, and providing the Sigler firm with picture perfect computer copy and discs.

To these two ladies goes my profoundest appreciation.

Laura Plambeck

Ruth Schultz

Sincere thanks also go to Frank Holdmeyer, editor of Wallace's Farmer, and Jerry Perkins, farm editor for the Des Moines Register, and many other editors and broadcasters who have lauded the books so generously. To all of them, I say, "Thanks A Million."

A very special thanks to the John Deere Company for their contribution to the success of this two book set and to their part in shaping the history of Iowa farms.

INTRODUCTION

Iowa's Sesquicentennial was observed in 1996 in countless ways as Iowans throughout the state, and former Iowans all over the nation, noted and celebrated Iowa's 150th year of Statehood.

Virtually every city, town, and village in the state marked the state's 150th birthday in some way or another. Folk festivals, parades, programs, county fairs, church events, farm gatherings and conventions, youth festivities, stock shows, airplane flyovers, wagon trains, radio and television features, magazine and newspaper articles and editorials, horse shows, classic auto and tractor events, art galleries and displays, quilt shows, and hundreds of other events highlighted the Sesquicentennial.

The Iowa Legislature and other government and civic bodies strongly supported the "once in a lifetime" event.

Nor was the celebration limited to Iowa. The renowned Smithsonian Institute in Washington, D.C. included the Iowa Sesquicentennial celebration in a National Folk Festival held on the Washington Mall in late June and early July.

More than a million visitors from all over the world and every state in the nation attended the "IOWA - COMMUNITY STYLE" displays and demonstrations.

Featured were Iowa agriculture, foods, cooking, crafts, quilts, girls' basketball, musical groups, seminars and panel discussions.

Another Sesquicentennial project of special interest to countless Iowa families is the recognition of Iowa pioneer family farms. These farms were established as early as 1834, and in the years before, or soon after, Iowa gained statehood in 1846. More than 300 of them are still in the hands of the same family that originated them so many years ago.

The Iowa Sesquicentennial Commission, with former Governor Robert Ray as Chairman and Scott Raecker as Director, in connection with the Iowa Department of Agriculture and Land Stewardship, with Secretary of Agriculture Dale Cochran in charge, have collaborated to find the oldest Iowa farms where the owners can trace their family lineage back all the way through to the original homestead buyers.

Close to 400 responses were received. Obviously eastern Iowa, where Indian treaties were the first to be signed to make the natives move westward, had the most longtime family farms. However, other intrepid pioneers also loaded their family's household goods and primitive tools on covered wagons and prairie schooners pulled by oxen or horses, to stake claims on the virgin soil farther west. Central Iowa was being settled in the 1850s, and as the Indian population finally crossed the Missouri River to new homes or reservations in Nebraska, Kansas, the Dakotas, and other states further west, hardy Iowa pioneers started breaking extreme western Iowa prairie sod in the 1860s and '70s.

In March of 1996, at a special ceremony in the Iowa Historical Society Building, under the auspices of the Department of Agriculture, ten pioneer farm families, each the oldest in Iowa's nine crop districts, were announced and honored as the oldest family-owned farm in their District, and two state winners were named.

On the following pages, the ten winning families and their pioneer farms are acknowledged, after which the oldest individual Iowa pioneer farms who participated in the search will be summarized in chronological order, along with interesting facts about the families that have maintained them all through these more than 100 years.

Table of Contents

Section One • The Winning Farms

Section Two • Farms 162 to 150 Years Old

Section Three • Farms 149 to 132 Years Old

AN ACKNOWLEDGMENT OF A PIONEER AGRICULTURAL BENEFACTOR:

Iowa's Heritage of Pioneer Family Farms

Section One
The Winning Farms

STATE WINNER
THE SHAFF FARMS OF CLINTON COUNTY
Settled 1837

Heman B. Shaff and his son, John H. Shaff

The Shaff Farms of Clinton County are the source of one of the most fascinating summarizations of an Iowa pioneer farm history -- its trials and triumphs, its challenges and contributions -- the author of this book has ever encountered. In fact, with eight generations of the Shaff family to consider, and 159 years to cover, it could easily be a book within itself.

There can be little wonder why the Shaff family was chosen as one of the two Iowa families honored during the summer of 1996 at the Iowa Sesquicentennial Folklife Festival sponsored by the Smithsonian Institute on the Washington Mall leading to the U.S. Capitol in Washington, D.C.

It all started in 1837 when 19 year old Heman B. Shaff, the son of a German immigrant, left his native Wayne County, New York, home, accompanied by his widowed mother and two younger sisters and a brother, for the almost "unknown" West. Iowa was his ultimate goal. Two covered wagons pulled by two teams of dependable horses were their means of transportation.

It was a long, tedious, tiring journey, and when they finally reached Illinois, young Heman left his mother and siblings to rest with Illinois friends while he proceeded to cross the Mississippi. On looking around at Clinton County's rich soil, he laid claim to 240 acres in Camanche Township, to set the stage for "The Rest of the Story."

Right after registering the claim, Heman returned to the family in Illinois, made sure all was well, then with his brother took their team and wagon to Chicago to earn money as teamsters for several months -- money so essential to purchase the farm he had claimed.

In 1838, after young Heman, now 20, took his family across the river, paid $1.25 an acre to settle his claim, and built a log cabin for a home, he started to break the sod with a cast iron mold board breaker plow. It was tough going.

This was a period when much experimenting with farm tools was going on. Dozens of patents had already been issued to ambitious inventors on plows, broadcast seeders, slotted guard mowers, reapers, and horse-powered threshers. Of course, young Shaff had none of these. All of the planting, cultivating, and harvesting was done by hand.

However, during the winter of 1838-39, Heman heard of a blacksmith named John Deere at Grand Detour, Illinois, who had created a steel plow that could turn the earth smoothly.

It was claimed the new plow, made out of a large rotary steel saw blade, would prevent soil from sticking to the moldboard, called "scouring". Accordingly, in the spring of 1839, young Shaff went to Grand Detour and paid Deere $24 for one of the plows, thus bringing the first steel plow to Iowa. And with that plow, he broke much more ground, which, more than 150 years later, would be officially recognized as one of Iowa's oldest family farms. Today, that plow and another bought in 1840, which marked the beginning of the Shaff family dynasty, remain as treasured items among the family's collection of pioneer memorabilia.

Two of Iowa's rarest plows were handmade by John Deere and purchased by Heman Shaff in 1839 & 1840 at Deere's Grand Detour, Illinois blacksmith shop.

The next year, Heman went back to New York State to marry his boyhood sweetheart, Mary Russell, and bring her back to their log cabin in Iowa. Six children came from that union, four daughters and two sons. The youngest of these children was born in 1851 and named John Heman.

John Heman Shaff married Jennie Drips in 1873, and they had a family of five -- a daughter and four sons. In 1904, John and Jennie became the second owners of the rapidly growing farm. John and his father had actually already gotten the farm up to 1400 acres, of which 1000 acres was under cultivation. John and his father were instrumental in getting a railroad to serve their area in the 1880s, and they gave land for it. One station, known as the Shaffton Station, was built in 1884 and continued through 1925. In the early years, the Shaffs also gave land for a school that served the area up to

1960 and at one time had an enrollment of 80 pupils.

Long before rural telephone lines were built, John Shaff privately undertook the building of a 12 mile long telephone line to Clinton so he could talk daily to his daughter.

Of John Heman's four sons, two became prominent and well-known and respected Clinton County farmers.

One was John Ostrander Shaff whose first wife was Gladys Melick. After her death, he married Evelyn Purcell. Altogether, he fathered eight children.

Heman D. Shaff, third owner of the Shaff farm.

The other son was Heman Drips Shaff who married Esther Peterson and they had one son, Paul Heman Shaff.

Both brothers had large farms and both lost heavily in the 1929 through 1934 Depression periods. And both made remarkable comebacks and saw their sons and grandsons carry on in the highest of farming traditions.

Detailed information has been received about one of those farms, the one Heman Drips Shaff and his wife, Esther, had, and passed on to their son, Paul Heman, the present owner.

The following report applies to both farms in general; and toward the closing, to the one Paul Shaff owns and operates in particular.

Things have gone well on the pioneer farm through the years. Of course, oxen were first used when Heman B., the original settler, started farming back in the late 1830s, and John Deere's personally-made steel plow had made breaking the land so much easier. In fact, neighbors would come to rent the plow and use it at night, using lantern light before returning the plow to Heman, who would need it for daytime plowing. The demand was so great for the new plow that Heman went to Grand Detour again in 1840 and brought back a second one of John Deere's steel plows.

The first settler's crops were corn, wheat, oats, and buckwheat. Corn occasionally yielded as much as 50 bushels an acre those first years.

Cattle and hogs, along with chickens and turkeys, were raised. The cattle were fed to 1200 pounds or more. Hogs were also raised to heavy weights. Fat hogs were the thing in those days.

Dairy cattle also were raised and milked by each Shaff generation. Angus beef cattle were also featured through the years, and especially by Roger Shaff, Paul's cousin, on his part of the Shaff farms. Paul, himself, was heavily into dairying with Holstein and Jersey cattle for many years.

Horses started providing the field power in the 1840s and continued to be used 80 or more years, but in 1915, a Minneapolis-Moline tractor -- one of the first ones in the county -- was bought and the horse population started declining soon thereafter. Since then, John Deere, International Harvester, and Ford tractors have been used.

All through the years, beginning in the late 1830s through the early 1920s, on the farms Heman Shaff and his sons owned and operated, the Shaffs were among the first to accept the new machines. Not only was Heman the first to get the steel plow, and also other plows, but he and his sons were usually among the earliest to try out new planters, discs, cultivators, mowers, and other haying tools, reapers, binders, and threshers.

In 1916, one of the sons of John and Jennie, Heman Drips Shaff, and his wife, Esther, became the owners of the large farm. They had married the year before acquiring the farm. Their son, Paul Heman, the present farm owner, was born four years later.

More land was bought, but after World War I -- about 1921 -- land prices began to tumble, as did the price for grain and livestock. Soon problems started to show up, and by the end of the Depression years in the late 1920s and early 1930s, when Heman D. Shaff was the owner, the "roof caved in", as it did on thousands of other farm owners. The interest payments on mortgages on high priced land were just too great. The result was that over 1000 acres were lost on just this one farm alone. Only the original 240 acre homestead could be saved.

However bleak things must have looked, Heman D. and his son, Paul, worked themselves out of the depths of despair. Innovative ways and modern machines were combined in the process. In 1938, a two-row mechanical corn picker was used on the Farmall 20.

Angus steers and crossbred hogs also helped.

In 1939, a corn combine came onto the farm. Neighbors said combines would never replace corn shellers and threshing machines -- but the Shaffs proved they could.

Better seeds and the use of chemical fertilizers and herbicides also helped greatly. When hybrid corn and improved soybeans came in, they were quick to be put to use on Shaff farms.

In 1960, corn drying bins were built. Ultimately over 100,000 bushels could be stored.

In 1943, Paul married Myrna Strohbehn. Three sons were welcomed,

Jonathan Paul, Dan Atwood, and Sam Heman.

Jonathan married LeAnne Hood, and they had a family of four -- Steven, Sue Ann, Sarah Lee, and Stacy Lynn. Dan married Pam Clark. Two children were born to them -- Mandy Suellens and Korine Jaye. Sam married Andrea Grabosch. They had one child -- Jennifer Lindsay. The children of Jonathan, Dan, and Sam are the seventh generation. Jonathan, Dan and Sam have all remarried in recent years. Jonathan is now married to Linda Peterson, Dan to Julie Schrunk and Sam to Traci Shook.

Paul, Sam and Jonathan Shaff

Members of the Shaff family, or of the families into which they married, have served in many wars, even as early as the War of 1812. William Drips, grandfather of Jennie Drips, wife of John Heman Shaff, was in the 1812 battles. Joseph H. Drips was in the Civil War. Victor Prine died in WW I. One of Paul and Myrna's sons was in the Vietnam War.

The Shaffs have been involved in many organizations. Undoubtedly, John Heman Shaff or some of his four sons were in the Grange. Paul Shaff, the present owner, his father, and his sons, have been staunch Farm Bureau members. Paul is also a Mason and a Shriner, and in Kiwanis. His family are Presbyterians. Roger Shaff was active in the Clinton County Cattleman's Association, as well as in Iowa legislative circles, and in community organizations.

The Shaff family has also been very active and influential in Iowa politics. John Ostrander Shaff, Roger's father, was elected to the Iowa Legislature in 1917 and to the Iowa Senate in 1920. He played a big part in getting Iowa "out of the mud" in good roads efforts. Both Roger and David, great grandsons of the Shaff family's Iowa founder,

Paul and Myrna Shaff, current owners.

served multiple terms -- David as a Legislator in the 1952 session and as a Senator in the 1954 session, when he authored the "Shaff Plan" for Iowa redistricting. Roger was a Senator from 1967 to 1979, which included his successful campaign in behalf of approving Ethanol fuel.

During his lifetime, 1817 to 1904, Heman Blakely Shaff gave an acre or more of one of his farms for a Township Cemetery as a burial ground for family members and friends. It is now known as the Shaff Cemetery with many members of the family, including Heman B., buried there. It is regarded as "Sacred Ground" and is kept up by an association which includes members of the family.

In 1951, Paul and Myrna built an attractive, modern farm home and with the family's heritage in mind, preserved and incorporated some of the sections of the stone walls that were a part of the stone home built by Heman Shaff and his wife, Mary, Paul's great grandparents, exactly 100 years earlier.

As for the Shaff farms of today, they are back in full strength following the heartaches and losses endured during the Depression more than 60 years ago.

The two large farms are now each about 1000 acres. Roger owns one which he farms with his son, John, and grandson, Peter. Paul owns the other and farms it with two of his sons, Jonathan and Sam.

What the future holds for the Shaff Farms dynasty is not yet clear. There are grandchildren and great grandchildren, some bearing the Shaff name, others now with other surnames because daughters married into other families.

One thing is clear, however, and that is that for the present, and hopefully for the future, some 2000 acres of Clinton County land remain in the capable hands of a family that has been respected "Stewards of the Soil" for 159 years.

The Shaff farm is marked with a 500 pound stone, two original John Deere plows and a Sesquicentennial sign.

Present Shaff farm home in which several stones from the original 1837 home have been incorporated.

STATE CO-WINNER
THE GARRETSON FARM
OF
HENRY COUNTY
Settled 1837

The boulder that marked the centennial of the Garretson farm.

Another Iowa pioneer family farm also dating back to 1837, and also chosen for special Sesquicentennial recognition both in Iowa, and in Washington, D.C., is the Garretson farm of Henry County. Although the Garretson story is quite different from the Shaff family story noted in the preceding pages, it, too, is an account that could easily fill the pages of a sizable book.

Unlike some of the other nine winning farms in the Iowa Sesquicentennial Commission's search for Iowa's oldest farms in the state's nine crop districts, the Garretson family cannot boast of prize-winning livestock or record crop yields. Instead, theirs is a fascinating story centered around people and compassion for the enslaved, etc.

The Garretson Farm was established by Joel C. Garretson back in 1837, when what we now know as Iowa was only a part of the vast Wisconsin territory. Eighty acres were bought for $1.25 an acre from the Federal Government's Land Office in Burlington.

The eighty acre tract was in what is now Henry County near what became a Quaker village called Salem. The eighty acres first bought by Joel C. Garretson is now only a small part of the 820 acres of the current Garretson farm owned and farmed by Joel H. Garretson, Sr., Joel H. Garretson, Jr., William Garretson, Doris Garretson, Loren Garretson, and Keith Garretson.

To go back to the beginning in 1837, Joel C. Garretson, a native of Ohio, who was the great-great grandfather of the present owners, had ar-

The Garretson family members taken on February 20, 1886, at the home of Joel & Elizabeth Garretson on the occasion of their 50th wedding anniversary. Joel and Elizabeth are in the foreground with their children behind them. Albert, Emily and Julia are in the middle row with Amos, Owen and John in the back row.

ranged for his wife and parents, a brother, John, and a younger sister to join him and his brother, Isaac, as soon as the two of them had settled on some land. That took place in June of 1837, and very shortly thereafter, Joel's wife, his sister and younger brother came to make the family complete once again.

Within weeks of buying the land, the men in the family started building log cabins for the several families. Then, as soon as they could, they started clearing land so plowing and planting could be done the next year. Corn was planted and oats seeded by hand. Raising of sheep, goats, cattle and hogs also began. Oxen were first used for field work and hauling. Horses displaced the slow-moving oxen later.

More land was purchased from the government from time to time. The first additional land was purchased in 1841. Other purchases were made in 1870, 1900, 1920, and even as recent as 1995.

In the earlier years, Joel and his brothers, John and Isaac, Jr. had operated grist mills in Ohio before coming to the Midwest. After coming to Iowa, they also made a mill to grind corn for their own families and some neighbors.

Joel married Elizabeth Goodson the year before coming to Wisconsin territory. Six children were born to that union. They were Amos, Emily, Julia, Albert, John, and Owen. All six received advanced education.

Although living near a Quaker village and associating with Quakers daily, Joel Garretson was not a Quaker. Nevertheless, he was as much of an abolitionist as any of his neighbors, and became a leader in what is known as the Underground Railroad, a system designed to help slaves gain freedom from their white owners and masters.

In the late 1830s and 1840s, although well before the Civil War, slavery continued to be the rule in all southern states, including Missouri. Meanwhile, some Missouri slave owners were beginning to set slaves free, but others were adamant about maintaining the authority over the hapless black Americans.

As a result, quite a number of runaway slaves entered southern and southeastern Iowa. Especially was this true around Salem where refuge was often found in the most unique ways. Slave owners were often in hot pursuit of their slaves, so there was danger involved in hiding the runaways. Moreover, slavery was still enforced by federal law.

Nevertheless, Joel Garretson and others devised ways of hiding slaves in secret basement, compartments, barns, in orchards, under sacks of bran in wagons going to market, in cubicles under loads of hay, in corn shocks, and in many other ways. One of the most unusual of all was dressing a Negro man in women's clothes, bonnet and all, and seating him beside a wagon or buggy's driver, and taking him to a safe refuge while those searching for him would pass by. Joel's fearless wife once found refuge for one of the runaways in an orchard hiding place.

One day, close to 100 irate slave owners were able to surround Salem, denying both access to, and exit from, the town. They posted a $500 reward for the capture of Joel Garretson. Fortunately, Garretson learned of the price on his head, mounted his fastest horse before the posse arrived, and got away unmolested.

One of the daughters of Joel and Elizabeth, Julia, became state lecturer of the Grange that was organized in 1867, and now was the dominant farm organization. Julia gained her position as Lecturer in 1870 and served a number of years.

Second to own the Garretson farm was Owen Garretson, Joel and Elizabeth's youngest son. He bought the farm in 1895. He married Emma Dilts, and they also had a family of six, all sons -- Wendell, Sumner, Alvin, Herman, Joel Howard, and Gilbert.

Owen had already made quite a name for himself as a farmer and community leader. Among his responsibilities up through World War II were Henry County Supervisor, Memorial Hospital trustee, Whittier College trustee, fuel administrator for Henry County, and assisted in the Liberty Loans program during World War I.

All six sons became college graduates, and they all served in positions of responsibility. Wendell and Howard became doctors. Alvin and Herman were insurance executives. Gilbert was a University professor, and Sumner became a farmer and real estate agent.

Sumner and his wife, Florence, Howard and his wife, May, and Gilbert and his wife, Ethel, inherited the farm in the 1930s, with Howard and Sumner doing the managing.

The 820 Garretson acres are financially secure, partly because many in

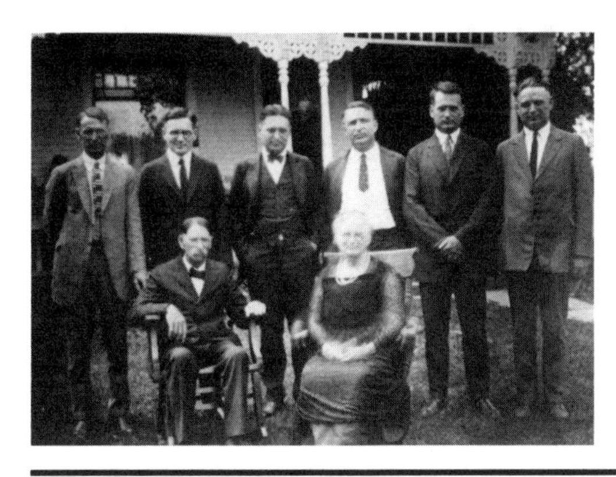

The Garretsons circa 1910. Owen & Emma, seated, with sons Sumner, Wendell, Alvin, Gilbert, Joel (Howard) and Herman.

the family have shares in the property, but more importantly because there seems to be a universal resolve that the land is never to pass out of the family.

Latest to buy into the farm is Joel H. Garretson, Jr. and his wife, Marlene, who bought 70 acres in 1995.

Others involved include those previously mentioned and their wives, as well as Josephine Garretson Bainter, wife of Harlan Bainter, a retired Iowa District Court Judge; Doris Garretson, who has a home on her share of the land where her son, Kenton Gill, now resides and where Joel H. Sr., and his wife, Joyce, and their son, Bob, help with the farming. Joel, Sr.'s share of the land is mostly timber hay ground and pasture and where a small cow-calf operation is carried out. Their son, Bob, who is Joel, Jr.'s brother, has land focusing on timber pasture, trees, and recreation. Loren Garretson maintains the large farm house built by Owen in the year 1900.

Absentee land owners include O.L. and Keith Garretson, who have much of the best crop land, which is now rented out to neighbors for corn and soybean production and for cattle; Virginia Woolis, Joel, Sr.'s sister and wife of Floyd Woolis, who live in Puerto Rico and have forty acres of hay ground; and William Garretson of West Des Moines, and his nephew, Con, who own much of the original 80 acres bought by Joel C. Garretson 159 years ago.

Although no member of the family was either in the Civil or Spanish American War, three Garretsons were in WW I -- Wendell, Alvin and Herman. Five Garretsons were in WW II. They were Ronald, Frank, Joel, Keith, and Charles, who was also in Vietnam.

In summarizing the report Joel Garretson, Jr., says, "We may not have prize winning crops, but we are proud that our farm has produced good people who are proud of their Iowa roots. It has produced doctors, housewives, lawyers, teachers, caring mothers, engineers, businessmen, entrepreneurs, pharmacists, sociologists, professors, journalists, orators, criminal justice majors, and environmentalists, and others -- all of them proud of their ancestors, and of their roots."

DISTRICT WINNER
CROP DISTRICT #9 - SOUTHEAST IOWA

THE CAMMACK FARM
OF
HENRY COUNTY
Settled 1838

Levi Cammack, who established the 158-year-old farm.

Nellie Cammack, a maiden lady, helped raise her brother's six orphaned children.

1838 was quite a year. It's the year Samuel Morse patented the telegraph with its dots and dashes to send messages coast-to-coast, and the year Herman and John Avery Pitts created the first portable grain thresher that was a Godsend to grain farmers for a half century.

It was also the year that mustaches became popular with men, and girls were told to stop riding horseback because it would "interfere with their future womanly duties."

It was also eight years before Iowa became a state, and Indians were still to be seen on all sides. And it was the year when Levi Cammack bought 80 acres of Henry County land from the U.S. Government at a cost of $1.25 an acre and was established as one of the first farm homesteads in Henry County. Levi Cammack was the great grandfather of Dale Cammack, the present owner and operator of a 234 acre farm.

Levi was the grandson of one James Cammack, who was born in Scotland, but had moved to England before emigrating to North Carolina in 1780, right after the American Revolution. Later, James moved to Ohio to become one of the Buckeye State's first farm settlers. There, his son John Cammack was born, one of a number of children.

John Cammack, Levi's father, continued the pioneering tradition by settling his family on the Indiana frontier in 1816, building a log cabin, and enduring all of the pioneering hardships of that era. There, Levi was born into the Quaker household.

As time went on, Levi grew up and married, and with his wife, Elizabeth, daughter of the Frazier family, farmed in Indiana a few years.

Evidently Levi was not born with a silver spoon in his mouth. He frequently told that to earn money to buy suitable clothes for his and Elizabeth's Quaker wedding, he proceeded to split rails for which he received the princely sum of 37 cents for every 100 rails he split. However, the pioneering spirit that had become so obvious among his own ancestors had gripped him and Elizabeth, too.

Thus it was that when they left their Indiana farm in May, 1837, along with their two older children and with several other Quaker families, they journeyed west to what was then Wisconsin Territory.

It was a long, slow, difficult journey. A total of 45 Quakers were on the trek. The Cammacks had three yokes of oxen to pull their covered wagons with all their worldly possessions. Levi had a grand total of 12 silver dollars in his pocket and vowed that if he had spent half of that before they had reached the half-way point in the westward journey, he would turn back the oxen and return to Indiana. Evidently he didn't spend six dollars by the time they were half-way, so the Cammacks carried on.

The trip to the Mississippi River took six weeks; and then after finally getting across the river, the family settled in the tiny village of Salem, not far from the Skunk River.

The next spring, after doing some looking around, Levi found an 80 acre tract to his liking and bought it for $1.25 an acre. First order of business was to build a home, using bricks from a nearby plant. Then it was breaking a few acres of the prairie sod and planting some winter wheat that autumn.

Later, corn and oats were added to the cropping program, hogs were raised, along with a herd of cattle, and a livestock dealership established. Success crowned his efforts, eventually enabling Levi to acquire several thousand acres of land in southeastern Iowa.

Meanwhile, the family grew until there were 13 children.

The farm that they bought not only included corn, wheat, barley, oats, and other crops, but it also had a large orchard providing apples, pears, cherries, peaches, and other fruits.

With success in his livestock dealings and land purchases, Levi Cammack became very generous, helping other families get started farming. However, when the recession of the 1870s struck, he found he had extended himself too far. The result was he lost all of his land holdings, except for 160 acres that are still part of the Cammack farm four generations later.

Second owner of the farm was Nathan Cammack, one of Levi's sons, who had worked closely with his father on the farm and with the livestock dealership.

Nathan married Jane Pigeon and they started their large family of 15 children soon thereafter. Meanwhile, Nathan was running the 160 acres that had been saved.

In 1876, Nathan and Jane bought 80 acres of the farm. They also built an 11 room frame house to accommodate their growing family. They also remained steadfast in their Quaker faith and embraced the Society of Friends.

Large as their family was, they all received the best education possible. One son, Albert, even graduated from Iowa State College and became a Professor of Agriculture at Colorado's Ag College. Another son, William, studied medicine at Northwestern University

The next owners of the farm were three of the Nathan Cammack daughters, Nettie, Laura, and Nellie. All three of them had been prominent teachers in early Iowa schools.

Their brother, Ray, and his wife, Laura Irene, had six children, but never saw them reach maturity. In 1932, both Ray and Laura were taken by pneumonia. Ray's sisters, now the owners of the family farm, and the aunts of the orphaned children, took them to their previously childless home.

The children ranged in age from 14 to 6 when their parents died. Dale, the future owner of the farm, was 13 and the second oldest. He and his older brother set forth immediately to earn money after school hours and during summer vacations to help meet family expenses.

Dale and Marcia Cammack, present owners of the Pioneer Farm.

Despite the hardships caused by their parents' deaths, their aunts made sure each child got a college education, three of them from the University of Iowa.

Dale's bent was agriculture. After serving in WW II with two of his brothers, he married, and in time, he and his wife, Marcia, became the owners of the pioneer

The Cammack farm today.

farm which had grown to 254 acres.

As for the farm, beginning early on, corn, oats, wheat, and hay were mainstay crops on the farm for many years, and fruit was sold from the orchards.

Angus beef cattle, a flock of Shropshire sheep, crossbred hogs, Jersey and Holstein dairy stock -- all were raised in the livestock area. Percheron horses furnished the field power for all the years until a Fordson tractor came to the farm in the 1920s. It was followed by an International 10-20, then John Deere and Allis Chalmers tractors.

There were some rough years in the 20s and 30s when low prices, drought, and Chinch bugs struck, and 1993 when rains never stopped, and 1995 when no corn could get planted, "but otherwise," says Dale, "we've had a lot of good years."

The Dale Cammacks are deeply involved in their community, including the school board, 4-H clubs, Boy Scouts, a teacher's association, and Sunday School superintendency in their Methodist Church, as well as working in soil conservation. They are also active in the Farm Bureau and the American Legion. Two of their sons served in the Vietnam War.

Congratulations to the Dale Cammacks and their four children, and all their ancestors, not only for their pioneer farm family record and reward, but also for their contribution to their community these past 158 years.

DISTRICT WINNER
CROP DISTRICT #3 - NORTHEAST IOWA

THE MOLONY BROTHERS FARM
OF
DUBUQUE COUNTY
Settled 1840

Dubuque County, Iowa, is a land of history. It was in the Wisconsin Territory that later would become Dubuque County where Iowa's first white settler was found. He was Julien Dubuque, a French Canadian adventurer who began mining lead ore near where the city of Dubuque is now located. He made friends with the Indians and learned to speak their language. He died in 1810, thirty-six years before Iowa became a state.

During the Civil War, shot for the North's Civil War weapons was made in a high tower located in Dubuque.

In the first part of the 1830s, some of Iowa's first farm settlements took place in Dubuque County, and so did tragic farm disputes. In her book, "Iowa -This Is The Place", Margeret Posten refers to lawlessness and murder at the Dubuque lead mines. She also tells about a bloody disagreement in one of Dubuque County land ownerships dating back to 1833, even before Iowa was a territory. A man named Woodbury Massey claimed some land near Dubuque. Another man named Smith, and his son, also claimed it. Massey ordered the Smiths off his claim and Smith retaliated by shooting and killing Massey. One of Massey's brothers then swore revenge on the Smiths if they did not leave. The Smiths stayed, so the Massey brother shot and killed the eldest Smith. Then the younger Smith vowed he would shoot the other Massey. At that point, Massey's sister, Louisa, shot at Smith but a billfold in his breast pocket spared his life. However, that near fatal shot convinced Smith he had better leave Iowa.

Of course, the Massey-Smith debacle was an extreme case of trying to settle land ownership questions. Virtually all others were settled peacefully and in 99% of the claims, there was no dispute whatsoever.

So it was in the case of the Molony farm, which is one of Iowa's oldest family farms, and one of the ten recognized by the Sesquicentennial Commission and the Iowa Department of Agriculture in the search for the oldest pioneer family farm in the state's nine crop districts.

Richard Molony, along with his wife, Margaret, and two of his brothers and three sisters emigrated from Ireland in the early 1830s. Richard was a Greek and Latin scholar in Ireland, but when he came to America, he had to settle for work in the salt mines near Syracuse, New York. That was not to his liking, so in 1840, when he heard that he might be able to acquire farm land in the Wisconsin Territory, he and other family members joined a wagon train that wound up in what is now Dubuque County, Iowa. At that time, it was still the Wisconsin Territory.

Soon after their 1840 arrival in Dubuque County, each of the Molony brothers purchased a half section of farm land from the U.S. Government at the standard price of $1.25 per acre.

Just how he did it is not explained, but Richard paid for his 320 acres with 80 turkeys.

In addition to raising corn, oats, hay, and livestock, Richard also served as township squire, where he settled land disputes in a much more sensible way than the Masseys and Smiths had done.

Apparently Richard and Margaret had only one child, which was a rather surprisingly small number of offspring when most pioneer farm couples had six or eight or even more. Some even had as many as a dozen or more. Of course, the larger the family, the more hands there were to do the endless work on pioneer farms.

Richard and Margaret's lone child was named John Richard; and, of course, he became the logical and only heir to the land his parents had accumulated.

John Richard married some time before he became the owner of the farm. Unlike his parents, John Richard and his wife had many children born to them - thirteen in all. Unfortunately, only two survived to adulthood. They were Michael and his sister, Meg.

One of the Molony families' favorite stories is that one of their four-year olds was kidnapped by a band of renegade Indians. Fortunately, he was not harmed. Apparently fearful of retaliation, the Indians abandoned him at Washington Mills, not far from the Molony cabin. There, his frantic parents found him later in the day, to their prayerful relief.

John Richard did not live to become an old man. His son, Michael, had to take over the farm at an early age. Of course, Michael's mother held title to the land and was always consulted by Michael on major decisions.

The family did add land to the original 320 acres from time to time. Cropping programs remained largely the same for many years until soybeans were added after about 1935.

Livestock operations, however, changed a lot through the years and are still changing. At first, it was only hogs and a few cows, along with chickens and turkeys. Later, Hereford beef cattle, sheep, and dairy cattle were added.

Looking over part of the land bought by his great grandfather in 1840, is Rich Molony on the left, the present operator. His father, Richard, is on the right.

Photo from Iowa Farmer Today.

Belgian horses were the source of all field power up to 1930 when a Fordson tractor was bought, but as many as 12 horses were in harness well into the 1930s. Since that first Fordson was bought, other tractors used on the farm include John Deere, Farmall, Allis-Chalmers, Ford and Massey-Ferguson.

Michael and his wife had a family of ten. They became the owners of the farm in 1920. Their sons included Michael, Jr. (better known as Mike), John, James, Richard, and Patrick. The sons took possession of the farm in 1955 and were responsible for the farm becoming known as the Molony Brothers Farm.

Three of the Molonys have been in uniform. James was in WW II. Patrick and Dick were in the Korean War.

The farm now totals 820 acres, 500 acres more than the original pioneer, Richard Molony, bought 156 years ago. The Sesquicentennial questionnaire returned by Richard indicates that the sixth and current generation of Molony brothers to own the land are Mike J., John, and Richard, plus Richard's son, Rich.

The Molonys belong to St. Patrick's Catholic Church, the Farm Bureau, and the American Legion. They are proud of their farm with its woodlands and pastures, and its productive Dubuque County soil. Producing corn, oats, hay, cattle and hogs keeps them busy. Winning the eleven county crop district pioneer farm family award has added another dimension of pride to the Molonys, and rightfully so.

DISTRICT WINNER
CROP DISTRICT #5 - CENTRAL IOWA

THE WORTH FARM
OF
JASPER COUNTY
Settled 1845

The Worth family of Jasper County has certainly proved its "worth" in pioneering and in farming.

It was in 1845, one year before Iowa became a state, that Joel B. Worth, a native of Kentucky but then farming in Illinois, heard of a treaty signed by central Iowa Indians. The treaty would have the natives travel farther west and open central Iowa for homesteading.

Joel Worth apparently lost no time in pursuing the opportunity to get productive, inexpensive land in Iowa. Family records show that late in 1845, Joel came through Keokuk and kept on going until he reached Jasper County. There he staked out a claim of 80 acres about two miles west of the village of Monroe. Joel was the great-great grandfather of the present owner of the farm, Wayne Worth.

When Joel Worth first established a homestead, Newton, now the Jasper County Seat, had not yet been founded, and Des Moines was little more than a frontier post. Joel Worth and other early Jasper County settlers would have to travel all the way to Fairfield for supplies or farm tools. Nevertheless, Joel Worth built a log cabin and started to plow prairie land and plant crops in early 1846.

The purchase of his 80 acres did not become official until 1848, when the government accepted the $1.25 per acre payment. It marked the end of a long, but successful effort to acquire a homestead.

Joel and his wife had a family of six. Work on the farm was demanding and difficult. A yoke of oxen was used in the fields. Corn, oats, and hay were the crops grown. Cattte, hogs, and chickens were raised.

In the first years of their farming, if there was wheat or corn to be milled, or flour or other food products, or farm machinery to be purchased, it meant going to Fairfield which was 90 miles away. That was a long 180 mile round trip haul for a team of horses, and it would take the better part of a week to make it.

One of the six children, a son, Samuel Frederick Worth, Wayne Worth's great grandfather, became the second owner of the farm in 1892.

Samuel Frederick and his wife also had six children. They were the owners of the farm until 1930, just when the Depression years were beginning. As was true of countless other farms, there was danger of losing the Worth farm.

Samuel Boyd Worth, one of the six children of Samuel Frederick, was the son who became the farm's third owner. His ownership began during one of the most trying periods in American farm history. Samuel Boyd was Wayne's father, and in recalling those trying years in the early '30s, Wayne tells about an especially scary moment in his boyhood.

One day when he was in the house, a man knocked at the door. When the door was opened, the man announced he had come to serve notice of foreclosure of the farm and that he needed to give the papers to Wayne's father. Fortunately, Samuel Boyd Worth was working in a distant field that day. No one in the house gave away Samuel's whereabouts. Reluctantly, the man left, and for some strange reason did not come back. Wayne remains convinced that if his father had been home that day, the farm would have been lost.

Although it was a difficult start, what with fear of losing the farm, drought, chinch bugs, and other insect problems, and abysmally low prices for grains and livestock, Samuel Boyd and his wife, Stella, survived. They also encountered good fortune later on. Hybrid corn produced greatly increased yields. Soybean production was started. Purebred Jersey cattle were purchased to establish a high-producing herd. An F20 Farmall tractor was purchased in 1938. Duroc hogs were raised and crossed with Hampshires.

Samuel did not do it all alone. His wife, Stella, raised about 450 Leghorn hens every year and sold hatching eggs. Samuel and Stella had three children, and when Wayne and his siblings became old enough, they were put to work and were dependable helpers. Samuel also had some good horses, as had also been true of his father and grandfather.

Improved machinery also helped make the Worth farming project more productive and the work easier. Helping make this possible were a two bottom tractor plow and a ten foot binder in 1938, a three bottom plow in 1946, an International 20 mechanical corn picker in 1953, and an Allis Chalmers grain combine in 1950. A four bottom plow and larger International corn picker were purchased in 1964, and a 205 International self-propelled combine in 1969.

Samuel Boyd Worth was a WW I veteran and was active in Masonic Circles. He was a 32 degree Mason and a member of the Za-Ga-Zig Shrine, as well as a member of the American Legion, and the American Jersey Club. He and his family were also active in the Monroe United Methodist Church.

In 1967, after Samuel Boyd had the farm back on solid ground, it was declared to be Jasper County's oldest farm and received the Iowa Centennial Farm Award.

In 1973, Wayne Russell Worth and his wife, Donna, became the fourth generation to own the pioneer family farm. The dairy operation was stopped under his ownership and a beef cow-calf project has taken its place. Hogs are still being fed, and corn, soybeans, oats, and hay are now the cropping program. Much of the row crop land is now being rented out. The farm now totals 210 acres compared to the original 80 acres.

Wayne Worth family, Wayne and Donna in the back with Dennis and Mary Sue in front.

Wayne and Donna have a son, Dennis Wayne, and a daughter, Mary Sue. The whole family has been active in 4-H projects.

Looking back, Wayne says the farm's worst years were the drought years of 1934, 1957, and 1972. The weather in 1972 cut the corn average to three bushels an acre. Meanwhile, 1994 has been the farm's best year with a 150 bushel corn average.

Wayne is a Korean War Veteran, and has also been active as a Mason and in the American Legion. His family are also members of the Methodist Church.

Dennis and Mary Sue are the fifth generation raised on the land their great-great grandfather staked out 151 years ago. They can take great pride in how their Worth family has proved its "worth" from pioneer times through today.

DISTRICT WINNER
CROP DISTRICT #8 - SOUTH CENTRAL IOWA

THE DENNEY-HIATT-DOOLEY FARM OF APPANOOSE COUNTY
Settled 1848

The farm chosen as the winner of the 1996 search for Iowa's oldest farm in the South Central Iowa Crop District is the LaRoy Virgil and Juanita Hiatt Dooley farm located near Centerville. The farm is a classic example of how Iowa farm families have met and overcome adversities.

Purchased in 1848 by Reuben Denney, the step-great grandfather of the present owners, it was a 40 acre challenge of hardship from the beginning. Yet, today, it is a farm expanded to 350 productive acres that has made a good living for the fourth generation of the Denney-Hiatt-Dooley family.

The 40 acres where Reuben Denney started homesteading 148 years ago was purchased from the government for $1.25 an acre. The patent for the land was received in 1849.

Reuben Denney was a native of Ohio, but, strangely enough, lived most of his younger life in North Carolina, where he married and had three children, although only one survived. It was there that he first learned that land was going to open up in the Wisconsin Territory and that Iowa was about to become the newest state to be admitted to the Union.

Denney had become a widower when he made his journey to seek land west of the Mississippi during the spring of 1846, just before Iowa would gain statehood on December 28. He came as far as Fairfield, Iowa. There he met Nancy Tucker Hiatt, who had lost her husband on the westward trek to Iowa. Nancy had a young son named John Lewis Hiatt.

Reuben and Nancy married soon after coming to Fairfield and lived there over a year, waiting for land to open up after Indian's moved farther west. That waiting period ended in 1848 when Reuben claimed those original 40 acres.

A log cabin was built, land was broken, and crops were planted and harvested. Livestock also was introduced to the small Appanoose County farm.

Family history tells that the Denney home soon became a stopping off place for families on their way westward as they also sought to buy new land when it became available. However, in one instance in the fall of 1850, the overnight visitor stayed longer than just for the night.

The guest was Mrs. Denney's former mother-in-law, also journeying west. The November evening she arrived amid much rejoicing, a major snowstorm started and raged on for several days, closing all roads. The result was the overnight visitor remained as a "guest" all winter long.

The Denneys replaced the log home with a larger, more convenient, and permanent home in 1885. They also opened what they called a "hostel" store, which was similar to the general stores that became popular late in the 19th century.

Reuben had three children by his first wife, but two of them had died. Nancy had John Lewis by her first husband, but she and Reuben had four more children, two of whom did not reach adulthood.

Evidently Reuben died in 1876. Records show that Nancy became the farm owner that year. Her son, John Lewis Hiatt, who had become Reuben Denney's stepson, was the third to own the farm which had already started to expand beyond the 40 acres.

John Lewis Hiatt and his wife had four children, one of whom was named John Lester. John Lester was the fourth to own the growing pioneer

Thanksgiving Day 1914

farm, purchasing it in 1910. He and his wife, Clara, also had four children that included the daughter, Juanita, who now owns the farm along with her husband, LaRoy Virgil Dooley, who is best known as Virgil.

Juanita vividly remembers some of the adversities her father and mother faced during the Depression years. For one thing, her father had bought a Model A Ford for $900 at 6% interest just before the difficult years began. That interest payment was $54 a year, and, at no time during the Depression did the farm make more than $54 to meet those interest payments and other expenses, so he could not pay off the debt on the car until a good crop was raised in 1938, by which time the Model A was nearly ten years old.

In the meantime, banks failed, prices of land, hogs, and grains dropped to all time lows. And on top of all that, grasshoppers, chinch bugs, and burning heat destroyed crops. One year, only one load of corn was harvested from the total ten acre field planted to corn.

LaRoy Virgil Dooley, 82, and Juanita Hiatt Dooley, 78.

1935 was the year Juanita and LaRoy Virgil Dooley were married. The heat was so intense that temperatures soared to 110 degrees or higher in the daytime, and in order to get sleep at night, the young couple had to move beds out under trees in the yard to escape the heat in the house. They lived that way for six weeks of seemingly endless heat and drought. The dust blown from fields was so bad that Juanita would have to dampen sheets and hang them over doorways to keep the dirt from blowing into the house.

Juanita also cannot forget the battles against chinch bugs. She and her young husband would go out early in the morning to dig post holes into which they poured oil or creosote in a rather futile effort to keep the bugs from entering fields. Other farmers plowed a furrow around the entire field and poured creosote in the furrows, only to see billions of the insects crawl over the first waves of victims in the furrows and devour the crops.

Difficult as things were some years, the Hiatts and Dooleys survived and carried on. Virgil and Juanita had three children, making for a fifth generation of the family to live on the pioneer farm which they bought in 1956.

Land was added from time to time to where the farm now totals 350 acres. The Dooleys have farmed it themselves for forty years, but rented it out for the first time in 1996.

Records are not complete for the earliest years, but it is known that great pride has always been taken in caring for the land on which corn, oats, and hay have long been the major crops, with soybeans added later.

The livestock program over the years has included beef cattle, hogs, dairy cows, and sheep. Juanita's mother also always raised about 1000 chickens annually. Virgil and Juanita raised a flock of laying hens and sold hatching eggs for years. They used kerosene heaters to incubate the eggs. When they finally got electricity, it was so much easier to do the incubation. Today, corn, hay, and beans, and a herd of stock cows get the emphasis.

Juanita can trace her ancestors back to the Revolutionary War in which her great-great-great grandfather served. Virgil and Juanita's sons, Roy Lester and Alan Lee, both served in the Vietnam War.

The early Hiatts were Quakers, but the current generation is Methodist. Virgil and Juanita are Farm Bureau members, as well as members of the Genealogy Society, Appanoose County Beef Producers, and Douglas Township Club. Virgil has also served as Appanoose County Fair Superintendent.

Juanita says it's been a peaceful life despite the hardships, and they are happy to have had so many years on their Appanoose County farm, and proud to be the family to win the South Central Iowa Sesquicentennial award.

DISTRICT WINNER
CROP DISTRICT #7 - SOUTHWEST IOWA

THE MCDONALD-ROBERTS-LUHRS-SLIGHT-JENSEN FARM OF ADAIR COUNTY
Settled 1849

Oldest farm in Southwest Iowa found in the Pioneer Family Farm search conducted by the Iowa Department of Agriculture and the Iowa

Sesquicentennial Commission, is known as the Roberts Farm of Adair County.

The 235 acre farm near Dexter, Iowa, was found to be the oldest in Crop District #7, which includes eleven counties in the southwestern part of the state.

The farm was established in 1849, not by a Roberts, but by an Ohio native named William McDonald. One of his daughters, Emily, married John Roberts and the Roberts family has managed to own all, or part, of the property ever since.

William McDonald was the great grandfather of Ivan and Claude Roberts, two of the current co-owners of the farm. The others are sisters Alice Luhrs and Cora Slight, and the children of another sister, Violet Jensen, who is deceased. Her children are Sherri, Chris and Lisa. Ivan and Claude Roberts moved to the farm and started farming there sixty years ago and still live there.

Before coming to southwest Iowa, McDonald had lived in Illinois and Missouri, as well as his native Ohio, but apparently it was always his ambition to farm in Iowa. That did not happen until 1849, when he staked his claim in the early fall and built a log cabin. That job took most of the winter.

In the spring of 1850, McDonald went back to Missouri to get his wife and four young children and move them into the new cabin.

This done, he then broke ground with oxen and planted seven acres of corn. That corn is said to be the first corn ever grown in Adair County.

Sadness also was felt that year. The couple's 11-year old daughter died in September. Her grave was the first in a cemetery then located on the farm.

Deeds, or patents as they were then called, for the 214 acres could not be obtained until 1853.

The McDonald's nearest neighbor was ten miles away. To get corn ground, they had to go to Winterset, and to get flour they had to go all the way to Indianola, sixty or more miles away.

Each year, more of the prairie was broken and more crops raised. Livestock also was added to the farm after a barn was built.

In 1860, Emily, the oldest daughter, married John Roberts, the son of another early Adair County settler and one of eleven children. His family was native to Kentucky and had planned to go to Kansas with two yokes of oxen and two teams of horses hitched to covered wagons. However, when they reached Nodaway County, Missouri, the mother of the large family died. After her death, the wagon train headed north and ended the search for land in Adair County. This explains how John and Emily met, and how the Roberts name started to displace the McDonald name on the farm's official documents.

John and Emily lived on a rented tract five years before they bought 80 acres, where they lived and farmed 19 years. During that period, they welcomed seven children, six sons and one daughter.

In 1887, Emily's father sold the original homestead to Emily and John. The Roberts family then moved to the larger farm in 1888. William McDonald came to live with his daughter and son-in-law until his death in 1891, which took place in the home he had built years before.

Youngest of John and Emily's children was a son who was also named John. He lived with them through his boyhood and youth, took over the work on the farm, and married Mary Rudolph in 1923. Mary took care of Emily until her death in 1924. John and Mary bought the homestead farm in 1936.

In the meantime, five children were born to Mary and John. It is interesting to note that those five children all went to the country school that had been built on land that once belonged to their grandfather, who had practically given the land so a school could be built there.

The children all graduated from the Dexter high school, often having to walk two miles from home to where they could catch the school bus.

After graduating, two of the sons, Ivan and Claude,s worked with their father on the farm and eventually took over the operation, although both also served three year hitches in the Korean War -- Ivan, 1950-52, and Claude, 1953-55.

Their sister, Violet, who married Darrell Jensen, passed away in 1936. Her three children -- Sherri, Chris and Lisa -- now share her part of the ownership of the farm that their great-great grandfather had established 147 years ago.

Claude and Ivan's other sisters -- Alice, now Mrs. Dean Luhrs, and Cora, now Mrs. Andrew Slight -- are the two other co-owners.

Claude and Ivan farm the 235 acres in partnership. They also own, or rent, some 470 additional acres of land in partnership. Neither one is married.

When their great grandfather started the farm in 1849, it was a highly diversified operation with corn, oats, wheat, hay and other crops grown. Cattle, hogs, chickens, turkeys, and other poultry were raised.

Today the Roberts brothers largely grow corn, soybeans and alfalfa hay. They also still feed out hogs and Angus cattle, a breed that has prevailed on the farm for many years.

They belong to the Farm Bureau and have also held NFO memberships and are members of the Iowa Cattlemen's Association and the Veterans of Foreign Wars.

Oxen were first used in the fields by McDonald, but he soon changed to horses. The first tractor, a Fordson, was introduced in 1937, followed by John Deere and International tractors.

Other great-great grandchildren of William McDonald, like Violet's three children, include Alice's two children -- Delene and John -- and Cora's seven children by her first husband, Dale Plymesser -- Connie, John, Nancy, Gale, LuAnn, Mary and Stella -- all of whom are in the fifth generation along with Sherri, Chris, and Lisa.

A sixth generation is also very much in evidence and numbered no less than 18 at the last count.

No mention of Adair County happenings in the early years of farming there would be complete without mention of the notorious outlaw, Jesse James, and the Great Train Robbery he staged near Adair on July 21, 1873.

One of the Robert's farm cows in a field calving pen with her twin calves.

Word had reached his gang that the Rock Island express train, with tracks through Adair County, was carrying $75,000 worth of gold. Knowing the fast express would have to be derailed to get the gold, Jesse had the spike removed alongside one rail and a rope tied around the rail so that one of his henchmen could pull the rail out of place a second or two before the speeding locomotive hit that spot.

That is exactly what happened. The locomotive shot off the tracks and upset, and the cars behind it crashed into it, and into each other. The engineer was killed instantly, and many passengers were seriously injured.

The outlaws quickly boarded the wreckage, robbed the passengers of several thousand dollars, but failed to find the gold. They had to make their getaway almost empty handed.

For all pioneer Adair County families, the "Great Train Robbery" was the topic of discussion for a long time. And for all their desendents, the same is true of President Truman's National Plowing Match visit in 1949.

DISTRICT WINNER

CROP DISTRICT #4 - WEST CENTRAL IOWA

THE LONSDALE FARMS OF GUTHRIE COUNTY

Settled 1853

The Lonsdale family of near Stuart in Guthrie County has the distinction of owning the oldest farm in West Central Iowa. Their farm was established in 1853 by John Lonsdale, who was born in Yorkshire, England, in 1818, and who came to America at age 23.

Not only are the Lonsdale Farms the oldest farm in Crop District #4 owned by the same family all these years, but the family also can claim one of the most interesting records of any of those to win recognition in the Iowa Sesquicentennial Commission's search for the state's oldest pioneer farm family. As a matter of fact, few farms featured in this entire book can match the Lonsdale story. To Mary K. Lonsdale and her husband, James, who is a great-reat grandson of John Lonsdale, must go most of the credit for the research done to compile their story. Space limitation will permit only a part of the many pages of information about the Lonsdales' background, their challenges,

John Lonsdale, standing to the left of his wife Brittann who is seated, with other family members in front of their 1861 home.

and their achievements.

After arriving on our eastern shores in 1844, John Lonsdale settled first near Rochester, New York, before moving to Ohio to form a partnership with Enoch France to operate a woolen mill.

While in Ohio, he married Brittann Dye, a native of New York whom he had met while in the Empire State. The year was 1846.

Brittann added much to the family lore. Her family traced its history back to Richard Warren, one of those who reportedly came over to the "New World" on the Mayflower. Her mother also bore a famous name. She was Ascenath Beecher Dye, a cousin of Harriet Beecher Stowe.

By early 1853, John wrote his sister in England telling her about the glories of America and of his improved health since doing work outside the woolen mill. He also told of some good earnings working on the railroad and cutting down trees for a sawmill. Then he closed the letter by telling her he planned to go west to Iowa and buy farm land.

A few months later, with the blessings of his wife, he went to Iowa with his partner, E.H. France, and bought 392.40 acres of Guthrie County farmland for $1.25 an acre. They then went back to Ohio and closed out their interest in the woolen mill. John then bought a team and wagon, loaded up his wife and children, and headed west to the new farm in Iowa.

In 1858, after getting his family settled and farming for a year, John built a dam and woolen mill on the Raccoon River, which flowed through his farmland. After starting on a small scale rolling and carding wool in the new mill, he started manufacturing blankets. They must have been good blankets because his establishment was soon known as the "Lonsdale Blanket Place."

The fact is, his establishment became a major market place for the wool being produced on nearby sheep farms, and also a place of employment for many residents of the area. The demand for Lonsdale blankets continued to

James and Chad Lonsdale seated on a millstone used as a hitching post. John D. Lonsdale is standing in this early 1900's photo.

be heavy during the last part of the 1800s, when he sold out.

John and his sons soon found little time for their farming, but John's nephew, Thomas Towler, who had come over from England in 1856, stepped into the void and took over the farming operation until the Civil War broke out. Then he enlisted and served through the entire war. After the war, he came back to take over the farm management again, and continued to do so until he was killed in a farm accident at age 72 on the farm he was managing.

John Lonsdale must have been doing well in the woolen business, and with his farm ownership. He kept buying land through the years until he had accumulated 2500 acres.

He also had much to do with establishing Dale City. He laid out the town in 1862, and saw it grow to include his woolen mill and office, a general store, some blacksmith shops, a post office (of which he became postmaster), livery stable, school house, church, and a number of homes.

The Dale City church (foreground) and school attended by Lonsdale family members prior to 1950.

Coming back to his earlier farming enterprises, by 1869, he had 900 acres under the plow and was stressing the "Three C's" in his farming venture - "Corn, Clover, and Cows". Hereford cattle were bred and six teams of horses were used in the fields regularly. In addition, there were 15 brood mares that produced foals every year, thus enabling him to supply many neighbors with work horses. He also had as many as 20 Brown Swiss dairy cows and quite a few hogs on feed. Chickens were also raised.

Records show that the school house he built in Dale City had as many

Joseph, Robert and Charles Lonsdale seated on the millstone hitching post in the mid 1940's.

as 22 pupils in a year, and that he was highly in favor of taxes that benefited schools. His own children went through high school and two of them went to college. His daughter, Mary Alice, was an early graduate of Iowa State College. His oldest son, James, became a medical doctor.

John Lonsdale died in 1892. His property was divided among his four children. His son, Charles, became the owner of that part of the land that included the original 392 acre purchase, as well as buying a partnership in the woolen mill.

Charles married Clara Downing. They were the second generation to eventually own a good portion of the farm. They had only one child, a son, whose name was Frederick.

It was during Charles' lifetime that the woolen mill project had to be given up. The dyes for the wool -- dyes that had been imported from Germany -- would no longer be available after the start of World War I.

Charles passed away in 1930 and his son, Fred, then inherited the farm. In the meantime, Fred, after attending Iowa State College, had been working with his father on the farm. Fred had also married Cecile Patterson in 1917.

Shortly after the marriage, Fred enlisted in the Army and left for training at Louisville, Kentucky. He became a WW I Second Lieutenant and was sent to France.

On his return from war service, he was happy to get back to the farm where he became quite a horse trader and an enthusiast for purebred Polled Hereford cattle.

Fred and Cecile had a family of six, three sons and three daughters. As the family increased in size, the house that had been built in 1861 had to be enlarged to a total of eight bedrooms and all the other necessary rooms.

A spring house, as it was called, provided a fine supply of good water. Large gardens, an orchard, milk and cream and butter, eggs, and fresh meat made the farm totally self-sufficient, yet Cecile and her daughters were expected to also bake two pies and a cake daily to satisfy the large family and hired help with tasty desserts.

World War II had quite an impact on the family. One of Fred and Cecile's sons, Robert, spent almost all of WW II in service, most of it in Europe where he was in several major battles. A daughter, Barbara, joined the WAVES. Another daughter, Ruth, was married to Gifford Covault at Lackland Air Force Base in Texas, where he received his Air Force training. He was a 2nd Lieutenant. Still another daughter, Mary, was in California working at Hughes Aircraft.

Fred Lonsdale in full uniform shortly after enlisting in 1917 for World War I.

Fred and Cecile's other two sons, Charles II and Joseph, stayed on the home front and worked hard with their father on the farm. After Fred's death, they continued to operate the farm and the herds.

Charles II married Elizabeth Jones and they had two children. One was a son, James, who married Mary Wagner. James and Mary welcomed four children -- James Scott, Teresa (now Mahlstadt), Lisa (now Sherman), and Martin Charles.

In 1970, Charles and Elizabeth and James and Mary purchased all of the Lonsdale farm land from the other heirs. James is now in charge of the farming of the 812 acres to which the farm has grown. Some additional acres are also rented. Corn, soybeans, and oats make up the present crop rotation. The large livestock herds are now gone, but a small cow-calf herd has been kept.

During some of the very busy periods, James' father and his sons help with planting and harvesting.

The 1980s were stressful years. Inflation, high interest rates, and sky-rocketing land prices, followed by disastrous decline, took their toll. The floods of 1993 were also rough. At one time, 230 acres were totally under water, with one field under 13 feet of flood waters.

Family records have been meticulously preserved and are highly interesting and revealing.

Among the things Mary Lonsdale's report includes are that electricity was brought to Dale City and Lonsdale Farms by Iowa Electric as early as 1919, and that the Dale City Ladies Club has been in existence many years,

A group of younger Lonsdales with their cousin, James Artig, who is seated on his horse. The Lonsdales are (left to right) Ruth, Mary, Joe (in Ruth's arms), Robert, Charles and Barbara. Early 1930's.

---

providing dinners for community funerals and other functions.

The records also note that beginning with John Lonsdale, many of the men in the family have been active in Masonry, and that family members have helped build churches and schools. James and Mary are now active in All Saints Catholic Church in Stuart.

The family were early abolitionists and involved with the Underground Railroad that helped run-away slaves to escape from their owners and masters. A hidden room in a hillside near Dale City helped in this dangerous undertaking.

Of special interest in the family records is a reference to Indians camping on a bluff near John and Brittann's pioneer cabin. John would have friendly visits with the natives, and the family still has axes, an old bow, moccasins, and other gifts given to John by the Indians.

As for military service beginning with Thomas Towler and the original James Lonsdale's service all through the Civil War and Fred Lonsdale's enlistment in WW I, the family has had many other members in uniform. Charles' oldest son, Jerry, became Navy Chief radarman in Vietnam. Robert's oldest son, John, volunteered for duty in Cambodia in 1963, and was killed in action there. Joseph's oldest son was also a Vietnam veteran.

James and Mary have five grandsons. They are James, Phillip, and Andrew Sherman and Alexander and John James Lonsdale. They also have five step granddaughters.

Martin Lonsdale and his wife, Maureen, and Marty's son, Alex, live in the large old family home with Marty's grandfather, Charles. This house was the one built by John Lonsdale in 1861 and has been home to each generation since -- most of that time has seen several generations living there at the same time. Hopefully, this will continue for many generations to come.

Don Muhm, nationally respected former farm editor for the Des Moines

Christmas 1992, Mary and James Lonsdale seated with James' parents, Elizabeth and Charles.

Register, was chosen to present the Lonsdale story at the Sesquicentennial awards ceremony. In his introduction he said he was "pleased and proud" to present James and Mary K. Lonsdale as representatives of the Lonsdale family.

Everyone who now knows the Lonsdale story can understand Muhm's pride and delight in introducing the West Central Iowa pioneer farm family winners.

DISTRICT WINNER
CROP DISTRICT #2 - NORTH CENTRAL IOWA

THE "L" WOOD FARM
Owned by THE THORSON FAMILY
of MITCHELL COUNTY
Settled 1854

He was born in Norway. His name was Erik and he was the son of Thor. So, in keeping with a long-time Norwegian tradition, his name became Erik Thorson.

While in Norway, Erik became a young shoemaker, but word got to him about the opportunities and freedom -- and availability of land -- in America. So when, in 1853, he learned that a group of Norwegians called "The Clausen Colony" was about to embark for the land across the seas, he joined them.

Once on board the ship, Erik learned the Clausen Colony had a destination in mind. It was a place in the midwestern part of the United States called Iowa. It didn't mean much to him at the time, but it certainly would within a few more months and for the rest of his life.

After disembarking on the East Coast, the group headed for the place called Iowa, stopping in Wisconsin enroute. Then the Clausen group decided to stick together once they got to Mitchell County. This is said to have resulted in the founding of the town of St. Ansgar, now a full-fledged city.

Thorson, however, was intrigued by the countryside with its timber, springs, and small lakes and its prairie grasses. On September 5, 1854, he filed a homestead claim on eighty acres of mostly timberland. That marked the beginning of his farming ventures, and set the stage for the Thorson family to receive one of the Iowa Sesquicentennial Commission's highest farm honors.

The Commission, working in cooperation with the Iowa Department of Agriculture and Land Stewardship, set out to find the oldest farm, still in the hands of the descendants of the original pioneer settler, in each of Iowa's nine crop districts. When the search was completed in north central Iowa, the farm Erik Thorson founded 142 years ago was declared the District Two winner.

Annis Thorson, age 87, Erik's grandson, and the owner of the farm, was already very ill when he learned of the search. However, he was glad to learn his farm was one of dozens of farms under consideration in the District's eleven north central Iowa counties.

On March 12, after the judging committee had finished its deliberation, a call went to the Thorson home to advise Annis and his wife, Rose, that their farm had been named the north central Iowa winner. Although Annis was on his death bed when the call came, Rose says the news was so gratifying that he experienced a sense of joy at the recognition for his farm. It can be said he died happy less than 24 hours later. Annis' funeral happened to take place on the very day of the public announcement of the ten state winning farms, of which his was one.

Going back to 1854 when Annis' grandfather first claimed the 80 acres, it must have been quite a challenge to clear land, build a crude cabin, break prairie sod, plant and harvest, but that is what Erik Thorson did for eleven years.

Then in 1865, he went back to Norway where a lady named Ragnild, who must have had the patience of Job, was waiting for him. They married there in Norway and when they got back to the Mitchell County homestead, Erik built an attractive two room log cabin for Ragnild in 1866. A year later, their only child, a son named Ole, arrived.

Farming now was undertaken more earnestly than before. A sizable barn was built, along with a corn crib and other farm buildings. Livestock was added to the farm enterprise. More land was bought and cleared.

As Ole grew up, he and his father worked closely together, and when Erik passed away in 1901, Ole inherited the farm.

Ole E. Thorson

Ole, who was born in 1867, lived on the farm his entire life until his death in 1938. In 1889, when he was 22, he married and he and his wife, Amelia, continued to work on his parent's farm all the while.

Ole and his wife outdid Ole's Norwegian parents considerably in the children's department. They had a family of nine. Annis, who eventually became the farm's sole owner with his wife, evidently was the oldest.

The farm has a long grove shaped like the letter "L". Amelia felt the property should be known as the "L" Wood Farm and the name has stuck ever since. The farm has grown to 183 acres, of which 166 are tillable.

On June 5, 1943, tragedy struck. Fire broke out in the machine shed close to the house after a tractor in the hands of a hired worker backfired, starting a blaze. Amelia, on seeing the smoke, quickly summoned the fire department. The flames spread quickly to a granary and chicken house. While watching, Amelia collapsed and died from a heart attack.

The next year, Annis and four of his siblings -- Clifford, Leon, Donald and Mildred -- bought the farm from Ole and the other four sisters and brothers and their spouses.

In 1969, Annis and his wife, Rose, bought out the others in the family and became sole owners of the property. They had two children. One of them is a son named Merlyn who continues to this day to help with the planting of crops and other details, including yard work around the house.

At one time, many different crops were raised on the Thorson farm, but now only corn, soybeans, and oats are grown. The planting, cultivating, and harvesting is done on a custom farming basis by Marvin and Roger Hanson.

Whereas cattle, hogs, and sheep were all raised for many years, there is no livestock in the yards anymore. However, Rose makes it clear she still has seven ducks to be cared for during the Sesquicentennial year.

A Farmall tractor displaced most of the horses in 1940.

The barn built back in the 1870s is still being used for storage. When the present house was built, Annis and Rose incorporated some logs as reminders of the first house their pioneer grandparents built of logs and stone.

The First Lutheran Church in St. Ansgar was built with generous help from Erik and his wife, Ragnild.

Annis was once a key figure in the U.S. Farmers Association and served as its president at one time.

The Thorson home.

DISTRICT WINNER
CROP DISTRICT #1 - NORTHWEST IOWA

THE WEST FARM
OF
EMMET COUNTY
Settled 1867

This sign is now posted on Wayne West's farm near Estherville, calling attention to Northwest Iowa's oldest family farm.

This is the story of Emmet County's oldest recorded pioneer farm family -the West Family. They were one of the ten families recognized in the Iowa Sesquicentennial Commission's search for the oldest farm in Iowa's nine crop districts. Because Emmet County is in extreme northwest Iowa, the area of the state which was the last to be settled, the West farm is the youngest of the ten farms honored by the Commission and the Iowa Department of Agriculture in 1996.

The story begins with George West and one of his brothers emigrating from Ireland to America in early 1861. Like so many thousands of other young Irishmen, they had lived through the aftermath of the potato famine that had literally destroyed the Emerald Isle in the late 1840s.

The island's population before the disaster caused by a severe blight that struck the potato fields was over eight million. Potatoes had been grown so successfully for untold years and had become about the only staple food in the entire country. So it was that when the blight destroyed the entire crop, more than 750,000 persons died of starvation.

Moreover, the disaster left virtually everyone poverty stricken and floundering, so that more than a million others left the "Olde Sod" for America or other lands. George West and his brother were two of them.

They did not come directly to Iowa in 1861, but they both had heard of the productive soil and of farming opportunities in Iowa and Illinois. However, the Civil War had just broken out when they reached New York, and any dreams they may have had then for settling in the Midwest had to be abandoned. Later, however, George spent the rest of his entire life in the Hawkeye State.

1861 was a time of great consternation. The war draft was on. Some wealthy families were able to hire a young man to take their son's place in the military. Young George was offered $100 to serve under another man's name, but he refused. Now that he was an American, he chose to enlist and serve under his own name.

When the bloody war was over, George was discharged, and, as payment for his service, received military certificates good for two quarter sections of land to be chosen somewhere west of the Mississippi. He probably lost no time in choosing Iowa because of the stories of its abundance and the fact that Emmet County was fast becoming an area of many Irish settlers.

He also lost little time in finding a bride, and on the westward journey to his Iowa land, he stopped for a time in Ohio where he found, and married, pretty Ann Cousins. Together, they then came by wagon train to their new home near Estherville in Emmet County.

Two additional acres were allotted in the military grant for the purpose of providing wood for a log cabin. However, with the winter coming on and severe cold approaching, West chose to erect a sod hut, believing it would be better protection against Old Man Winter's worst northwest Iowa blasts.

The next year, they did build a large log cabin which served them well for a number of years and was the birthplace of most of their eleven children, all but two of whom made it to adulthood. In time, however, George and Ann built a large frame house to accommodate their large family.

Wayne West, the present owner of the farm and a great grandson of George and Ann, says that although a fire destroyed all family records and pictures, stories handed down through the generations tell of the harsh winters and the wolves and other wild animals encountered by his early ancestors. It was a hard life, with land to be cleared and virgin prairie to be broken, and with markets far away. A trip to Algona by oxen and wagon to have a load of wheat ground into flour required three days. Much of the land needed drainage, and tiling had to be done by hand.

Wheat, corn, oats, and hay were grown; and cattle, hogs, sheep and chickens were raised. Horses soon started displacing the slow-moving oxen.

By the time George had the farm well established, the National Grange had become the nation's leading farm organization. By 1875, Iowa already had 924 sub-ordinate Granges with more than 42,000 Grange members, or Patrons of Husbandry as they called themselves.

While there is no record of George having joined the Grange movement, it is known his son, William, and probably most of his other sons, were Grangers.

Second owner of the farm was William West, one of George and Ann's nine grown children. William's wife's name was Martha, and they acquired the land in 1911. William raised purebred Shorthorns and sold breeding stock.

The crops he grew were much the same as his father's, but by then, more modern machines were making the work much lighter. However, field power still had to be provided by horses and mules. As many as 12 head were harnessed daily some years, including a couple of broncos.

The first tractor on the farm was an 18-36 International. It was bought in 1927 and was the forerunner of several makes of tractors on the West farm later, including John Deere, Case, Allis Chalmers, Oliver, and another International.

A tornado struck the farm in 1936, destroying several buildings.

William and Martha had only two children. One was a daughter, Ethel, and the other was a son, Arthur. Arthur, who became Wayne West's father, gained ownership of the farm in 1948. He and his wife, Gladys, were the farm's third owners. They had a family of four.

Arthur continued breeding Shorthorn cattle and raising hogs and sheep. He also was already in the farming picture when hybrid corn and soybeans started to become universally accepted. By 1948, corn yields were approaching 100 bushels an acre.

Wayne West, the present owner of the 160 acre farm, and his wife, Annette, had a family of ten children, one of whom died in infancy. The other nine were Timothy, Thomas, Tami, Theresa, Tony, Treva, Todd, Theodore (Ted), and Tricia.

Five of the seven remaining children in the Wayne West family. Tony and Theresa are in front, Treva, Tami, and Tricia are in back.

Wayne and Annette bought the farm in 1959. They switched from the Shorthorn cattle raised and bred by Wayne's father and grandfather to an Angus herd. They also were the first in Emmet County to bring in Simmental bulls for cross breeding.

They have concentrated on corn and soybeans as compared to the more diverse crop rotations used by those preceding them on the farm. Hogs were also raised until a few years ago.

Wayne and Annette continued to farm the land until 1994 when Annette was struck by a serious illness, but they still live in the home built on the farm in 1974. Annette has now regained much of her health. The farm is being rented to Kenneth Reinhardt.

Wayne says it has not been easy to provide for a family of nine. The children were never the most expensively dressed, but always clean and presentable with pride. He also tells of a family sweet corn project started when the older children were 9 or 10. It was quite an acreage and he and the children would go out early in the morning to harvest up to 200 dozen ears, then sell them to stores and from roadside stands. It was a special help financially, and taught responsibility to the children as well as giving them early business experience.

Tragedy struck the family twice in recent years. Both Tim and Tom were lost to Hodgkin's disease. It was a hard blow, but a supportive family and what Wayne calls "a wonderful community of neighbors" helped him and Annette to overcome.

Five grandchildren -- Matthew, Marci, Donald, James and Tyler -- and one great grandchild -- Samantha -- now brighten the West family home.

Wayne served in WW II in Italy, and is now an Emmet County Supervisor. The family is Catholic.

The great grandfather helped form what is known as the Woodmen's Lodge and proudly watched his seven sons join the organization all on the same day.

Youngest daughter Tricia, with her parents, Wayne and Annette, on her wedding day.

Iowa's Heritage of Pioneer Family Farms

Section Two
Farms 162 to 150 Years Old

LATTY FARM
OF
DES MOINES COUNTY
Settled 1834

Members of the Latty family of Des Moines County firmly believe their farm, which they assert has been in the hands of their family for 162 years or more, is the oldest family farm in Iowa. Family lore indicates the first Latty family member to come to Iowa as having arrived in the state as early as 1833.

Patricia Bischoff Latty, wife of John Coe Latty, the current and fourth owner of the farm, supports the family's contention with numerous written accounts. They include newspaper reports and obituaries, and the "History of Des Moines County" published in 1915. On page 512 of that publication, Mathew Latty is credited with becoming the first settler in the county's Benton Township on April 17, 1834.

However plausible the Latty family's conviction may be — and there seems little doubt that Mathew Latty and his wife, Sarah, staked a claim for a large parcel of Des Moines County land as early as 1834 — the land was not actually purchased until 1839. That is two years later than several other families in other Iowa counties had been able to obtain official documents verifying the date and place of 1837 farm purchases.

Be all that as it may, the Latty farm and family story is a kaleidoscope of conditions, problems, challenges, sorrows, and triumphs of pioneer farm settlers in the 1830s.

To go back to the beginning, Mathew Warren Latty, who came to Iowa before the mid-1830s, was born in Maryland in 1795 and was of Irish descent. When he was only five years old, his family moved to Kentucky where he grew up. He was only 18 when he joined the Kentucky militia in the War of 1812 and fought in the Battle For New Orleans.

In 1827, he married Sarah Rice and they became the parents of ten children, of which only five reached adulthood. In their desire to move West, they reached Illinois in 1831. By then, three children had already been welcomed.

In 1833 Mathew set out alone to explore land in what was known as the Black Hawk Purchase, west of the Mississippi. He reached Des Moines County and decided that was where he would like to settle. He then returned to Sarah and the children, then already numbering five. During the winter, he arranged for a covered wagon and a yoke of oxen. They left for Iowa in late March on what would be a journey of intense sorrow. Cholera, then a rampant epidemic among Indians, struck them soon after they left Illinois. One by one, the five children died and had to be buried along the way.

They ferried across the Mississippi on April 17, 1834. A log kept by Mathew shows they reached Des Moines County the morning of April 18. After traveling only a few miles, Sarah, grief stricken, exhausted, and pregnant, could go no farther. It was then and there that Mathew staked out 320 acres of the pioneer claim. It was in what would later be called Benton Township and would become the family's farm five years later and for all the years since then.

After building a log cabin, Mathew began breaking the prairie sod with his oxen and planting a few crops. On June 6, Sarah gave birth to another child, a son named John, the first white child to be born in the area. Within the next ten years, four more children were born. They were named James, Joseph, Mary and Sarah. All grew up to adulthood.

Among the many interesting things found in the Latty family records is the fact that an Indian trail was close to the cabin and that Sarah had to hide anything that was bright or shiny because it always appealed to the red men who would want to take the objects.

According to Patricia Latty, Mathew found he could not buy the land he had claimed in 1834 for another five years. Therefore, he had to wait until February 25, 1839, before he could demand making the purchase. It was not until October 21 that year that he was given a receipt from the Land Receivers Office in Burlington showing he had paid $200 for the first 160 acres of his 320 acre claim. The family still has the original document and it was not until December, 1841, that Mathew received a land patent bearing President Tyler's signature.

In 1850, a new frame home was built on the farm. Later, when the Civil War broke out, James Latty, the family's second oldest son, joined up and was in several of the historic battles during the War Between the States. After the war, he became the Sheriff of Des Moines County.

In 1867, Mathew sold a strip of his farm for $1 to the Burlington to Cedar Rapids Railway. A small village called Latty's Station sprang up alongside the new tracks on the Latty farmland. A post office, weighing station, general store and a few other buildings were soon erected. Mathew was also instrumental in the building of a school and a church. However, the only services held in the church were in the German language, so the Latty family, with its command of English and an Irish brogue, did not attend.

Mathew Latty lived to be 83, under 18 Presidents beginning with George Washington all the way through Ulysses Grant.

John, the oldest son, was killed in a horse and buggy accident, so Joseph Warren, the remaining son, took over the farm in 1882. He and his wife, the former Lucetta Ross, had a family of seven, one of whom was given the unusual name of Hallie Iowa. Their youngest son, John Penny, eventually became the third owner of the Latty farm, after he bought out his six siblings in 1939.

John Penny married Helen Gregson Coe in 1938. Their two children were John Coe and Carolyn Rose. In 1960, when his father died, John Coe inherited the farm. The next year, he was married to Patricia Bischoff, who is the party that has kept a record on the Latty family history since her husband's great grandfather arrived in Iowa.

John Coe and Patricia also have a son and a daughter, John Paul and Julia Ann. John Paul and his wife have a daughter, Emma, who represents the sixth generation of Lattys in Iowa.

John Coe has added to the farm's acreage, which now totals 700 acres.

HEDGES FARM OF DES MOINES COUNTY

Settled 1835

Des Moines County, in extreme Southeastern Iowa, certainly was one of the first counties in Iowa to become settled. One of the very first pioneer farms to be claimed, and where the present owner still has the same surname as his great-great grandfather, is the Hedges farm established in 1835. Now 161 years old, that farm certainly is one of Iowa's oldest.

Frank C. Hedges, who acquired the property in 1980, is the sixth member of the Hedges family to own the 450 acre place near Oakville, in what is often referred to as the "Heart" of the Mississippi Valley.

Frank's great-great grandfather was Joash Hedges. When Joash first acquired the farm from the U.S. Government in 1835 for $1.25 an acre, the prairie had to be broken before corn could be planted, or oats, barley, or wheat could be seeded. Much of the farm was left in prairie grasses for feed for the horses and the beef and dairy cattle bred on the farm. Hogs and chickens were also raised.

Joash's son, Jerome, whose wife's name was Elvira, gained possession of the farm in 1875, 40 years after it was first homesteaded. He was Frank Hedges' great grandfather. After his death, Elvira became the owner.

In the meantime, Percheron horses, Hampshire hogs, and Shorthorn cattle had been established as the livestock mainstay in the enterprise.

Jerome and Elvira had two children, one of whom was Benjamin , who became the next owner in 1930. By then, the acreage of the farm had already increased considerably, and a number of more modern machines had been purchased.

Fourteen years before Benjamin, Sr., and his wife had bought the farm, they became one of Iowa's earliest tractor owners. It was in 1916 and the new contraption that had some of the neighbors shaking their heads was a Waterloo Boy. A self binder that saved a lot of bundle-tying was purchased in 1918.

Benjamin, Sr. and his wife had two children. One of them was a son named Benjamin, Jr., who eventually became the fifth owner of the larger farm in 1954. He and his wife are the parents of the present owner, Frank C. Hedges, who had married Nita. They bought the 430 acres in 1980 and had decided on a name for the farm beforehand. Frank's nickname is "Sandy", so the combined parts of his nickname and a "Fran" ahead of her given name add up to an abbreviated farm name, "San Franita".

Frank and Nita have three children. All three are sons and all are still very much involved with Agriculture and "San Franita Farm". Steve works with his father on the farm. Dave is a farm mechanic. Steve lives on the original homestead place.

Hogs are now farrowed and finished on the farm. There are also about 60 beef cows now and their calves are fed out. The rest of the farm is devoted to grain farming.

Frank Hedges and some of the family's predecessors have kept copious notes, or diaries. There is sufficient material from which a full book could be written. Unfortunately, space in this book does not permit much elaboration. However, some special items should be mentioned.

For instance, during the Civil War, Benjamin Franklin Hedges was in the Battle of Arkansas where he was severely wounded and died three days later. Jerome Hedges, the second of the farm's owners and a Huron Grange member, received the Order of Patrons of Husbandry award for "Advancement of Agriculture". He was also an active debater.

When the Farm Bureau came to Des Moines County in 1918, both of Benjamin's parents were very much involved. Elders in the family also were on school boards, drainage ditch associations, and went to Washington to lobby for rural electrification.

In years since the turn of the century, members of the Hedges family have kept some interesting farm price records. Among them are those of 1918, when wheat was $2.05 a bushel; gas, 20 cents a gallon; eggs, 52 cents a dozen; and the 150-mile drive to the State Fair from Burlington on dirt roads took 12 hours. It was WW I and land prices started going sky high.

In 1936, corn jumped to $1.07 a bushel after drought ruined many fields, while cattle brought $6.40 a hundredweight, eggs were 15 cents a dozen, and soybeans, 63 cents a bushel.

In 1941, seed corn was up to $14 a bushel. By 1947, wheat hit a 50-year high at $3 a bushel and corn went to $1.81 per bushel for a 27-year top, while hogs brought 30 cents a pound.

Good neighbors were certainly on the job by then, too. In 1939, 133 men, 30 women, and 33 teams of horses and wagons came to one stricken Des Moines County neighbor to make short work of the corn harvest on that farm.

THE PRESTON FARM OF DUBUQUE COUNTY

Settled 1835

Dubuque County, Iowa, is replete with early American history. Names like Marquette, Joliet, and Julian Dubuque have long been associated with the famed old county along the Mississippi River.

Nor is it at all surprising that out of all the Iowa counties along the mighty Mississippi and everywhere else in the state, Dubuque County was one of the first to be settled by Iowa farm pioneers. Easterners seeking richer soil to farm started seeking land in Dubuque County, as well as some other eastern Iowa communities in the early 30s. By the mid-1830s, some claims were already recognized and recorded.

One such claim was that of Sylvester Bill Preston who paid the United States Government $1.25 an acre for 640 acres in 1835. Part of that land has remained in the Preston family's hands ever since. Now — 161 years later — 110 acres of it is owned and controlled by Donald Gustavus Preston and his wife Vineta. He is the great grandson of the original claimant.

Moreover, Donald Gustavus Preston's son, Donald R. Preston, and daughter, Greta Preston Hartman and her husband, Walter Hartman, represent a fifth generation active in the recognition of the Iowa Pioneer family farm.

Mrs. Hartman points out the family has authentic documents to prove theirs is the oldest farm in Dubuque County that has been continuously owned, operated, and controlled by the same single family. Some persons, including some historians, argue that the Preston farm is the oldest family farm in the state, although this claim is disputed by others.

Many pages would be required to tell the whole Preston farm story. Briefly, it should be pointed out that Sylvester Bill Preston — sometimes referred to as "Samuel" — was born in Maryland and was trained as a chemist. He came to Dubuque County from Mineral Point, Wisconsin, in 1835. He had served at erecting, testing and managing a copper ore smelter in the Wisconsin city.

That same year, 1835, he registered a claim for 640 acres in Mosalem Township. He and his wife, Ann, had five children, most of them born on the farm.

They resided on the claim for a short time after it was registered, but had to leave temporarily because of Indian problems. Then, as soon as the government secured the land, they returned.

The land was all along the Mississippi and very productive. Preston bought the large acreage partly for farming purposes, but also as an investment.

In the beginning, prairie crops grown on the large pioneer farm included potatoes, corn and wheat. Prairie grass grew so thick and tall that a man had to get on horseback to see over an entire prairie grass field. The 1850 census states that oxen, milch cows, sheep, hogs, and horses were raised on the farm. That year as many as six oxen could be yoked up at a time. Beeswax and honey were also produced.

Sylvester Preston himself was a busy individual, juggling his time between the farm and his profession as a mining chemist, constantly testing ore. He died in 1852 at a young age.

When only 12 years old, Sylvester's son, Gustavus Vasal, started to express interest in the farm. Soon he was doing much work in fields and with the cattle. Recognizing that interest, his father gave him a few acres to work with, and ultimately about 112 acres to use as his own. By the time the Civil War broke out, he had cleared most of the timber and was growing grain crops.

When hostilities between the states broke out, he and his brother, David Hollingsworth Preston, both joined up, but Gustavus was discharged because he was under age. His brother became a corporal in the 21st Iowa Infantry and died from wounds suffered in the battle of Vicksburg. A brother-in-law, Dr. Jesse Hibbs, served as a surgeon in the war four years before he, too, was killed.

Soon after the war, Gustavus bought the 112 acres, expanding the cropping program to include corn, wheat, oats, along with clover and timothy hay, and started to increase the dairy herd and the hog drove. He and his wife, Melissa, had three children, two daughters and a son named David Orlando.

David Orlando Preston, father of the current owner, did a lot of the farming before becoming the farm's owner in 1932. He was a dairyman, adding some Guernseys to the herd to increase butterfat content. Hogs and sheep were also raised. He also added oats to the cropping program.

He and his wife, Anne, had only one child, Donald Gustavus, who, along with his wife, now operate the 110 remaining acres of the farm, which is now in the CRP Program. Before putting the land in the conservation program, however, David grew corn, oats, alfalfa, brome grass, and clover.

David Orlando Preston, the father of the present owner, was a Dubuque business college graduate who had earned his degree the hard way. It called for walking nearly five miles through the woods and along the railroad tracks every morning and late afternoon and then having his farm chores to do when he got home. However, with a business degree, he chose to farm the 1835 farm then called "Cottage Hill". His cropping program was much like his father's, but he added Guernseys to the dairy herd. He also had an orchard and a large garden producing produce for the Dubuque Farmer's Market.

David married Anna Johnson, a Swedish immigrant girl. They had two children — a girl, Gerde, who died as an infant, and a son, Donald Gustavus, who is now the farm owner. Donald married Vineta Kifer in 1938. They became the parents of Gerde Ann, who has provided all the information on the 161 year old pioneer farm, and a son, Donald Robert.

Like his father, Donald chose farming over University opportunities. He has continued the dairy, hog, and crop production enterprises for which the farm has long been known, but has also served the State Highway Commission. In addition, he and Vineta have held memberships in the Presbyterian Church and Farm Bureau. He has also served on the Election Board, Triple A Committee, Rockdahe Cemetery Board, Township Trustee, and School Board.

One hundred ten acres of the 640 originally claimed in 1835 was purchased by Donald and Vineta in 1943. It was renamed "Preston Sesquicentennial Farm" in 1986 after 150 years of ownership in the same family, and is now enrolled in the Conservation Reserve Program.

THE FOGGO-FOGGY-ABELL FARM OF LEE COUNTY

Settled 1836

Eliza Jane and Andrew Foggy, great grandmother & great grandfather.

James Foggo was born in Edinburgh, Scotland, in 1796 and came to America in 1820. After first settling in western Virginia (which is now West Virginia), he came to Iowa in 1836.

On the arrival of the Foggo family west of the Mississippi, they laid claim to a tract of land in what is now Pleasant Ridge Township in Lee County. At the time of the claim, the area was known as Wisconsin Territory.

State Historical Society records verify that in 1836 the census records show that James Foggo was able to make the final purchase of several tracts of land from the Government for $1.25 an acre on November 27, 1836.

James Foggo was the great-great grandfather of Jane Foggy Abell, who now owns the 160-year old farm jointly with her mother, Mrs. Glenn Foggy. Mrs. Abell provided dozens of pages of documented material, letters, copies of land patents, pictures, and other materials to prove the Foggo family's land acquisition took place in the mid-1830s. The Foggo name was changed to Foggy soon after 1838.

James married Margaret Aflack, also of Scotland, whom he had met on the long ocean voyage coming to America. They had seven children. Shortly after coming to Lee County in 1836, they built a log cabin in which some of their younger children grew up.

Andrew Foggy, son of James and Margaret Foggo, was a rugged, colorful, enterprising early Iowa pioneer. He learned to chew tobacco from Indian neighbors while only eight years old. His Kentucky long rifle, powder horn, bullet mold, leather money belt, and gold nugget from Colorado, and an ox

The barn in 1870 after a tornado had struck.

yoke he used in those long ago times are now in the proud possession of Mrs. Abell.

During his boyhood and youth, Andrew assisted his father on the farm, including hauling dressed hogs to town where the meat was sold for 1-1/2 cents per pound. Venison, however, brought 3 cents a pound, but prairie chickens, easily trapped or shot, brought virtually nothing.

Andrew was also something of an adventurer. In 1863, he drove two yokes of oxen pulling a wagon loaded with farm produce to Colorado. Two years later, he drove four yokes of oxen to Montana with a load of bacon, sugar, and coffee.

Andrew was 40 when he married Eliza Cooper, who was born in Ireland, the youngest daughter in a family of 15. She was only three years old when her parents took her with them to America. The Andrew Foggys were highly successful farmers, operating several hundred acres of land devoted to corn, oats, and hay land, and raised horses, cattle, hogs and sheep. They bought the farm in 1864.

They also raised two children, a son and a daughter. The son's name was John Cooper Foggy. He eventually became the farm's owner. John C., who was Mrs. Abell's grandfather, was born in 1873 and got his elementary education in Mt. Pleasant. He then attended business college in Quincy, Illinois. However, instead of launching a career in business, he went back to farming on his parent's 256 acres and then bought 124 acres of his own.

John was married to Leona Klopfenstein in 1898. They welcomed a son, Glenn, and a daughter, Fern. They continued to farm the home place and were able to buy it by 1915. They specialized in raising Percheron horses and Hereford cattle. They also added to the farm's acreage.

John Foggy also served as Township Clerk and as president of the school board. In 1944, he sold his farm to his son, Glenn.

Glenn Cooper Foggy, born in the year 1900, was Jane Foggy Abell's father. He married Loretta Markert, and Jane was their only child. She was the fifth generation in the family that had come to this country in 1820.

Glen and Loretta operated the farm much like their parents had, only with the benefit of tractors and other modern machines and with improved seeds and cultural methods. At Glenn's death, the farm, now 172 acres in size, was passed on to his wife who now owns it in partnership with their daughter, Mrs. Abell. The farm is now rented out to Melvin Moeller.

Jane and her husband, Charles Abell, were married in 1960. They have a family of four — three sons, Charles, John and Michael, and a daughter, Heather. They are the family's sixth generation representatives.

When asked the organizations and associations with which the Abell family is now identified, Jane's reply was simply, "Too numerous to mention."

WOODLAND HEIGHTS FARM of THE PARSONS-SMITH FAMILIES OF LOUISA COUNTY

Settled 1836

In a painfully hand-penciled, hard-to-read letter, plus a full set of answers he wrote on a questionnaire, Will C. Smith of Wapello has sent a wealth of information about what is certainly one of the oldest family farms in Iowa.

The 86-year old Louisa County farmer and community leader, whose memory takes him back almost to the turn of the Century, states that the Pioneer Farm of which he is the present owner, was established by his great-great grandfather back in 1836. That year, Andrew Jackson was still serving as President.

The first to purchase the land was Jonathan Parsons, who bought 360 acres from Wm. Toole and John Burris. They had homesteaded the property a year or two earlier when the Indians were about their only neighbors.

Josiah Parsons, son of Jonathan and his wife, Mary, became the second owner in 1848. He was Will Smith's great grandfather. Next, it went to a bachelor great uncle, before it was returned to the Parsons family in the person of Smith's great grandmother, Mary Coleman Parsons.

Mrs. Parsons had three children, one of whom was a daughter, Olive, who married a man named Smith and became the fifth owner. This is where the name "Smith" entered the procession of owners.

One of Olive Smith's children was Earl, who was the sixth generation to own the land and the father of Will Smith, the present 86-year old owner, who has two children, making it seven generations to be involved in what is now known as Woodland Heights Farm.

Wheat, corn, oats and hay were the first crops grown on the farm after the sod was broken. Cattle and hogs were also raised. As many as 20 horses and mules provided the power in the fields until the first tractor — a Ford — was bought in 1925. Prior to that, a Huber steam engine was used for threshing.

The first gang plow came in during the very early 1900s and a wire trip equipped corn planter in 1926. Electricity arrived in 1932, but there was no combine until 1948. After the 1925 Ford tractor became worn out, other tractors were bought including International, Allis-Chalmers, and Case.

It wasn't always easy to operate the 160-year old pioneer farm. In 1933, corn was selling for 10 cents a bushel and veal calves brought 10 cents a pound. 1934, '35, and '36 were drought years. That four year period was disheartening, to say the least.

The family also knows something about war. A great uncle, Bentley Coleman, was in the Civil War. A nephew, Dr. M.B. Nichols, was in the Korean conflict. Another nephew, David Swerly, was killed in the Vietnam war, while another member of the family, Doug Kaisau, was crippled there. Will's son served in the Army Reserves.

Interesting recollections came forth in Will Smith's letters. One told of his father trading a team of horses for a Model T Ford as early as 1914. Another told of the Civil War veteran, Bentley Coleman, going to Oregon right after the war and not keeping in touch for 35 years. Will's grandfather was a successful auctioneer for many years.

As for Will C. Smith and his family, the list of community activities and memberships is long and impressive. Some include:

Charter member, the Louisa County Conservation Board —
County Farmer's Home Administration Board 3 years —
County Condemnation Board for ten years —
County Farm Bureau Federation chairman —

Chairman of numerous church boards and a choir member —
Chairman of the Izaak Walton League several years —
Co-organizer of Indian Hills Golf Club —
Fifty year 32 degree member of the Masonic Lodge.

In addition, Mrs. Smith has served as Worthy Matron of Eastern Star.

It's surprising that Will Smith had time to do any farming on his 360-acre pioneer family farm, but he managed to squeeze that in, too.

THE ROBISON-BRUS FARM OF SCOTT COUNTY

Settled 1836

One of Iowa's oldest Pioneer Family Farms is a Scott County farm currently owned by Mrs. Violet Brus.

A resume received from Violet Brus tells that her husband's great grandfather was John Robison, an Indiana native who married Mary Elizabeth Oswalt McSkimens on January 28, 1836. Their "honeymoon" was in the form of an oxen-drawn covered wagon trip to the Wisconsin Territory.

On arrival on the west side of the Mississippi, they claimed a 160-acre tract near Davenport, then a struggling village. The first thing they did was build a log cabin in the timber near a spring in what is now Buffalo Township.

Their first child, named Joseph Parks, arrived in late November that year. Two daughters were born later.

They had two yokes of oxen to break the prairie, both on their own claim and for other settlers. Compared to the stony ground he had left in Indiana, Robison found the rich, black Scott County soil free of rocks, and a welcome contrast to what he had known back East.

Official title to the land could not be obtained until 1841. Five years later, he started building a two-story, six-room log house near a new road. The resourceful pioneer went to Wisconsin in the winter to cut pine logs and have them sawed into lumber, then floated the lumber down the Mississippi to Buffalo. He picked it up there and used it for floors, doors, etc. When the new home was completed in 1848, he had enough lumber left over to build a barn.

In 1850, Robison was killed when he fell under a run-away wagon loaded with sacks of grain. His widow continued to live on the pioneer farm until her death in 1881.

Second owner of the farm was the Robison's youngest daughter, Eliza (born 9-24-1840) and her husband, Jacob Brus, who was born on 11-29-1829 in Prussia. He came to the United States in 1846 and moved to Iowa in the late 1840s. After serving as a hired farm hand for six years, he used his savings to buy, and use, a threshing machine until 1861, the year he married Eliza. With money earned from threshing, he started buying land, and eventually became one of Scott County's most successful, largest, and wealthiest farmers.

Jacob and Eliza had eleven children.

One of their daughters, Lena, married a Muscatine County youth whose surname was the same as hers. He was John Henry Brus, and they were the third couple to own the farm. They purchased the property in 1902.

John H. Brus must have been very fond of horses. At one time, he had 33 of them in his barn, and used them for pulling his many machines in the fields.

John and Lena had a family of five, one of whom is Walter J. Brus, who, with his wife, Violet, became the pioneer farm's owners July 2, 1958.

The farm had been 340 acres originally, but Highway 61 was built through the farm and then widened twice, so only 288 acres are left.

Now, in this Sesquicentennial year, the farm has been rented to Delmar Meyer. A beef cow herd makes up the livestock program, while corn and soybeans are now the cropping rotation.

In earlier years, dairy cows, hogs, and Shorthorn cattle were raised, along with Belgian horses and some turkeys and chickens. Corn has always been raised on the rich Scott County soil, but wheat and flax were other crops grown when John Robison and Jacob Brus were doing the farming. In 1932 and 1933, chinch bugs decimated crops for John H. Brus.

John's first tractor was a Rock Island, used as early as 1915, a real novelty in the neighborhood that early in the tractor era.

Mrs. Brus continues to be a member of the Farm Bureau and of the Blue Grass Community Club.

THE SCHWEER FARM OF LEE COUNTY

Settled 1836

The Schweer Family Story is not only one of the oldest of all the Iowa pioneer farm families, but certainly also one of the most fascinating.

It all started with Christopher Schweer, who was born in Hanover, Germany, in the early 1800s, but left his native country, family, and friends to go alone to the New World to see what fortune might hold in store for him. And he certainly found a lot.

After arriving in New Orleans, he came up the Mississippi and, lured by the promise of the unsettled and unsullied frontier, purchased a claim in Lewis County, Missouri, in 1835. Then he heard that the BlackHawk War in Iowa had opened land for claims on fertile river valley soil. His next move was to go up and see for himself in the Spring of 1836.

Schweer must have liked what he saw in what would soon become Lee County because he soon staked out a 160-acre claim, started working it, and then returned to his Missouri claim for the winter. However, by then he was totally convinced southeast Iowa, although still a frontier, was the place for him and his large family, then still in Germany.

In early 1837, he returned to what would become Iowa nine years later. He worked his claim hard, decided it would be his family's final home, and the following year returned to Germany to get his family.

While enroute to his homeland, Schweer dreamed about starting a nursery when he returned, so while Dora, his wife, and their seven children were busy packing, he bought hundreds of young fruit trees and took them to Iowa with his family. It was a month-long crossing through the sub-tropics, so the trees sprouted and leafed out before the journey ended, but enough were saved so that a large orchard could be, and was, established.

The German immigrant and his family found pioneer Iowa farm life difficult. Wheat had to be hauled long distances and brought only 25 cents a bushel. Awaiting their turn at grinding mills, they frequently had to wait a whole week before their grain could be ground.

One of Christopher and Dora's seven children was Conrad, who had been well-educated in Germany's schools. He became the second owner of the pioneer farm. Although highly proficient in German, he immediately set forth to master English as soon as he arrived in Iowa. Thus, with a good command of both languages, he became one of Lee County's most influential pioneer citizens.

In 1853, Conrad married Sophia Klinder, who had also been born in Germany. According to "A Biographical Album of Lee County", the couple raised eight children, added several hundred acres to the original holdings, and established one of the finest farmsteads in the county.

The "Album" stresses that each one of the children was given a liberal education in both English and German. As a farmer, Conrad Schweer was quick to accept the most modern farming practices of his time and bought costly machinery. He also developed one of the best purebred Shorthorn cattle herds of his day.

In spite of his foreign birth, Conrad Schweer, who was a strong Democrat, was elected to both the 13th and 14th General Iowa Assemblies. The "Biographical Album" concluded with the words, "As a farmer, he has no superior, and as a factor in the industrial interests in this area, he occupies a position that could scarcely be filled by any other man."

Third owners of the farm, which now totaled over 760 acres, were Louis and his wife, Emma, who had gained possession in 1894. They were the great grandparents of the present owners of the farm, Mr. & Mrs. Donald Schweer. The "History of Lee County" credits Louis and his wife as maintaining the farm and farmstead in the excellent condition in which it came into their hands. They also became the parents of eight children, five of whom survived. Louis continued to uphold the traditions of the Democratic Party and served in a number of Township offices, in addition to attending numerous Party conventions.

In 1934, several of Louis and Emma's children — Eva, Paul, Erich, Edward, and Walter — became joint owners of the property; and in 1945, Walter apparently bought out the interests of his siblings. Walter and his wife had three children, one of whom is Donald who now owns the farm with his wife, the former Lillian Kirchner. They first purchased part of it in 1963 and acquired the rest in 1971. Their daughter, Sandy, who married John Fedler, represents the sixth generation on the Schweer farm. Nor does the family story stop there. Sandy and John have a son observing his fourth birthday this Sesquicentennial year, 160 years after his great grandfather, seven times removed, first set foot on Iowa soil.

Donald and Lillian have done a wonderful job of tracking down the Schweer family history. They point out how wheat was the first crop back in 1836, followed by rotations involving corn, oats, and hay. Apples, cherries, and other fruits were also significant in the farm's total production for many years.

Wheat was abandoned many years ago, and soybeans have been added to the program for the last half century.

The farm now numbers some 300 acres and is devoted to the production of corn, soybeans, oats, and hay and to raising cattle, sheep and chickens.

Back in 1837, a log cabin was built, and three years later it was replaced by a large rock house. The rocks were hauled to the building site from a distant point by oxen. It must have been well built because it served as the home for four generations of Schweers, which totaled 25 children and their parents.

When she was an eighth grader, Sandra Schweer, daughter of the current farm owners, wrote a school essay about the "Old Rock House" in which she tells that the structure had seven large rooms, two big pantries, and an attic in which children loved to play. They even had a club house up there.

She adds that the outside walls were 30 inches thick, and that there also was a dark, dungeon-like basement. Then Sandra concluded her essay by saying, "If this old house could talk, it would really have some stories to tell."

Donald was one of the children born in the Old Rock House and has lived on the pioneer farm he now owns all his life. While an FFA member, he earned the Iowa Farmer Degree and sang in both the Future Farmer State and National choruses. He still remembers the first tractor he drove — a John Deere "B". Since then , a larger John Deere, a Fordson, and an I.H. tractor have been used. His father bought his first corn picker in 1951 and the first combine in 1953.

The family has been, and continues to be, active in the St. Paul's U.C.C. Church, and in the Farm Bureau, Iowa Sheep Producers, and the Iowa Soybean Association.

Their daughter, Sandy, was named Lee County's outstanding 4-H member and was listed in the "Who's Who" among high school students. She is now a Respiratory Therapist.

THE DODDS FAMILY FARM OF DES MOINES COUNTY

Settled 1837

Another one of Iowa's oldest farms is the Dodds farm near Danville in Des Moines County. It was first settled by William Drennan Dodds and his young wife, Mary, in 1837, nine years before Iowa became the 36th state in the Union.

Second owner was Aaron E. Dodds, one of William and Mary's youngest sons, who acquired the 640 acre tract in 1888, followed by one of his sons, Bert E. Dodds, in 1935, and then the present owner, U. Ellsworth Dodds, Bert's only son, in 1966. The farm now has been brought down to 120 acres.

Original cost of the land when William Drennon Dodds bought it from the U.S. Government by decree of President Jackson, was $1.25 an acre. Today, the average Des Moines County farm is valued at over $2000 an acre.

The Dodds family farm's story is almost a book within itself. William

Drennan Dodds was the oldest child of Joseph and Mattie Dodds of Kentucky. He was born in 1811 and moved with his parents to Illinois where he married 14-year old Mary Eads in September, 1834.

The next spring, the young couple got a team of horses and a covered wagon and set forth for Iowa. It must have been a crowded wagon. Besides William and Mary, it carried meat, bread stuffs, and other foods, some hay and feed for the horses, numerous sheepskins for bedding, four hens and a rooster, a brood sow , and some furniture. Behind it, they tied a milk cow.

Arriving at the Mississippi across from Burlington, they ferried across the swollen stream and went to a village called Pleasant Grove. However, by then, there was no feed left for the horses and the cow, so William cut down some tender young saplings to feed the animals.

During the night, the horses broke loose. William, after finding a nearby settler's young girl to stay with his pregnant wife, set forth on a two-day search for the horses. He finally found them where they had been caught and tied up by an earlier settler who refused to accept any reward for his kind deed.

That fall, Mary, then only 16, gave birth to William Elbert, the first of sixteen children, all of whom grew to adulthood except two. Second youngest, Aaron arrived in 1868, and later took over the farm.

By midsummer, 1835, most of their provisions were gone, but William was able to buy several barrels of corn meal from a steamship crew. Sixty chicks were raised and wild game was always available. Some roasting ears of corn had also been grown, and wheat for seeding came in from Illinois.

Although not hostile, Indians often came into the log cabin to beg or steal food those first years. One day in 1836, Mary was horrified when the Indians took her baby to their village, only to decorate him with beads and trinkets, and return him unhurt to the worried and grateful young mother.

Soon after the log cabin was built in 1837, right after the land was purchased, a barn was also built. Today, that old barn is still standing and is used for storing hay.

Before tractors came into the picture during Bert Dodds' tenure, Shire horses were the power mainstay on the farm. Several different makes of tractors have been used since 1935, including Allis Chalmers, John Deere, Case, and International.

Chinch bugs made life miserable in 1934, the last year Aaron Dodds owned the property. A wet spring and drought were worrisome in 1935 and 1936 just after Bert had acquired ownership. Incidentally, Bert Dodds was Des Moines County's State Representative for ten years. During the first years on the farm, an orchard was planted and the original owner, William, raised wheat, oats, corn and hay. Since then, Bert and Ellsworth added alfalfa and soybeans to the crop rotation.

In addition to horses and dairy cattle, the Dodd family had Shropshire sheep early on as well, and also purchased Chester White hogs that were raised and sold. Poland China hogs also were raised as were registered Brown Swiss dairy cattle. Of course, chickens were also raised, mostly by the family's women folks.

Ellsworth Dodds and his family, owners of the farm since 1966, are active in the Methodist Church, serving on the church board as well as on the school board. They also belong to the Farm Bureau. A son, Herbert Dodds, representing the fifth generation of the Iowa branch of the family, has been a member of the Iowa National Guard.

THE HOOK FARM OF LOUISA COUNTY

Settled 1837

Bill and Darlene Hook, 5th generation owners of Lonesome Pine Farm.

One of Iowa's oldest Pioneer family farms is the Hook Farm, now known as the Lonesome Pine Farm, near Wapello in Louisa County, established in 1837. Throughout these 159 years, Hook has been the only surname associated with the pioneer farm.

The farm was homesteaded by Elisha Hook, the great-great grandfather of the present occupant, William B. Hook and his family. A detailed record of every day of Hook family ownership of the original 80 acres has been furnished by the current owner and operator for use in this book.

The record shows that Elisha Hook and his wife, Jane, both born in the early 1790s, were both natives of Virginia. Elisha, of Irish and Scottish ancestry, was engaged in farming in Virginia when he, with his family, emigrated to Indiana in 1835.

They remained in Indiana only two years before they set forth for Iowa. In the spring of 1837, they crossed the turbulent Mississippi River and settled in the small village of Toolesboro, named for W.L. Toole. Shortly thereafter,

Great-great-great grandchildren of Elisha Hook, Randy Hook and Connie Hook Rohwer; Great-great grandson and present owner, William Hook; Great-great-great-great granddaughter, Jaime Hook.

Elisha entered a claim for 80 acres of good land not far from the Mississippi. A log cabin was built, a few acres of the prairie broken, and some corn (then known as "maize") was planted. Later, wheat and oats were also grown.

Elisha and Jane were staunch founding members of the Presbyterian Church in their community. Seven children were raised, one of which was George W. who inherited the land in 1853. He was also born in Virginia and was just 12 years old when he came to Louisa County with his parents and several younger brothers and sisters.

George W. Hook, the Hook farm's second occupant had quite a career before he started farming in 1853. After leaving home at age 22, he became a salesman for merchandise at a Yellow Springs, Iowa, store. After that, he went to Iowa City as a clerk for a year. Next he joined two others, Lorenzo Harman and Willard Mallory, in buying a yoke of oxen and set forth with them on the long trek to California where they did some gold mining and George got into a successful mercantile adventure.

Accordingly, he bought a good horse, and then, dressed like a poor, unsuccessful tramp, put $10,000 worth of gold in his saddle bags and rode back to Louisa County.

With that rather sizable pile of gold for the year 1853, he converted it into cash and was able to purchase 306 acres near his father's homestead and established a home on that property. He married soon thereafter, and became the father of nine, the oldest of which was a son, named Alonzo B. Hook, who took over the farm in 1895 at the time of his father's death.

Alonzo, of the third generation in the Hook family to have the farm which included the original 80 acres, and William Hook's grandfather, had the farm in his name until 1933, but experienced some difficult times during that period.

Most of the land was lost to unconscionably high taxes caused by the building of a huge levee along the Mississippi. Alonzo and his wife had three children, one of whom was Albert A. Hook, William's father, who took over the management of the land in 1933 soon after Alonzo's death. Albert and his wife had a son, who is William, now the fifth generation owner of the pioneer farm. William and his wife, Darlene, took possession in 1951, and stayed in partnership with his father until 1978, when Albert passed away.

William, known to many as "Bill", and Darlene are the parents of three — Connie, Randy, and George. They are the sixth generation to live on the farm which now totals 540 acres, including the 80 Elisha bought 159 years ago.

The Bill Hooks also have four grandchildren, who constitute a seventh generation of Hooks, but none live on the farm their great-great-great-great grandfather homesteaded back in 1837.

In 1981, the farm was incorporated and named "Lonesome Pine Farm" because of a lone pine tree on the property. Ownership is now shared with Bill and Darlene's three children. The farm now is devoted to grain farming.

Bill says the original early Patents and Registrations are not available on Elisha's first 80 acres because the county courthouse burned in 1837 and all of the earliest farm records burned with it. It is known the original eighty was acquired by Squatters Rights and claimed by markers of stone. Undoubtedly, Elisha Hook was a determined fighter to hold onto land so crudely marked, but there is no doubt he was able to do so.

There are precious few farms in Iowa older than 159 years, and even fewer where every owner and operator through all those years had borne the same last name as is true of the Hook family.

It should be added that throughout all that time each generation has sought to be a credit to his community. Through the years, the Presbyterian and Methodist faiths have been important to every family member, as has Masonry, and now the Order of Eastern Star, P.E.O. and T.T.T. as well. ASCS committee men's positions were filled for over 40 years.

Although there is no livestock on the farm now, records show that over the years Hereford and Angus beef cattle, Holstein dairy cows, and Hampshire hogs, along with chickens, were raised extensively.

Horses and mules furnished the power in the fields many years, but that changed in the 1930s when a Fordson tractor was bought, followed subsequently by Allis Chalmers, Massey Ferguson, Ford, Oliver, and White tractors. Two bottom gang plows, wire-drip corn planters, and a Delco Light plant were purchased in the early 1920s, a large grain binder in 1930, followed by a mechanical corn picker in 1940 and a combine in 1950.

Asked for the worst and best years of farming, the answer comes quickly. The droughts in the mid 1930s were the worst and the record yields of 1994 the best.

THE BELKNAP FARM OF DES MOINES COUNTY

Settled 1838

The sixth generation of Belknaps are now farming the Belknap Farm in Des Moines County, Iowa. They are brothers Mike and Craig Belknap, sons of the late William Belknap and his wife, Shirley.

Founder of the Belknap farming enterprise was Silas Gardner Belknap, great-great grandfather of Mike and Craig. Silas was able to buy 180 acres near a place called Hickory Point, now known as Northfield, on November 7, 1838. Cost was $1.25 an acre. A land patent on the property could not be obtained, however, until December 1, 1941.

Second to own the property was Silas' son, William Miller Belknap and his wife, Mary, in 1853. During William's period of ownership, 40 acres were sold to Orson Belknap, and some other acres changed hands several times, but most of the original acres Silas had procured were not sold.

In 1880, William and Mary's son, Louis Harrison Belknap, and his wife, also named Mary, became the owners of 153 acres bought from his mother. Louis also bought 120 additional acres nearby.

In 1921, Everett and Margarette Belknap started to farm the land, and he was able to buy 250 acres from the family and 40 more from a neighbor. That 40 acres was part of what Silas Belknap had originally homesteaded.

William Louis Belknap, the son of Everett and Margarette, started his farming activities when he was only 19. Later, he was married to Shirley Janssen in 1956. His mother sold the large pioneer farm to them on March 1, 1972.

In addition to operating the 280 acre family farm which he eventually owned, William also rented 596 acres, making his one of the largest farms in the county.

William's widow, Shirley, and her two sons, Mike and Craig, have been doing the farming since their father's death. The farm that is now owned by the Belknap family totals 235 acres. How much additional land is rented is uncertain.

Looking at the history of the various owners is interesting.

Silas, the original pioneer, who had been born in New York State, had married Naomi Miller in 1817. They later moved to New Milford, Pennsylvania, and became the parents of eight children.

In 1921, Louis and Mary retired and their oldest son, Everett Harrison, took over. Everett had married Margarette Todd in 1916, and they moved with their first-born, a daughter, to the old homestead in 1921. Three sons were born later.

Everett and Margarette got their first car, a Model T Ford, in the early 1920s and drove it to the State Fair.

The 1930s were hard years with the Depression, pitifully low farm prices, and droughts, but they survived and in 1949 bought the family farm. Four years later, they bought 40 more acres from a neighbor, thereby reclaiming the last of Silas Belknap's homestead and putting the original farm all back together.

As for William Louis Belknap (the husband of Shirley, the woman that sent close to 50 pages of information), he, too, was an outstanding farmer with all the latest of modern equipment and cultural practices at his disposal.

However, William Louis was only a Junior in high school when his father passed away. His older brother came back from the Air Force to take over the farming until William was 19 in 1955. William then took over the farm alone.

He bought a $1600 corn picker that fall, raised 120 pigs, and borrowed money from the bank for a wedding suit so he could marry Shirley Janssen the next year. Four children were born to the couple — Christina, Michael, Judith, and Craig.

For a time, William was in partnership with his mother on a livestock project, but he gave that up for grain farming. He rented a lot more land, bought more machinery, and in 1972 bought the pioneer farm from his mother. It was a $90,000 investment in 235 acres.

By 1977, he was raising 400 acres of corn, 300 of soybeans, 12 of hay land, and 8 of oats.

William has since passed away and the farm is now owned by Margarette in partnership with Shirley and Shirley's two sons, Michael and Craig. They are now the sixth generation farming the 158 year old farm first homesteaded in 1838.

THE LYON-ADAMS FARM OF JOHNSON COUNTY

Settled 1838

To properly set the stage for the story of what is now known as the Pioneer Oaks Farm, Bruce A. Adams, one of the present owners, writing from Phoenix, Arizona, early in Iowa's Sesquicentennial year, told about the "Dillon Furrow".

He says, "Of great historical interest is the location of the ancestral home on what was known as the 'Dillon Furrow', plowed by oxen from Dubuque to what was then called Napoleon (now known as Iowa City).

"The location of the pioneer family farm which apparently had some old oak trees on it is ten miles north of what is now Iowa City. In the early years, it was frequently used as a stage coach stop known as 'The Ten Mile House'."

That the farm is easily one of Iowa's oldest, and certainly must have been one of the first in Johnson County, is evidenced by Bruce Adams' account in which he refers to 1837. The account goes on to say:

"Robert Lyon, the original homesteader, moved from Venango County, Pennsylvania, to Iowa in 1837, arriving by boat at Bloomington (now Muscatine). He brought along his wife, Elizabeth, and six of their nine children. Leaving the family camped in the 'slough area' of Bloomington, he went on to Cedar Township in Johnson County to stake a claim, cut trees for a home, and clear a little land. On returning to Bloomington, he sickened with a plague and fever and died on July 26."

At the occasion of Robert Lyon's untimely death, the oldest son was only 15. Apparently, just before his death, the early pioneer had been able to give his wife the exact location of the claim, which was many miles from Bloomington.

Somehow Elizabeth managed to keep her family together that fall of 1837 and the long, hard winter of 1837-38. Early in the spring of 1838, she and the children, including the 15-year old, of course, managed to get to the claim in Johnson County.

With the help of kindly neighbors, a crude cabin of logs and stone was built and some crops were planted. The "Dillon Furrow" referred to earlier now enters the story. Dillon made the 75 mile furrow with a yoke of oxen.

Now a crude road, what had once been a single furrow from Dubuque to Napoleon (which is now Iowa City), led right by the Lyon claim. Money with which to pay off the claim was desperately needed, so Elizabeth sent the 15-year old son, oldest of the children brought to Iowa, up the Dillon Furrow to the lead mines near Dubuque where he could earn money to help pay for the land his father had claimed.

In the meantime, however, because the land had not been paid for when claimed, another family, wishing to have a home on the "Dubuque Road" as the Dillon Furrow came to be known, jumped the claim and paid for twelve acres. Fortunately, the Lyons were able to get title to the rest of the original 160 acres, but the property was reduced to only 148 acres instead of a full quarter section. The cost was $1.25 an acre, as was true of all other land purchased from the U.S. Government in 1838.

Elizabeth Lyon was Bruce Adams' great-great grandmother. One of her sons, Ebenezer, and his wife, Henrietta, became the second owners. They had a family of five, one of whom was John Lyon.

John married Isabel Keene Adams, and they were Bruce's grandparents. One of their sons, Richard, who married Lucille Shercliff, became the fourth owner, but had no children. However, they adopted Bruce, who was a nephew, as well as adopted son, and who eventually became the fifth and present owner of the land the family acquired in 1838.

In 1976, Bruce and his wife, Eloise, incorporated the farm and named it the Pioneer Oaks Farm. Stock in the farm, which has grown in the meantime from 148 to 425 acres through the 158 years of its existence, is now shared by Bruce and Eloise and their four children. They include their two sons, Brent and Robert, and two daughters, Barbara and Mrs. Margaret Tolbert. They make up the sixth generation of the Lyon-Adams family to own the historic property, established eight years before Iowa became a state, right along side of Dillon's famous furrow.

Reminders of those early pioneering days are still to be seen, including parts of the wood frame house, built in 1845 and still a part of the ancestral home, as well as a stone smoke house that is still standing.

Crops grown over those 158 years include wheat, corn, oats, barley, hay, and soybeans. Bruce's father, Robert, was both a farm crop winner, as well as a judge, at county fairs.

Blooded stock was emphasized. Registered Shorthorn beef cattle and purebred Hampshire and Berkshire hogs were raised, along with Guernsey dairy cattle. Some of the registered stock won prizes at the West Liberty and Tipton fairs.

Up to 18 horses were stabled and used annually for field power up until 1924, when the first tractor was bought, and for some years beyond. Numerous makes of tractors have been used including Fordson , Farmall, White, Cass, John Deere and Allis Chalmers.

A Delco plant furnished electricity as early as 1926 and by 1936, REA was furnishing the electric power.

Bruce Adams was a member of the U.S. Marines during WW II and saw action in the Pacific Theater. He took over ownership of the farm in 1949.

All members of the family have been involved in Masonry, dating all the way back to ancestors in Ireland.

Bruce's father was active in the Grange and Bruce himself served as Johnson County Farm Bureau President in 1960.

Pioneer Oaks Farm is now being rented by Robert Dvorsky of Solon, Iowa.

THE MAGRUDER FARM OF JOHNSON COUNTY

Settled 1838

When James Magruder was growing up in Chesterfield County, Virginia, where he was born in 1818, he could hardly have anticipated he would wind up in Iowa 20 years later. Nor is it likely he could have imagined that he would become owner of a farm and that five generations of Magruders would live on that same land all the way to Iowa's Sesquicentennial Celebration 158 years later. But that's exactly what has happened.

James and Millie Magruder in front of their home built in 1913.

A great-great grandson of James Magruder, Douglas Magruder, who is currently the fifth generation owner of what is now the Magruder Farms Corporation, tells the interesting story of what happened between 1818 and 1996.

"My great-great grandfather, James Magruder, was born the eldest of nine children in Virginia on April 19, 1818, which is where he spent his childhood. At the age of eighteen he moved to Indiana, where he spent nearly three years working in the carpenter's trade. In 1838, he again moved westward, this time to Johnson County, Iowa, and settled in what is now called Fremont Township.

"He was married to Ruth Stover, a native of Indiana, in 1839. Upon their marriage, they built a homestead on the 240 acres of land he had obtained from the government. This land was entered in Johnson County as the first land sold that far west of the Mississippi River."

The first thing the young couple had to do was build a log cabin not far from a spring-fed creek. Next, sod had to be broken the hard way using a plodding yoke of oxen. Corn was planted and oats seeded. Hay land was also established from timothy and grass seed. A herd of beef cattle was started and hogs and chickens were also raised.

Seven children were born to the couple, but unfortunately four of them died in childhood. However, George, James, and Mary survived.

Douglas speaks highly of his great-great grandfather, saying:

"James was known to be a leader in Johnson County. He sat on the first jury held in the county, was the first constable in Fremont and Pleasant Valley Townships, and served as the first trustee. Another first was the payment of the first tax in Johnson County. He was an active member of County Agricultural Society for years, as well as a member of the Democratic Party. James was also a member of the Christian Church and a member of the Old Settler's Association of River Junction."

Incidentally, the Old Settler's Association still exists and Doug is one of its present members.

Records show that James Magruder assisted in burying the first white man to die in Johnson County. James Magruder's pioneering spirit is also evidenced in that he used a "Prairie Schooner" along with a yoke of oxen, and had much to do with creating some of the first roads in eastern Iowa.

When James Magruder died in November, 1893, the farm was passed on to his son, James, Jr. James, Jr. continued to farm the land and married Millie Norris. Born to James Jr. and Millie were Alice, Edna, and Lloyd. James, Jr. was noted to be the president of the River Junction Lumber Company, and president of the Pleasant Valley Telephone Company in 1914. He also served as president of the Old Settler's Association of River Junction. One of the early plows was obtained and used during this period.

During James, Jr.'s ownership, several depressions, drought years, chinch bug invasions and other problems were weathered and the family managed to hang on. When James, Jr. passed away, his son, Lloyd, Doug's grandfather, became the third owner back in 1935.

Lloyd and his wife, the former Nell Rayner, had a family of three — Edwin, Harold, and Gladys. It was during Lloyd's tenure the horses were replaced with tractors. The first one was an Allis Chalmers purchased in 1945. Since then, John Deere tractors have furnished the field power.

Lloyd continued to own the land until 1972 when his son, Harold, took over. Harold married Charmain Pratt and they welcomed a family of five — James, Douglas, Pamela, Kevin and John.

It was while Harold and Charmain owned the farm that it was decided that a farm corporation should be formed. The name chosen was "Magruder

Farms Corporation" and it was finalized in 1978.

During Harold's period of ownership, the Vietnam War was raging and Douglas, his second oldest son, was one of thousands of Iowans who answered the call, serving in the U.S. Navy.

After his return from sea duty near the jungles of that long-suffering country, Douglas joined the Magruder farming operations by renting land and raising some livestock. He married Debbie Brenneman. They have three children — Renee, Ryan, and Robyn.

Doug now serves as president of the Magruder Farms Corporation, which now has expanded to 800 acres, largely devoted to growing corn and soybeans and is basically farmed like a family farm.

Members of the Magruder family have served both in Methodist and Presbyterian Churches, and in the Old Settler's Association. Douglas also belongs to the American Legion. With Doug and Debbie's youngsters representing the sixth generation and now growing up, it appears that the Magruder Farms will continue.

THE NEWBERRY FARM OF LEE COUNTY

Settled 1838

The Newberry family of Lee County is another one of those families that can look back all the way and find the same surname used on every patent, land grant, abstract, or any other official paper, related to ownership of their land.

James W. Newberry was the first in the family to acquire Iowa land. A native of Orange County, New York, where he was born in 1817, he was about 21 when he first set foot in Iowa. That was in the year 1838.

Not long after coming to Lee County, Mr. Newberry was able to homestead a fairly large tract of land, some of it extending into Missouri. And, not surprisingly, he soon decided he needed a life partner. It didn't take him long to decide Edith Benedict, who had come to Iowa from Canada, was just the partner he needed.

They were married in Des Moines Township in Lee County where they immediately settled on J.W.'s homestead. There they raised a family of ten and worked hard at producing crops and raising livestock. Although they had started with limited means, they were able to buy additional land from time to time until at one time they owned a total of 1117 acres, 312 of them in Missouri.

Always community minded and deeply religious, J.W. Newberry was one of a committee of three that bought a tract of land for over $900 in 1893 for the purpose of building a community church.

Mr. & Mrs. Newberry were themselves members of the Josephites Division of the Latter Day Saints. It was a branch of the Mormon Church that did not believe in the plurality of wives. However, the Community Church they helped to build is known as The Union Church and not only embraces the Josephites and other Latter Day Saints, but also Presbyterian and other faiths.

Second owner of the Newberry farm was one of J.W. and Edith's sons, Charles D. Newberry, Sr., who was a breeder of Shorthorn beef cattle and Duroc Jersey hogs. Charles D. and his wife had a family of eight, one of which was named Charles D., Junior, and who became the third owner, after farming with his folks for a time. C.D., Jr. and his wife had three children, one of whom was Dave, who now is the Newberry farm owner.

There was a time when a combination of drought years, along with blight hitting crops, that they had to sell off the beef herd to make ends meet. Flocks of laying hens provided eggs with which to buy the family groceries.

Corn, oats, wheat, soybeans, cowpeas, and hay were all growing on the farm at one time or another.

Horses had to give way to tractors as early as 1937 when International tractors started taking over. However, electricity on the farmstead did not come until 1951.

Dale Newberry and his wife, Betty, now own the farm. Their son, Steven, and grandson, Jason, are now doing the farming that includes raising and feeding cattle and hogs and growing corn and soybeans, as well as ten acres of woodland. Dale adds that he runs errands and helps a little.

The family has been active in 4-H projects. In fact, Dale was a 4-H leader and on the Extension Council for a number of years. He is also a member of the Lee County Fair Board. Moreover, he was a Pioneer Seed representative for 37 years before his son, Steven, took over.

THE NICHOLS-MEACHAM FARM OF MUSCATINE COUNTY

Settled 1838

Samuel Nichols of Ohio was a veteran of the War of 1812, and a friend of Iowa's first Territorial Governor, Robert Lucas. In 1838, at the Governor's invitation, Nichols rode horseback from Chillicothe, Ohio, to Muscatine County, Iowa. It did not take him long to become impressed with a 320-acre tract in Pike Township in Muscatine County. Accordingly, he bought the claim from the Carothers family, who had been the first white settlers in the area. The price is said to have been only $1.12-1/2 an acre.

The same parcel of land has remained in the Nichols family ever since and is now owned and operated by Chris Meacham, one of Samuel Nichols' great-great grandsons.

After establishing his claim, Samuel rode back to his family in Ohio, only to find his wife, Mary, very ill. Mary, the mother of four daughters and two sons, was the granddaughter of two Revolutionary War colonists. Her illness progressed rapidly and she died soon after Samuel's return, leaving him with five six children.

In 1840, Samuel returned to Iowa with Benjamin, his oldest son. They started to work the land claim and built a log cabin on the banks of the Wapsipinicon river.

In 1842, Samuel married Nancy Searles, widow of a doctor, and he and Nancy raised his children in that riverbank cabin. In the meantime, he had received a land grant for his services in the War of 1812, so the 320 acres officially became his.

As the children grew up, more room was needed, so a five-room brick house, with a loft over two rooms, was built. The new house soon became a "Half-Way House", often used by settlers going to or coming from Muscatine.

When the railroads moved into Iowa, Samuel Nichols became very interested in a line called the Burlington, Cedar Rapids and Northern Railway, and soon was a stock holder. After his death, his son, Benjamin F., gave land for the construction of a station known as Nichols Station, named in honor of his father. It later became the town of Nichols. Benjamin operated a store there for a time, then returned to the farm.

Second owner of the farm was Townsend Nichols, Chris Meacham's great-great uncle. Townsend was the son of Benjamin and his wife, and inherited the farm in 1893. Based on information available, Townsend Nichols had no children.

Third owner was also named Townsend. He was Townsend B. Nichols, son of Benjamin F. and his wife, Susan, and great grandfather of the present Nichols farm owner.

A 1911 issue of "The History of Muscatine County" points out that Townsend B. increased the farm acreage to 600 acres, and raised high grade cattle, hogs and horses. However, his business acumen extended far beyond his own farming enterprise.

For one thing, he was also called upon to manage his uncle's 2200 acre holding. He was also a member of the Board of Directors of the Nichols Bank. He also served as township clerk and as president of the school board. In addition, he filled most of the chairs in the Nichols Masonic Lodge and embraced the Democratic Party.

He and his wife, the former Tetitia Sutton, had two children. One of them, a son, also named Benjamin F., eventually became the fourth owner of the property. He was Chris Meacham's grandfather, and was a veteran of WW I.

As fourth owner of the farm, he carried on in the same manner as his predecessors. He and his wife, Ora, had four children. They were the grandparents of the current farm owner, Chris and Diane Meacham, who are the parents of one child, the seventh generation of the family. Chris's father, Maynard Meacham, evidently did not own the farm at any time. He was a WW II veteran.

The Samuel Nichols' brick house built in 1871, is a typical 19th Century farm home with the main block a two-story rectangle style, with a one-story rear wing. The added area has a gabled room with dormers. The 125-year old house in which Mr. & Mrs. Meacham live is presently undergoing extensive restoration.

For many years, registered Aberdeen Angus cattle were raised on the farm, but there is no livestock on the farm now.

Chris and Diane are active in the Nichols Christian Church.

BROWN-CILEK-KROB FARM
OF
JOHNSON COUNTY

Settled 1839

A 560-acre farm in Johnson County has been known as the Glen Devey Pork Farm since August, 1920. However, long before that, it was known as the Brown Farm, beginning as early as 1839 when Edwin A. Brown bought 160 acres from the U.S. Government.

The first home was a log cabin, but was replaced by a more permanent home built of stone in 1860. Two buildings constructed during Edwin Brown's ownership are still in use as a barn and a shed.

Edwin and his wife had a family, although there is no report of the actual number. It is known, however, that one of the children was a son named Alonzo, who eventually succeeded his father on the farm in 1888.

During his ownership, Alonzo joined his father in raising cattle and horses. The cattle were Herefords and the horses were purebred Clydesdales and were of top quality. In fact, some were even exported to England where the Clydesdale breed originated. Unfortunately though, a fire in 1936 destroyed most of the Brown family's horse records and much other information.

Oats, corn, and hay were the pioneer farm's first crops.

Alonzo and his wife had two children. One of them was a son named Vernon, who eventually succeeded his father on the farm. However, it was a long time in coming. When Alonzo passed away in 1906, his widow, Ethie Adams Brown became the owner, and it wasn't until 1952 that Vernon actually gained possession

During the period after his father's death, Vernon often served his country in uniform — first as a member of Company A Engineers in the Iowa Guard, then in the U.S. National Guard, and then on the Mexican border in 1916. Then in less than two years, Vernon was in the U.S. Army in WW I, serving in France.

During the years that followed WW I, soybean production was added to the corn, oats and hay field rotation, and cattle feeding was the main livestock project. Today, it's corn, soybeans and hay in the fields and stock cows and calves are in the pastures on the 560 acres the farm has grown into.

Ethie Cilek and Betty Krob, daughters of Vernon and his wife, Martha, became the owners of the large farm in 1965. By then, Vernon had thoroughly convinced those who were to follow him that John Deere tractors were the way to go. So, beginning in 1934, the farm has had a John Deere GP, Model G, Model B, and Model 3020, 4020, 4400, and 8430.

Rural electrification did not come until 1959.

Now operating the 560 acres is Kevin Krob, son of Betty Krob, who owns the farm with her sister, Ethie Cilek.

Church has been important for the Brown family through the years, and to their children. Vernon and Martha were active in the Universalist Church, while their daughter, Ethie Cilek, is a member of the Solon Methodist Church. Vernon is a member of the Solon American Legion Post and his daughter, Ethie, founded the Solon American Legion Auxiliary and was its first president.

THE CHESNUT FARM OF LEE COUNTY

Settled 1839

Virginia and Robert Chesnut in front of a tractor bought in 1950 and still in use today.

It would have been fascinating to have known and visited with Bob Chesnut, the first. In fact, an entire book about him would have been exciting. Not only would it have told about how he staked out a farm claim in Lee County in the mid or late 1830s, but also what happened before and afterward. It would be interesting reading.

To put a small part of "Old Bob's" story in words, he was born in Pennsylvania in 1815, and was just 20 and had already learned some carpentry when he joined a party that planned to establish a grist mill in western Illinois. The party of more than 20, including wives and some children, "flatboated" down the Ohio to St. Louis. The flatboat not only had all the members of the group, but also furniture, tools, food, milling supplies, and 30 barrels of whiskey.

At St. Louis, the group boarded a steamboat and went up the Mississippi to what is now Warsaw, Illinois. There, Chesnut left them and went further north to a village called Flint Hills on the west shore. Chesnut found the village (now Burlington, Iowa) had one frame house, a couple shanties, a sawmill, and a trading post.

Built in the early 1850's, this house was home to four generations of Chesnuts.

Circa 1906, pictured are three generations of the Chesnut Farm homestead.

Others of the original party soon joined Bob there, and they found an ideal spot for the proposed mill on the fast-flowing Skunk River near Gibson's Ferry. Chesnut used his carpentry skills to help build the mill, said to be Iowa's first flour mill. After completing the dam and mill, Chesnut opened a carpenter shop, but a flash flood swept it away, tools and all, a few weeks later. That is when Bob Chesnut's career as a farmer began.

The original claim was somewhat over 80 acres, later purchased from the Government for $1.10 an acre.

It was a time when Indians were still very much around. Chesnut claimed the first Indian he met was Chief Keokuk. He also became acquainted with Chief BlackHawk. On one occasion, he saw 20 canoes filled with Indians going up the Skunk River.

Soon after acquiring the land, he went back to Pennsylvania and brought back apple and peach tree seedlings to start a sizable orchard. Corn was the major field crop.

Bob Chesnut married Mary Haynes in 1838. They had six children, the oldest of which was a son named Napoleon. Napoleon grew up to be the "farmer" of the group. Even as a boy, he helped his mother operate the farm when Bob caught the "Gold Rush Fever" and went to California to make a fortune. He did come home "rich" in experience, but with a "fortune" of just $2.40.

Although Ted Sloat, a writer for the MADISONIAN, has credited Robert Chesnut I with filing his claim in 1836, Robert Chesnut III, the present owner of the land, disagrees. As a great grandson of the farm's founder, he has documents indicating it was 1839 when the original deed was filed, followed by a purchase in 1840.

Second owner of the farm was Eldon Chesnut, one of the sons of Robert I. However, he did not make the purchase until 1906, only a year before his father died at age 92.

Robert I had been a long time member of both the Lee County Pioneers and the Old Settlers Association.

Eldon and his wife had three children, one of whom was a son named Robert II. He was a veteran of WW I where he had served in France.

Robert II bought the property in 1941. He and his wife had a family of five. One of them is Robert III, who now has the 69 acre farm, which he purchased in 1968. He and his wife have six children who represent the fifth generation to have lived on the pioneer farm.

The land is now rented to a neighbor with corn and hay the major crops and some cattle being raised.

The original cabin on the farm was made of hewn logs and stood until demolished in 1968. An ox yoke found in one of the old buildings indicates that oxen were used in the fields before horses furnished the power.

The first tractor was a Ford purchased in 1950. Now, 46 years later, it is still in use.

FOX-WHITMARSH FARM OF LEE COUNTY

Settled 1839

This Sesquicentennial Pioneer Farm Family Report must begin with a meeting held in New England back in the mid 1830s.

Clayton Edward Whitmarsh, who is the fifth generation on one of Iowa's oldest Sesquicentennial farms, writes to tell that a Reverend Asa Turner was on a fund raising tour in 1834. One of his stops was in Ipswich, New Hampshire. There he told about the rich soil and cheap land in Illinois.

Among those in attendance was a pair of brothers-in-law, Timothy Fox and Lewis Epps, who were partners in a pork packing business, and a William Brown. So impressed were they about the possibilities out toward the western frontier, they decided to take advantage of them. Accordingly, in early 1836 they, with their families, started the long journey to the West.

However, on arriving in Illinois, they found all that land had been bought up. So it was that they went farther, crossing the Mississippi near Burlington. Once into Iowa, they learned of a Burlington resident who had squatters rites on a large parcel of Lee County land. When they found it was for sale, the three New Englanders took the $200 they had between them and bought much of a square mile of land where the town of Denmark now stands.

Just why they called it "Denmark" is not known, but records show that the town founders laid out a village site three-fourths of a mile square, outlined blocks, made up both inner and outer plots, and provided for a town square and for a burial grounds.

The three families put up a double cabin in which to live that winter, then started selling the lots. Hay from nearby farms was piled up in the future village square, which caused the village to be first known as "Yankee Haystack."

Handwritten abstract records are confusing and there is no exact date of when Timothy Fox acquired what has ever since been known as the Whitmarsh Farm. However, there is one abstract dated November 28, 1838. In any case, it is known that Fox obtained 80 acres from the Government that year and that he was the father of Charles Whitmarsh's wife, Charlotte. Charlotte was one of Timothy and Mary Fox's 15 children. The "History of Lee County", an official publication, reveals that Charles and Charlotte already acquired 200 acres, including the original 80 acre homestead.

The first cabin on the farm was built of logs from oak, elm and walnut trees, and the second included some pine wood as well. Then in 1849, a brick home was built that has served four generations of Whitmarshes. A large barn for livestock was also built early on. In 1906, the original barn was added onto, making a 38 x 50 foot structure in which eight or more horses were stabled and the cows were milked.

Back in Civil War times, Charles E. Whitmarsh, the farm's second owner, enlisted in 1862 and served to the end of the war as his Company's blacksmith. Timothy Whitmarsh also enlisted early and was "drummer boy" for a Missouri Engineer's Unit for three years.

Charles and Charlotte, who were Clayton's great grandparents, had a family of four. One of them, a son named Timothy Fox Whitmarsh, and who married Addie Hart, became the third owner of the pioneer farm in 1889. Timothy and Addie had two children, one of which was a son named John, who married Hattie Taylor. John, who was Clayton's father, acquired the farm in 1911. John and Hattie had seven children. They were also the first to own the farm clear of debt.

Over the years, beginning with Charles Whitmarsh, the farm has grown wheat, oats, corn, timothy, brome grass, clover, and orchard grass for hay. Horses, Hampshire and Chester White hogs, Shorthorn milking cattle, and chickens were raised for many years. However, by 1942, some horses were being replaced by a tricycle type, used R.C. Case tractor, and subsequently, all of them, by a string of tractors, beginning with a Ferguson-Ford, and then by several John Deeres, followed by a Case and now a new Case-International.

John's father and grandfather were early users of steel plows, reapers, binders, wire-trip corn planters, and the first types of corn pickers.

Clayton, who is now 76, had to assume farming responsibility at a young age. His father died when he was only 12. His older brother and a hired man then handled the farm until Clayton graduated from high school and took over. He credits his Vo Ag teacher and his FFA courses for helping him a great deal, and good neighbors who gave him both advice and help. During his tenure, more modern equipment was added. He continues his livestock interest with Hereford and Angus cattle and a confinement hog operation.

The farm is now rented on a share basis to David and Kathryn Houston. Clayton says, "They are just like family."

Ever since Timothy Fox became one of the founders of the Denmark Congregational Church in 1838, Whitmarsh family members have been attending. Fox also gave land for the new church as well as for a school, a park, an academy, and a cemetery.

Later on, Timothy Fox Whitmarsh, the third farm owner, led the Denmark Community Band, and Clayton, who now has the farm, has served on the school board, as a Township clerk, all the Congregational church offices, president of the Lee County Farm Bureau, and Cemetery Endowment Fund Treasurer for 47 years. He is also a member of the Mississippi Valley Farm Business Association.

THE HOWELL FARM OF JEFFERSON COUNTY

Settled 1839

The Howell family of near Lockridge is another of those Jefferson County families whose farm pre-dates Iowa Statehood several years.

Established in 1839 by Thomas Howell, great grandfather of the present owner, Thomas M. Howell, it is one of the larger farms purchased by early pioneers and has become even larger since. The original purchase made from the government for $1.25 an acre was 400 acres. Today, now held by the fifth generation of Howells, it has increased to 660 acres.

Before coming to Iowa, Thomas and his wife, Leletha, who were both born in Virginia, were married, and the first of their nine children were born there. They then moved to Illinois where three more children were born.

When they first arrived in Iowa, they lived in VanBuren County several years, and this is where their last four children arrived. Then in 1839, they moved to Round Tree Township in Jefferson County and made that their permanent home, first building a one-room cabin with a fireplace for heat and cooking. However, the bread was always baked in a Dutch oven outside.

Thomas Howell was also a Baptist minister as well as a farmer, and was commonly referred to as "Reverend Thomas".

One of their brood of nine was a son named Albert who married Druscilla Gregory. They proceeded to operate the large farm on their own. Four children were born to them. Then in 1873, they were able to buy the farm shortly after Albert's father's death.

Four sons were born to Albert and Druscilla, but two of them passed away. Thus it was that the two surviving brothers, Thomas N. , who was Thomas M's uncle, and Parvin, his father, inherited the farm.

The partnership continued for 15 years when Parvin was able to buy out his brother's family's interest.

Parvin and his wife, the former Helen Thomson, were married in 1911. To this union six children were born, four girls and two boys.

One of those sons was Thomas M., who farmed with his father until the latter's death in 1963. In the meantime, in 1947, Thomas married Rachel Riepe, an elementary teacher. The couple has spent all of their lives on the farm ever since and were able to buy it shortly after his father, Parvin, passed away.

The couple has no children, but they still continue to raise crops — corn, soybeans, oats and hay.

Earlier generations farming the large tract also had a significant livestock program, including Guernsey dairy cattle, Shorthorn beef cattle, Shropshire sheep and Duroc Jersey hogs. Chickens were also raised.

One of Thomas' ancestors served in the Civil War.

Thomas and his wife belong to the Methodist Church and are members of the Farm Bureau and the Odd Fellows Lodge.

For the most part, the large farm holding was on solid ground throughout its long tenure. But in the Depression along with drought, cold, heat and burned out crops in the early '30s, it was a case of just barely making it.

1996 will mark the Howell's second Sesquicentennial.

The first was in 1989 at the time of the farm's actual 150th anniversary, with close to 100 relatives, neighbors, and other friends in attendance. The second one is the statewide celebration now in progress in which millions are marking Iowa's 150th actual birthday, with the Howell farm already in its 157th year.

IDLE WILD LIMITED FARM OWNED BY THE COOP FAMILY OF JEFFERSON COUNTY

Settled 1839

A Jefferson County Farm called "Idle Wild Limited" has been owned by the Coop family since 1839. It is not only one of Jefferson County's oldest farms, but it is also one of Iowa's oldest to be owned by the same family with the same surname for 157 years.

William J. Coop is said to have bought the farm in 1839, although he could not get a land patent on it until 1843. He and his wife had nine children, so the oak log cabin with a foundation of rocks found on the farm must have gotten rather crowded before a larger home could be built.

Wheat, corn, oats, and hay were the original crops, with sheep, hogs and cattle the livestock that was raised.

The second to own the farm was one of the pioneer's sons, Lafayette Coop, who bought it in 1865 at the close of the Civil War. Several members of the Coop family were engaged in the conflict between the states; and William J. Coop, the original owner of the Coop farm in 1839, had also been in the Black Hawk War of 1832.

As a matter of fact, some member of the Coop family is said to have taken part in every war since, and including, the 1832 Indian War. Included are the Mexican War of 1848, Civil War, Spanish-American War, the two

World Wars, etc.

Lafayette Coop and his wife had six children and held the farm until 1919, the year after WW I ended, when one of their sons, Albert L. Coop, and his wife took over. Their family numbered eight children. One of their sons, Raymond M. Coop, became the farm's owner in 1946, the year after WW II came to a close.

Raymond and his wife had seven children, but none of them became the fifth generation representative to take over. Instead, one of their cousins, Bernard Coop, and his wife (the parents of six) acquired the property and kept the farm in the Coop family name. That was in 1964.

However, in 1975, Michael B. Coop, a great-great-great grandson of William J. Coop, the founder of the farm, was able to buy it from his Uncle Bernard, thus getting the land back in the direct line of descendants. He is now the sixth generation with the surname Coop to own the farm in this Sesquicentennial year.

Not every year in this more than a century and a half has been a bumper year. Michael, the present owner, says family records show that drought hit hard in 1934, '36, '83, and '88, while heavy rainfall in the year 1947 and 1993 also took its toll.

THE LEWIS FARM OF LINN COUNTY

Settled 1839

A Cedar Rapids Gazette article carried in 1909 is headed by a caption, "Passing Of A Notable Pioneer". It refers to the death of 99-year old "Uncle" Thomas Lewis of Palo, Iowa, one of Linn County's earliest settlers.

The article speaks in glowing terms of the pioneer farmer who was born in Pennsylvania in 1809, and who moved westward until at the age of 30, he and his wife filed a claim in 1839. There is an official record in the Linn County recorder's office showing the claim to have been for 160 acres at a cost of $1.25 an acre. However, as time went on, the Lewis farm holdings increased to 620 acres.

It was reported that the Lewis farm was one containing some of the richest soil in Linn County. It was not until April 29, 1842, that a cash certificate officially declaring the land to be Thomas Lewis' was granted. The land patent was signed by President John Tyler.

Seven children were raised by Thomas and his wife, the former Mary

White, also a native of Pennsylvania. The Gazette article credits Thomas Lewis as being a progressive and ambitious farmer, as well as a kindly father and a model citizen. He and his family belonged to the Methodist Church, and he was a well-respected neighbor with many friends. A lifelong Republican, he held various local and county offices. His death came only a few months before what would have been his 100th birthday.

Second of the six generations to own the pioneer farm was a son of Thomas Lewis, Thomas Clark Lewis, and his wife. They were the great-great grandparents of the present owners.

Thomas Clark Lewis was born in 1865, right after the Civil War came to an end. Like his father, Thomas C. was an ardent and ambitious farmer, working with his father until he and his wife became the owners of the land themselves. Thomas C. is said to have brought the farm to a high state of cultivation, and to have grown quality cereals such as corn, wheat, and oats. He also grew high grade livestock, mainly cattle and hogs.

He and his wife, the former Alice Railsback, one of a family of eleven children, became the parents of two sons, one of whom was Thomas Orland Lewis, who became the third owner of the farm.

In politics, Thomas C. did not follow in his father's footsteps. Instead, he became a lifelong Democrat and was elected to serve as Township Trustee. He and his wife were members of the Methodist Episcopalian Church and both enjoyed the respect and confidence of all who knew them.

After Thomas Orland's death, the farm remained in the hands of his widow, until it became the property of a son, Thomas Harlan Lewis, and his wife.

No further information has been supplied about the family or the farm except that the farm now comprises 400 acres. Corn and soybeans, and a cow-calf herd, are now getting the central emphasis.

The application for the Sesquicentennial pioneer farm recognition was signed by Thomas John Lewis and Lee Craig Lewis, who evidently are the fifth generation to be involved in the Linn County farm homesteaded by their great-great grandfather back in 1839, seven years before Iowa became a state.

THE LEWIS-ANDREWS FARM OF LINN COUNTY

Settled 1839

John Lewis came from Ohio in the late 1830s to, as the saying goes, "seek his fortune in Iowa". He did not stop the minute he crossed the Mississippi to settle in the first eastern Iowa county he set foot on. Instead he went on farther west and finally stopped in Linn County.

The year was 1839 and Indians were still on all sides, although none were particularly hostile. In any case, Lewis settled on an 82 acre claim near what is now the town of Palo. It was his homestead, but he could not get an official abstract until September 12, 1844.

In the meantime, he proceeded to use oxen to plow sod and to get crops started. He and his wife had several children, one of whom was a son, William Lewis, the great grandfather of the present owner.

Third to own the land was William's son, Charles Wesley Lewis. Apparently, he and his wife had no sons. In any case, one of their daughters, Ruth, married Lewis Andrews. They became the parents of Carl E. Andrews who now owns the farm. The farm has increased in size to 135 acres, where corn, oats and hay make up the rotation.

The present home on the Linn County farm was built in 1950.

No further details about the farm, or the families who have lived on it since its inception 157 years ago, have been provided.

THE McDONALD-HOBBS FARM OF DES MOINES COUNTY

Settled 1839

1839 was one of those very early years of farming undertakings in Iowa. It was a time of oxen and covered wagons, of log cabins and rail fences, of wooden plows and cradles on scythes, of spinning wheels and wax candles, and of endless hard, hand work.

One of those who had the courage to initiate an Iowa farming venture 157 years ago was John McDonald, who bought an 80 acre parcel of Des Moines County land from the U.S. Government on October 29, 1839. The price was $1.25 an acre.

Parrott McDonald with some of his cattle.

Oats, wheat, corn and clover for hay were the first crops grown after the prairie sod was broken with a yoke of oxen in the spring of 1840. Building a log cabin evidently also took some time that year.

John McDonald and his wife had a family of six, some of whom were born several years before 1839. One of those half dozen hardy pioneer youngsters was a son named Emmet who grew up working with his father on the homestead, and who became the second person to own the land. That took place in 1847.

Emmet and his wife also had six children, one of the oldest of which was a son, Parrott McDonald, who became the farm's third owner in 1883. He and his wife had only two children. Evidently both were daughters, and one of them, Elaine, would eventually become the fourth owner of the Des Moines County land.

However, long before that took place, much else transpired.

In the livestock yards, Hereford cattle were brought in from Hereford, Texas. Later the cattle herd was increased with some Angus cattle as well. Chester White and Hampshire hogs were bred and fed and sold from the hog lots. Elsewhere on the farmyard were coops of chickens, guineas, and bantams, largely cared for by the women and children.

Belgian and Percheron horses replaced the slow plodding oxen early on in the enterprise. As many as eight horses were fed and used every year until a tractor was bought to replace them in 1930.

Grasshoppers wiped out crops in 1874, but in 1929 wheat produced on only 33 acres brought in enough cash to buy a brand new Nash automobile.

Alfalfa was added to the cropping program in the early 1900's. Wheat and barley production was dropped by the 1920's and soybeans were introduced around that time.

In WW I, two McDonald sons, Paul and Austin, answered their country's call to help stop Germany's Kaiser and to be reminded that some of their ancestors had been in George Washington's Colonial Militia to fight and defeat King George's "redcoats".

The bank failures in the 1920s and 1930s, plus the droughts, chinch bugs, and Depressions of the early 1930s, and another drought in 1936, made it so difficult that at times there was hardly enough money to buy a loaf of bread.

When WW II came along, two more McDonalds, Robert and John Austin, donned uniforms to help end the dreams of Germany's Hitler and Japan's Tojo.

Parrott McDonald's daughter, Elaine, married a man whose last name was Hobbs. They had two children, one of whom was a son named Ronald. However, Elaine and her husband did not gain possession of the farm until 1957, 74 long years after her parents had bought the farm in 1883. Then in 1987, after Elaine had owned the land 30 years, Ron bought it. Corn and soybeans remained as the major crops.

Ron's father was a member of both the National Farmer's Organization (NFO) and the Farm Bureau.

The family members have been active in Eastern Star and Masonic orders. Church membership over the years has included both Presbyterian and Methodist churches.

THE PRICE-MOSHER FARM OF HENRY COUNTY

Settled 1839

What has been known as the "Lone Road Farm" in Henry County, is one of the few Pioneer family farms acquired as early as 1839. It is located near Salem, Iowa. Despite the fact that the farm has been in the same family's hands for 157 years, only three generations are shown as owners, although the fourth generation members now operate it.

First to own it were Mr. and Mrs. Robert Price who obtained 160 acres in 1839 by way of a U.S. Government Patent. The Prices were childless, but had several nephews and nieces, one of whom was named Martha. She became the wife of Alonzo Mosher. She was the grandmother of J.L. Mosher, who is now the farm's operator.

Alonzo Mosher bought 80 acres of the farm from Mrs. Price for about $22 an acre in 1869. He and his wife, Martha, had ten children, one of whom was a son, James J. Mosher, who became the third generation representative to own the land. James J. made the purchase in 1906. He and his wife had a family of five, one of whom is J.L. Mosher, who is now on the farm which is still in the estate of his late father, James J.

Native lumber was used to build a home on the farm soon after the land was purchased. There is still some bark to be seen on the sills under the first floor. An amazing thing is that the house is still standing. Even more amazing is the fact that it is still serving as the farm home, and that J.L. Mosher still lives in it. "They just don't make 'em that good anymore," would be a good way to describe the century and a half old structure.

Wheat, oats, corn and hay were the crops being grown when the land was put into cultivation. Pasture for cattle, sheep and horses became quite an acreage, too, as was the hay land.

Hogs and chickens were also raised.

A grain binder was purchased by James J. Mosher in 1925, and a Fordson tractor in 1933, just a year before the drought of 1934.

Soybeans were added to the crop rotation after the trying '30s.

The farm now numbers 185 acres and is rented to Ronald Overberg. Ownership of the property remains in the estate which includes J.L. Mosher; his sister, Anna Watts; a nephew, Norval Mosher; and nieces Joan Berkland and Arevel Merrit.

During the Civil War, David Mosher joined the Iowa Cavalry in October, 1861, and was captured the next year. That meant spending time in the notorious Libbeyville prison before his transfer to a Federal Prison where he died on May 19th, 1865.

One of J.L. Mosher's nephews, Gordon Watts, served three years in WW II. Another nephew, Neil Watts, was in uniform from 1954 to 1956 when rumblings of the Vietnam War were beginning to be heard. This was also true of Norval Mosher in 1953 through 1955.

All of J.L. Mosher's ancestors were Quakers, but J.L. and his brother and sister belong to the Congregational Church. J.L. is also a member of the Farm Bureau.

CAMPBELL-BREITENSTEIN FARM OF LEE COUNTY

Settled 1840

Another of the pioneer Lee County family farms originated in 1840 is the 200-acre tract purchased from the United States Government by Michael Campbell. The purchase was made for $250 on June 1, 1840.

Michael Campbell was the great-great grandfather of Lawrence Breitenstein, who is the fifth, and current, owner of the pioneer farm.

Part of the original purchase was sold off in 1878, but 110 years later, Lawrence Breitenstein bought 120 acres of it back, so Michael Campbell's homestead of 1840 is all back in the family's hands again. Breitenstein and his wife, Ginger, live on the farm now, and farm all of it with the help of their son, Darin.

When Michael Campbell started the long-time family farm, the main crops were hay, corn for fodder, milo, pasture and cow pumpkins. Oxen were used for the field work those first years. The first home was a log cabin built on a stone foundation.

Besides oxen, the first livestock on the farm was cattle, hogs, and sheep. Chickens were also raised. Horses came later.

Second family member to own the farm was Uriah Campbell, a son of Michael and his wife. Uriah is Lawrence Breitenstein's great grandfather. He acquired the property in 1847, twelve years before the Civil War broke out.

During the Civil War, Lawrence's grandfather on his father's side joined the 3rd Iowa Volunteers and served in no less than six crucial battles, most of them fought down in Mississippi, including the battles of Greentown, Tupelo, Old Town Creek, Talehatchie, Big Blue River, Osage, and the Battle of Independence, all within six month's time in 1864. To survive that many Civil War battles must be some kind of a record.

During Uriah's ownership, crop production, in addition to those his father had grown, also included milo and sorghum. Draft horses also came into the picture during those years, as well as riding horses.

Uriah and his wife had a daughter, Mary, among their four children. Mary (who was Lawrence's grandmother) and her husband were the third generation to own and operate the farm. However, the name changed from Campbell to Breitenstein during that period, which began in 1881.

Records show that sometime during the farm's history, probably when Mary Campbell Breitenstein owned the land, dairy cattle were also introduced into the livestock program, and as many as eight horses were used in the field work annually.

Mary and her husband had a family of seven, one of whom was a son, Walter Breitenstein. Walter took over the farm in 1931 and became the father of nine children, one of whom was Lawrence.

During Walter's ownership, horses had to give way to tractors, with the first one, a John Deere "H", bought in 1946. Since then, several other tractors have been used, including another John Deere, a Case, and several Internationals.

Lawrence was a Navy veteran of two Far East cruises during the Vietnam War and is a member of the American Legion and the Farm Bureau. His father was active in his Masonic Lodge and his wife in the Methodist Church.

In 1970, Lawrence and Ginger bought the farm, which they now own in cooperation with their son, Darin, who is one of their three children.

THE CASADY FARM OF VAN BUREN COUNTY

Settled 1840

It was 1840, six years before lowa became a state, when William Cassady bought a small tract of land in Van Buren County. There he built a wood structure home and he and his wife raised eleven children. Like all other farms of that period of 156 years ago, land was plowed as soon as possible, probably with oxen on a heavy breaker plow.

Corn was planted, cultivated, and harvested by hand. It would take 75 or more hours of hand labor to grow 100 bushels of corn. By contrast, today, with all the modern machines that are used, it takes about two hours to grow 100 bushels.

Oats were also seeded by hand, and harvested with a hand cradle. Hay was also all handled by hand with three or four tined forks.

Along with cattle and hogs, chickens, geese, ducks and guinea fowl were raised.

Allen Cassady became the second owner of the farm in 1848. Allen and his wife had only two children, one of whom was a son named John. John gained possession of the farm in 1876, and with an interest in race horses, built a race track on the farm and held races there periodically. John and his wife had a family of five.

One of those five was a son, Alfred, who shortened the Cassady name slightly to Casady, and named the farm "The Casady Farm."

Alfred had the farm in his name for 51 years, and went through good years and bad. The worst years were the Dust Bowl years when drought struck nearly four years in a row in the early 1 930s.

He also saw the beginning of soybean farming, first when hardly anyone knew what to do with them, to where they now are found on half the crop acres on many farms.

Corn yields of open-pollinated corn were as low as 30 bushels an acre, but that changed radically when Alfred first tried hybrid corn. Yields were consistently over 100 bushels an acre when he quit farming in 1963.

A steel-wheeled 1940 Farmall tractor permanently changed the field power from horses to machines.

Alfred and his wife had four children, including a son, Paul, who built a battery-powered electric plant some time in the 1930s to make the Casady Farm the first electrified farm in their neighborhood.

Paul and his wife, Mary, took over the farm in 1963 and changed things from a highly diversified farm with milk cows, hogs, chickens, and corn, oats and hay crops, to a corn and soybean only farm project. They had a family of three.

In 1974, Mary became the farm owner at Paul's death, and now rents out the 115 acre farm to a neighbor.

Because there were veterans in the family, Mary belongs to the American Legion Auxiliary. She also belongs to the United Methodist Church in Cantril.

DONOVAN-McKENNA FARM OF JACKSON COUNTY

Settled 1840

Robert McKenna, of near Bernard in Jackson County, is a fifth generation owner of a pioneer family farm first established by his great-great grandfather back in 1840. He was Jeremiah Donovan, father of five, and a hard-working pioneer settler.

The land was purchased from the Government, presumably for $1.25 an acre. It was mostly prairie land as was true of most purchases made 156 years ago.

One of the Jeremiah Donovan's family of five was a son named Daniel, who became the second owner of the property. He was the father of six, one of whom was a son, Benjamin, who was Robert McKenna's grandfather.

Benjamin, the third of the farm's entrepreneurs, and his wife, had an even larger family. There were seven children who all grew up on the pioneer farm. Corn, oats, and other crops were grown, as had been true of their ancestors, and hay land provided feed for beef cow herds — and also enabled the children to have fun bouncing around in the new mown hay. One of those children was Florence, who married Lawrence McKenna, and became Robert's mother.

In 1981, Robert acquired the old Donovan farm from his father. It now totals 160 acres and is both a livestock and grain farm, with emphasis on feeding beef cattle and hogs.

In looking back on the farm's history, McKenna found the first home back in the 1840s was a log cabin. He says the drought years of 1934 and 1936 were the roughest years on the farm. He also found that horses started to be replaced for field work in 1929 when a McCormick-Deering tractor was purchased. Subsequently, an International and a Ford tractor have been used. The Ben Donovan family evidently were pioneers in the use of farm electricity. A home Delco plant was installed as early as 1918.

Robert McKenna also reports that an uncle, Richard McKenna, was killed in the Korean War.

Members of the McKenna family have been active in St. Patrick's Church many years.

THE FRAZER-LICHTENWALTER-MITZNER FARM OF CEDAR COUNTY

Settled 1840

Richard Mitzner of Tipton, of the Mitzner Family Trust, has provided the Iowa Sesquicentennial Commission and the Iowa Department of Agriculture and Land Stewardship with basic facts of a Cedar County farm homesteaded by his great-great grandparents, Mr. and Mrs. Benjamin Frazer, 156 years ago.

Benjamin and Sarah Frazer laid claim to 80 acres of good Cedar County soil on May 21, 1840. The payment made to the U.S. Government was $1.25 an acre.

Second to own the property was one of Benjamin's sisters, Catherine Frazer, who was a great-great aunt of the present owner. She evidently married a man whose last name was Lichtenwalter. In any case, the third owner was Margaret Lichtenwalter, who must have been a daughter of Catherine and her husband.

John S. Lichtenwalter, believed to be the son of Margaret and her husband, is shown as a grandfather of Richard Mitzner and his brother.

Apparently John and his wife had a daughter, also named Margaret, who married a man named Mitzner, and who became the mother of the current Mitzner Family Trust shareholders.

The application shows the farm now totals 153 acres and is devoted to crop farming featuring corn, soybeans, and hay.

The present home on the farm was built in 1875, 121 years ago.

No additional information about the families who lived on the 156 year old farm, or about the farm itself, was provided.

THE McDONALD-MOEHLMAN FARM OF LEE COUNTY

Settled 1840

Eighty-five year old Mrs. Gladys Moehlman of Danville, Iowa, made certain the land her great grandfather, John McDonald, originally purchased in three separate Lee County parcels would be acknowledged in this book. In a painstakingly pencil-written letter on note paper, Mrs. Moehlman listed all the details.

John McDonald purchased the first 40-acre tract on October 16, 1840. It was bought directly from the U.S. Government.

The second parcel of 40 acres was originally purchased from the government's land office on the same day by Simeon Lawson Parriot, and his wife, Sarah, who turned right around and sold it to John McDonald.

The third 40 acre parcel, however, was also obtained directly from the U.S. Government and also in late October, 1840.

However, land patents for the first and third tracts could not be obtained until December 1, 1841, and not until May 29, 1843, for the second parcel that had first been obtained by the Simeon Parriots.

John Emmet McDonald, son of the farm's original owner, and his wife were the second to take over the 120 acres.

Third to own and operate the farm was a son of John Emmet and his wife, Parrot McDonald. He was brought in to the farm's management at an early age because his father, John Emmet, died while still quite young. Parrot and his mother were able to hold things together and keep the farm.

Hogs and Hereford cattle were raised and fed out for the Chicago Union Stockyards. This was true of what countless other eastern Iowa farmers did during that period.

Mrs. Moehlman, the daughter of Parrot and his wife and present owner of the farm, reports there were two especially bad years in the farm's 156-year old history. In 1874, grasshoppers devastated the crops; and exactly sixty years later, in 1934, it was chinch bugs that destroyed the grains and the corn.

Parrot was a progressive farmer all his life and was active in community projects, including serving as a bank director during the difficult depression years. He lived to age 89.

After his death, two of his sons-in-law took over the farm. One of these was Gladys' husband. He lived until 1992. Gladys, who is now the farm's owner, rents most of the land out to a neighbor.

Mrs. Moehlman has a son, Donald, who is a representative of the family's fifth generation; and who, in turn, has a son who is now interested in a Red Angus herd which is being raised on the farm's pastures.

NEWTON-AVERY FARM OF LEE COUNTY

Settled 1840

The Newton family of Lee County has made quite a heroic effort to keep much of a Sesquicentennial Pioneer Family Farm in the Newton name the past 156 years, and has pretty well succeeded in doing so.

Samuel Newton, the great-great-great uncle of Joyce Newton Avery and her brother, Daniel W. Newton, gained a land patent on 160 acres of Lee County land back in 1840.

Half of that land was sold to a William Samples in 1850. Samples was not a member of the Newton family, but through the years, it has come back into the family's hands again and again. In 1865, Orson and Harriett Newton, great-great uncle of Joyce and Daniel, bought it. However, five years later, it was sold to Leonard Hoff, who also was not a family member.

Hoff, in turn, sold it to T.C. Robinson in 1888. Thus, it remained out of the family until 1923, when Dan Hazen Newton, Joyce and Daniel's grandfather, reclaimed it for the family, and now an uncle, Richard Newton , son of Dan Hazen has had it since 1963.

As for the other half of that original 160 acres, it has remained in the Newton family now for 156 years.

Charles Newton , a brother of the original homesteader and great grandfather of Joyce and Daniel Avery, acquired it in 1851. He and his wife had a family of four, and their son, Dan Hazen Newton, grandfather of Daniel W. and Joyce Avery, was the next to own the pioneer farm. He bought it in 1901. He and his wife, Nettie, had four children, and upon his death, Nettie held the farm until 1963, when the brother and sister, Daniel W. and Joyce Newton Avery, were able to gain possession of it. Their sons — Ralph farmed the west half, Richard, the east.

Joyce and her husband had four children and her brother and his wife had two. They kept the pioneer Newton family farm until this Sesquicentennial year, when 60 acres were sold to their first cousin, Marvin Newton (Richard's son). Marvin and his wife, Carol, also farm many additional acres.

Joyce has retained 20 acres of the original tract, so between her and her cousin, Newton family members have managed to keep half of Samuel Newton's 1840 purchase intact and in the Newton family for five generations.

Meanwhile, Marvin and his wife have three children, who make part of a sixth generation.

Joyce and Daniel Avery's daughter, Linda, who married Kevin Pender, represent a sixth generation actually living on the 156-year old family farm.

It should be added that another Newton couple, Ralph and Kathryn, lived on and farmed the place from 1936 to 1961. They were the parents of Joyce and Daniel W. and their mother lived on the farm until 1989. She was a beloved school teacher in this area for 35 years.

Over the years, wheat, corn, oats, and alfalfa and timothy hay have been in the crop rotation, and soybeans have been added in more recent years.

From 1930 on, Holstein dairy cattle, Poland China hogs, Belgian horses, and some sheep were raised, along with flocks of chickens.

In WW I, horses raised on the farm were taken by the Army; and one of those horses, with unquestionably distinct markings, was later seen near the Western front in France by a neighbor who was in WW I service "over there".

Ralph Newton came very close to being inducted in WW I, while Joyce's brother, Daniel W., served in the U.S. Navy in 1957; and Marvin Newton, the present owner of part of the original farm, was with the Seabees in Vietnam.

Long, long before that, one of the family's ancestors, David Newton, was with a Vermont Militia Unit in the Revolutionary War.

Insofar as community organizations are concerned, the great grandfather who owned the land from 1851 to 1901, spent part of his time as the secretary of the posse organized to prevent horse thieving. His son was also a member of the posse. During his tenure on the farm, Ralph Newton, Joyce and Daniel W.'s father, was active in the Denmark Congregational Church, Odd Fellows Lodge, Farm Bureau and was God's Portion Day organizer.

PEET-HOLTHAUS FARM OF JONES COUNTY

Settled 1840

Iowa's Sesquicentennial Committee, in its quest to find Iowa's oldest farms, has unearthed a treasure chest of remarkable stories about life on the Iowa frontier 150 or more years ago. One of those stories is the trials, triumphs and hardships of the Gideon and Abigail Peet family in their long, difficult journey from the East Coast to Iowa Territory back in 1840.

Gideon and Abigail's fascinating story begins long before their arrival in Jones County, but it is essential that readers know about that early period that eventually caused them to make the long journey to the Midwest.

Soon after she became a bride in the early 1800s, Abigail found herself riding a horse, with her young husband walking alongside, from Stratford, Connecticut, destined for central New York State, in hopes of establishing a home in the wilderness. As she rode, she clutched tightly to a bag holding all their worldly possessions. They had already traveled nearly a week and had already chopped marks in an effort to blaze a trail in the wilderness so others could find their way into the woods or they could find their way out. There Gideon felled trees and built a cabin. There they established a farm and had 12 children. Nine boys and one girl grew to adulthood.

Then in 1839, one of their sons had ventured West and had scouted the good soils of eastern Iowa. It must have been a glowing report to his parents, because despite his age of 60, Gideon decided the East was becoming too crowded so he came west to Fairview, Iowa, where more land was available for his six unmarried sons. It has been said that he was offered 160 acres of land for his team of oxen in what is now downtown Chicago.

The records given the author of this book gave few specifics, but it is assumed that after getting settled in Iowa, some of the sons went back East to get their mother, sister, and younger brothers, and possibly a future bride as well. It is known that the young wife of Gideon II had been a teacher in New York state before coming to Iowa.

The progression of ownership of the land Gideon I formally claimed in 1840 shows that a Cordelia Wilcox married Gideon Nelson Peet, a son of Gideon I and Abigail. They also homesteaded on the frontier in 1866 and started their family in a log cabin.

It was anything but an easy life in those early pioneer days. The hardships endured by the women as well as the men are told in such events as occurred one day when Gideon Nelson was away at court and his wife, Cordelia Wilcox Peet, was at her spinning wheel when she heard a noise and saw a band of 17 Indians in the yard. Too terrified to do anything else, she kept on spinning while they entered the house, ransacked her cupboards, picked up the babies, Collis and Theresa, who were playing on the floor, talked to them, finally leaving the house and executing a dance in the yard. One turned to the door and said, "Brave white woman, Indian no hurt!"

As time went on, that log home frequently became a stopping place for travelers.

Gideon I lived only four more years after coming to Iowa, but his sons took on the responsibility of developing the land. They also enlarged their holdings greatly. One or two of the sons are said to have owned up to 2000 acres at a time. It is told that in early years, all the land on both sides of the Military road between Fairview and Martelle was owned by the Peet family.

Information provided for this section shows that Cordelia, the wife of Gideon II, owned the Iowa homestead for a few years, indicating that her husband, who had been the second owner of the farm, must have passed away while still fairly young.

While it is not known when Gideon II died, it is known that his widow, Cordelia, lived to be 80, and that, at age 77, she attended the 1893 World's Fair in Chicago. Just before her death, she expressed the wish she could live another 50 years "to see the development that is certain to come."

Third to own the homesteaded land was Eber Peet, one of the sons of Cordelia and Gideon II. Eber's wife's name was Orianie. They had eight children. Orianie also outlived her husband a number of years and was listed as owner of the land beginning in 1916.

Her son, Clarence B. Peet, and his wife, became the next owners. They were the parents of a daughter, Gloria, and two other children. Gloria married Burdette Holthaus, and in 1968, they became the sixth owner of the land that had been in the Peet family's name for over 125 years. Two children were born to Burdette and Gloria, making for a seventh generation.

Burdette was a veteran of WW II in which he served 52 months, first in Ireland, then North Africa, then Italy and finally in France.

The farming and stock raising done by the Peet family over those 125 years was not unlike that of other pioneers. The prairie had to be broken first, then corn, wheat, oats, and hay were the crops. Oxen, hogs, sheep and chickens were raised, followed by horses brought in to replace the oxen. Spotted Poland China hogs and milking Shorthorn cattle were the livestock mainstay for a time.

When Burdette and Gloria took over after WW II, the tractor age had changed the farming operation to a corn, soybean, oats, and hog program.

The farm is now rented to a neighbor, Phillip Niehaus.

The Holthaus family members belong to the Martelle Methodist Church and the Farm Bureau.

THE RONALDS-MCDILL-JACK-ZEITLER FARM OF LOUISA COUNTY

Settled 1840

The present home was built by George McDill in 1917.

A Florida resident, Patricia Jack Zeitler, has supplied detailed information on an Iowa Sesquicentennial Pioneer Family Farm located in Louisa County. The data is far more complete than the pages of this book can accommodate. All are extremely interesting and thorough.

The great-great granddaughter of the original owner of the pioneer farm, Patricia Zeitler, now is a 50% owner with her mother, Mrs. Faith McDill Jack, who owns the other 50%.

The first owner was John Ronalds, who was born in Vermont and then moved westward in steps. He first moved to Ohio, then to Indiana, after that to Illinois, and finally to Iowa. He served as a Colonel in the War of 1812. He married Martha Killbaugh in Ohio in 1822.

Nine children were born to the couple — four in Indiana, two in Illinois, and three more in Iowa. Their mother was only five feet tall and her babies were all small. The first born was so tiny it was said her father's shoe would have been large enough for a bed for her. Marion Emily, their seventh child, arrived on December 3, 1836, and was the first white girl to be born in

Louisa County.

In 1840, John and Martha obtained 80 acres to homestead in Louisa County. The purchase was for $1.25 per acre and came through the Government's General Land Office.

As soon as the purchase was approved, John Ronalds fashioned the timbers for the framework for their first log home. It had to be a reasonably large home to provide for their large family. He made his own mortar and did his own plastering. Rails made by splitting logs were used for fencing.

It was hard work using oxen to break the prairie, and doing the planting of corn and seeding of wheat, oats, and hay land by hand. Scythes and cradles were used to harvest the grain and hay. The corn had to be husked by hand, of course. More land was purchased for a total of over 280 acres.

That John Ronalds was a leader as well as a pioneer is seen in the fact that he was a member of the 1846 Constitutional Convention when Iowa became a state and also was a member of the Commission that established the Capitol in Iowa City.

Martha Ann, the second oldest daughter, married Joseph McDill, who became the second owner of the farm. They were the great grandparents of Patricia. At Joseph's death, three of his and Martha's sons divided the 288 acre tract. One of them was George McDill, Mrs. Zeitler's grandfather. He and his wife, the former Elizabeth Dodder, lived on the homestead and had three children.

One of those children was named Faith, who married Carl Jack and became Particia Zeitler's mother.

A paragraph or two about the hardship and challenges the wives and mothers of those pioneer years had to contend with day and night is very much in order.

Not only were there usually a large number of children to care for and feed and clothe, but in some cases, to help educate as well.

Martha McDill had seven children and one of the reports about her dedication to her family tells how she not only washed and carded the wool shorn from the sheep on the farm, but spun it on her spinning wheel as well. And as though that were not enough, she also wove it into cloth to be used to clothe the children. All this was done in the evening by the light of candles she had also made and molded from tallow.

The old pioneer saying, "The men work from sun to sun, but women's work is never done," most certainly applied to Martha McDill.

In other information secured from Mrs. Zeitler, it is revealed that her mother still lives in the three-story brick home with 23 rooms built by her parents in 1917. A system of batteries built in the basement provided electricity for the home as early as 1918.

Some interesting statistics were also furnished by Patricia Zeitler. A few that deal with prices that prevailed at different times that may be of interest are:

1900 - Wheat sold for 60 cents a bushel

1933 - Corn , 10 cents a bushel

1946 - Soybeans, $2.00 a bushel

Back in 1900, men could get a shave for 10 cents and a pound of butter was 18 cents. In 1910, a dozen eggs was 14 cents and was usually traded for groceries.

In 1919, 40 rods of wire fence cost $21.96 and a pair of overalls with matching jacket could be had for $4.00. A year's subscription to Wallaces Farmer was only a dollar. Gas for the Model "T" was 28 cents a gallon.

However, not everyone was satisfied with a Model "T". George McDill purchased a new Buick in 1931 for $1000, but the corn he had to sell only brought 24 cents a bushel.

The 276.93 acres now in the pioneer farm, including the 80 acre, 156-year old homestead, is now rented on shares to Job Keltner, Jr., who raises corn and soybeans and does it well. In 1994, his corn averaged 221 bushels an acre and soybeans averaged 68. Ninety acres of the farm are still pasture land where some 50 head of a cow-calf herd are being raised.

THE STEPHENS FARM OF WASHINGTON COUNTY

Settled 1840

Stephens is an exceedingly well-known name in Iowa agricultural circles for several reasons. One reason is that a large Washington County farm was homesteaded in 1840 — six years before Iowa became a state — by Samuel Stephens and has been owned and operated by one or more members of the Stephens' family for 156 years. Another reason is that one of those owners and operators of the farm was Richard L. Stephens, Iowa Farm Bureau Vice President for a number of years.

As indicated, the first Stephens name to appear was Samuel, great-great grandfather of the present owners, who bought 160 acres of good prairie land from the government in 1840. An official document with the signature of President Tyler proves Mr. Stephens' original ownership. Indians were still around at the time, and breaking the prairie sod with oxen and horses was no easy task before wheat, corn, flax, and other crops could be grown.

Richard Stephens, Vice-President, Iowa Farm Bureau.

The Civil War period in the 1860s was also difficult for pioneer farmers, as well as everyone else. Sons, badly needed on the farm, were called to service early in the conflict to save the Union. Such was true of the Samuel Stephens family. One of their sons, L. A.. Stephens, later to become the farm's owner, was called and gained the highest non-commissioned rank in Company "C" of the 8th Iowa Volunteers, an infantry unit.

After surviving the war and the hard times that followed, L.A. became owner of the farm and the second generation of Stephens' to do so.

He, in turn, saw one of his sons, Dewey D. Stephens, grandfather of the present owner, take possession of the farm in 1909. Dewey and his wife, Blanche, became the parents of seven children, one of whom was Richard L., the member of the family referred to earlier as the long-time vice president of the Iowa Farm Bureau. In 1945, at the close of World War II, Richard became the farm's owner.

By now, the farm had increased in size to 440 acres, but not until some trying times had been survived, particularly the period of 1929 through 1935.

Boyd Stephens, one of Richard L.'s sons, who is now a member of the Richard L. Stephens Trust, of which Richard A. Stephens, another son of Richard L., is also a trustee, tells of some of the trials the Dewey Stephens went through during their period of ownership during a period of "boom and bust". In a memo to the author of this book, written during the Sesquicentennial year, Boyd Stephens says:

"Dewey and Blanche, who had taken over the farm and the mortgage in 1909, and had raised seven children, provided monetary and moral support to three sons to start their own farms. In the "Boom Years", which ended in 1930, as the family had grown, so had the mortgages.

As a result, Northern Trust of Chicago started to foreclose on the farm. An agreement, that in the next five years for every dollar paid, two dollars would be forgiven, was finally reached.

It was quite a challenge, but finally, in 1938, Dewey and Blanche took a train to Chicago to pay off the mortgage. It was their first trip together since they were married.

While there, Richard, the oldest son, called to tell them all the buildings, except the house, had burned. Then, at the age of 64, Dewey went to his timber and worked out the lumber to rebuild. In the following two years, he constructed two large barns and a crib in addition to farming the 440 acres."

That's the kind of stuff some of our forebears were made of in years gone by,

Presently the farm, while still owned by the Stephens Trust, is farmed by their tenant, Kenneth Robertson, who is a grain farmer. Some of the land is also in the Crop Reserve Program.

When Richard L. was doing the farming, hog production was a major enterprise and was done so efficiently that Richard (or "Dick", as he was universally known) became one of Iowa's earlier recognized Master Swine Producers, a project started early in World War II in response to the nationwide call to grow more meat and other foods to help "Win The War and Write The Peace".

Richard L. further made the Stephens' name stand out when he was named one of Iowa's Master Farmers, and served in the State Legislature 18 years, both in the House of Representatives and in the Iowa Senate.

CLOVER LEAF FARM OWNED BY THE WILSON-JOLLY FAMILIES OF LOUISA COUNTY

Settled 1840

Born in New York City in 1815, James X. Wilson could hardly be expected to become an Iowa farm pioneer 25 years later, but that's just what happened. Soon after his birth, his parents moved and took him to Pittsburgh, Pennsylvania. A few months afterwards, his mother died.

He was then taken to Washington County, Pennsylvania, where he lived on a farm with a family by the name of Toner until he was ten. It was during this time that he received most of his formal education.

In the fall of 1824, at the age of 19, James X. accompanied his father, John, to Preble County, Ohio, where they spent the winter and his father remarried. In the spring of 1825, the family settled in Union County, Indiana.

In 1842, at the age of 25, James went West as far as Iowa and was so impressed with Louisa County soil and the county's future possibilities, that he staked out a claim on Honey Creek near a place known as "Bottom Patch". There he built a log cabin close to the creek.

After a couple of years of working his claim and harvesting some crops, he went back to Indiana in 1843 to marry the girl who had promised to wait for him. She was Martha Ellen Miller. The wedding bells rang on June first, and shortly thereafter the young couple got back to what was then commonly referred to by Easterners as "The Wilds of Iowa".

Upon their settling in the Honey Creek log cabin, James first took care of weeding the crops and then began making some of the first bricks manufactured in the county. Some of those bricks, made in Wilson's first kiln, are still to be found in the chimney of the brick home the couple built some time in the late 1840s.

Soon after their first child, a boy named John, was born in the cabin in the "Bottom Patch", a "gully washer" of a storm came up, sending Honey Creek out of its banks. Family history indicates the high water reached the cabin and that James carried his wife and baby on his back to safety on higher ground.

James X. Wilson was both industrious and a good business man. He kept adding to the 40 acres originally homesteaded, and by the time of his death in 1891, had accumulated 207 acres for his ten children. His youngest son, Charles Brown Wilson, is the one who took over when his father passed away.

Charles and his wife, Anna Jane, built a new home in the late 1880's which is still the home on the farm, and oversaw a rock quarry as well as the farmstead, which had grown to 527 acres. Charles also served as the Louisa County Representative to the State Legislature through the early 1890's. He was one of the homeowners on one of the first Rural Free Mail Delivery Routes in the nation established in Morning Sun, Iowa, in 1896, exactly a hundred years prior to Iowa's Sesquicentennial. Incidentally, Morning Sun has established an R.F.D. Museum during Iowa's Sesquicentennial.

Charles and Anna Jane had five children, all born in the farm home, but only two lived to adulthood. Youngest of those two was a son, James Ralph Wilson, who became his father's right hand man. He married Martha Emma Hutcheson in 1929.

J. Ralph and Martha oversaw both the decline in the farm during the depression and the recovery and expansion in later years. They were active in the growth of Louisa County and opened a new quarry from which much of the gravel for county roads is still taken. J. Ralph also served the town of Morning Sun as president of the telephone company, encouraging the laying of underground cable and other technological advances that have served the region well.

The couple's oldest daughter is Gwendolyn Marie. Born in the same room in the current home as her father, Gwen also graduated from Morning Sun Consolidated High School and Iowa State.

Gwendolyn married Frank Jolly; and although they left for California soon after their marriage, they are the current owners of the 514.65 acres of land now in the farm. This includes the original "bottom patch", the 40 acres of "highland" in James X's claim of June, 1842, the old and current quarries, as well as other acres of timber, farmland and pasture land, now both rented out.

Frank and Gwendolyn's second child is Kathryn Jolly Vance. She has provided this information for featuring this 156 year old farm. She and her husband and their two children now live in the home her great grandparents built. Her children now attend the Morning Sun School, just as have the six generations of the family who have preceded them.

James X. Wilson's oldest son, James Wiley Wilson, served in the Civil War. Almost all members of the family have belonged to the Presbyterian Church.

Mrs. Vance sums it up with six meaningful words. They are "We certainly have a rich heritage."

WOOLEY-McALLISTER FARM OF WASHINGTON COUNTY

Settled 1840

Mrs. Wilma McAllister, the widow of Raymond McAllister of Washington County, not only has made a special effort to supply information on the beginning of the Pioneer Family Farm she continues to own, but she also has summarized some of her observations and memories of farming's changes.

In reporting on the farm's origin, and about the original owner, she says, "William Wooley came to this land in 1838. It was in 1840 when he and a neighbor traveled together by horse drawn wagon to Burlington from Indiana to purchase adjoining farms. William was born in Kentucky, but had been living in Indiana.

"Not only did William farm the land, he was also the first school teacher in the township. He also surveyed the first road that led from Washington to Crawfordsville.

William Wooley digging potatoes with a "one mule" digger.

"From the date of the original purchase to the present, a direct descendant has lived on this 80 acre tract and farmed it every year. I am the fourth generation to live here. My husband farmed it as long as he was living; and now my son and his son farm the ground. That makes six generations to make their living on these Sesquicentennial acres. Through the years, additional land has been purchased, but the home and buildings are still on the original 80 acres."

Records the Washington County farm owner has supplied show that William Wooley and his wife had a family of seven. One of those children, Cary Allen Wooley, was Mrs. McAllister's grandfather. He bought the farm in 1885.

Cary and his wife had three children, one of which was Wilma McAllister's father, William C. Wooley. He gained possession of the farm in 1923, four years before Wilma was born.

In addition to the many things her father told her about the change to mechanization on so many farms during his boyhood and youth, Wilma was also intrigued by what he said about a most unusual development that occurred in 1916.

In August of that year, the Wooley family was flabbergasted to be approached by an oil drilling crew. The drillers were convinced there was oil below the rich Washington County soil. The Wooleys gave permission to explore the idea on their land and the drilling began with much expectancy. However, after several days, the only thing they had hit was a great flow of well water. The drillers soon lost their enthusiasm as well as their energy. When the weekend came, they all went on a drinking spree and never re-

William Wooley amid his large turkey flock.

turned. Thus, the Washington County "oil boom" stopped almost as soon as it started.

Wilma's husband, Raymond, served in WW II. As soon as he returned, he became an active farmer. He farmed the Wooley pioneer farm and rented additional farm land.

Wilma became the fourth owner in 1980. Her son, Tom, has been operating the place since his father's death. Tom has a son who represents the sixth generation on the farm.

During her parents' time of ownership, the Depression and drought years hit very hard and the farm had to be mortgaged. A sheepskin deed with President Van Buren's signature also had to be surrendered. However, by 1942, the mortgage was paid off. About that time, Raymond also enlisted and served in WW II.

Jersey dairy cattle and Hampshire hogs, along with sheep and chickens, were raised by both the second and third owners. Wilma's father also raised turkeys and had a large incubator to hatch the turkey poults.

Horses and mules were used for power until 1930 when a Fordson tractor came on the farm. That tractor was replaced by a steel-wheeled John Deere A, and with other John Deere tractors since that time.

The Wooley family are long-time Presbyterians, tracing as far back as 1783 at Paint Lick, Kentucky. William Wooley was a founding member of Crawfordsville, Iowa's Presbyterian Church. All his descendants were also members.

Mrs. McAllister marvels at the changes seen in farming just in her lifetime alone. She writes, "From riding on my father's knee following the horse-drawn one-row corn cultivator, to driving a team of horses pulling the wagon picking up bundles for the threshing crew, to proudly being able to drive (with my father's supervision) the new Fordson tractor, to listening to the put-put of that wonderful John Deere A, to now riding with my son and grandson in the air-conditioned cab of the powerful John Deere tractor pulling 12-row equipment. And all on the same land!"

THE BEATTY FARM
OF
VAN BUREN COUNTY

Settled 1841

Warren Beatty, the present owner of a 155-acre pioneer family farm in Van Buren County that his great grandfather started back in 1841 with about 80 acres, has an unusually complete record of the first four transactions involving the property near Keosauqua.

The first year the land became private property was 1838 when one Claiborne Lea obtained part of it from the United States Government, back when Iowa was still part of Wisconsin Territory. His portion was 39.20 acres purchased on November 6 of that year. Mr. Beatty has a copy of the Patent, the wording of which is as follows:

United States
To — **Record of Sale and Issue of Patent.**
Claiborne Lea — *Date of Sale Nov. 28, 1838.*
Certificate No. 410.
Date of Patent Dec. 1, 1841.
Vol 1 page 413. U.S. Land Records.
Conveys: -Lot 5 being the North East 1/4 of the North West 1/4 of Sec. 19, Twp. 69, Range 9, containing 39.20 acres.
O-E. Book page 491-492 Van Buren County Records.

Second set of persons to be involved, as shown by a Warranty Deed, and including "Forty acres, more of less", were Harlehigh and Sophie Buckland who sold those 40 acres, "more or less" to one Marquis Strong, also on November 6, 1838. Consideration was placed at an even one hundred dollars. It is assumed that Mr. Buckland and his wife had obtained possession of the tract from the government earlier in the year.

Just what happened next is a question no one can answer now. However, the next paper involved in those early transactions was a Sheriff's Deed, dated February 2, 1846. Evidently Mr. Strong, who may have been a land speculator, had lost the property. In any case, the Van Buren County Sheriff, one Josiah Bonney, on behalf of the county, sold the land to Benjamin Beatty, the first member of the Beatty family to be mentioned as early as 1838, and the present owner's great grandfather, to officially own it. Consideration for the 80 acre package is listed at $256.50.

Marquis Strong's name comes into the picture again in what was termed a Judgment paper showing the action of Purdon versus Strong. There is no record of who Thomas and John Purdon were, but the Judgment shows the amount of the transaction was only $25, but that costs ran to $98.93. The important thing on the judgment paper is that it again lists that Benjamin Beatty paid $256.50, the full total of the full amount of the judgment, interest, and other costs necessary for him to get possession of the land. Soon after the purchase, a wooden home was built. Although remodeled several times, that home is still being used as a residence.

Benjamin Beatty and his wife had a family of seven. When he died, his wife, Margaret, became the owner of the farm in 1866, right at the end of the Civil War. After that, one of her sons, William Beatty, Warren's grandfather, became the owner in 1881.

Wheat, corn, oats, and hay were the standard crops on those pioneer farms, as was true of the Beattys. Hogs and cattle, both beef and dairy, were raised, and horses, of course, did all the field work and provided all the transportation.

One of William Beatty's five children — a son, Roy —took over the farm in 1918. He was Warren's father. In 1962, by which time the farm had increased in size, Warren Beatty and his wife became the present owners. They have five children, and are the fifth generation to be involved in the Beatty family farm. The farm is now tenanted by Robert Hamberg.

Corn, soybeans, hay and beef cattle is the farming program pursued by Mr. Hamberg today.

In looking back, Warren Beatty says a late 1930s model John Deere became the farm's first tractor. He also remembers 1950 as a vintage year because that year his father got a mechanical corn picker, and the whole family welcomed electricity. In the late '50s, only a few years before Warren became the farm's owner, a grain combine was added to the machinery line.

The Beatty family is active in the Methodist Church.

THE JUDY FARM OF LEE COUNTY

Settled 1841

CERTIFICATE No. 6865

THE UNITED STATES OF AMERICA,

To all to whom these Presents shall come, Greeting:

WHEREAS George Judy of Lee County Iowa Territory has deposited in the GENERAL LAND OFFICE of the United States, a Certificate of the REGISTER OF THE LAND OFFICE at Burlington whereby it appears that full payment has been made by the said George Judy according to the provisions of the Act of Congress of the 24th of April, 1820, entitled "An Act making further provision for the sale of the Public Lands," for the North East quarter of the South East quarter of Section Thirty two in Township Sixty eight North of Range Five West, in the District of Lands subject to sale at Burlington Iowa Territory Containing Forty acres

according to the official plat of the survey of the said Lands, returned to the General Land Office by the SURVEYOR GENERAL, which said tract has been purchased by the said George Judy,

NOW KNOW YE, That the United States of America, in consideration of the Premises, and in conformity with the several acts of Congress, in such case made and provided, HAVE GIVEN AND GRANTED, and by these presents DO GIVE AND GRANT, unto the said George Judy, and to his heirs, the said tract above described: TO HAVE AND TO HOLD the same, together with all the rights, privileges, immunities, and appurtenances of whatsoever nature, thereunto belonging, unto the said George Judy, and to his heirs and assigns forever.

In Testimony Whereof, I, John Tyler PRESIDENT OF THE UNITED STATES OF AMERICA, have caused these Letters to be made PATENT, and the SEAL of the GENERAL LAND OFFICE to be hereunto affixed.

GIVEN under my hand, at the CITY OF WASHINGTON, the first day of December in the Year of our Lord one thousand eight hundred and forty one and of the INDEPENDENCE OF THE UNITED STATES the Sixty Sixth

L.S. 47224

BY THE PRESIDENT: John Tyler

By R Tyler Sec'y.

J Williamson RECORDER of the General Land Office.

UNITED STATES
DEPARTMENT OF THE INTERIOR
BUREAU OF LAND MANAGEMENT

WASHINGTON 25, D. C. AUG [illegible] 1965

I hereby certify that this photograph is a true copy of the patent record [illegible] in this office.

Land Patent for George Judy in 1841.

Five years before Iowa entered statehood, George Judy got the papers he needed to show he had laid down fifty hard-earned dollars to acquire 40 acres of land in Lee County, Iowa. The paper was dated December 1, 1841, and bears the signature of President John Tyler.

Like all other papers required to gain possession of government land during those early years, it spells out in beautiful hand writing the exact location of the land. In Judy's case, it makes it clear that the 40 acres were "in the Northeast quarter of the Southeast quarter of Section Thirty-Two in Township Sixty-Eight North of Range Five West, in the District of Lands subject to sale at Burlington, in Iowa Territory, containing 40 acres."

The document goes on to refer to surveyors in the General Land Office and that George Judy was the purchaser. It also makes it clear that Judy, or his heirs, "have gained all the rights, privileges, immunities, and opportunities of whatsoever nature, and that they now belong to the George Judy family."

George Judy was the grandfather of the present owner, John Judy, and was the father of ten. One of those children was George E. Judy, who became the second owner of the 40 acres, and the father of John. John, with his wife, Elizabeth, now operate land that includes the original forty acres.

Few of our lowa Sesquicentennial Pioneer Family Farms, purchased more than 150 years ago are now in the hands of only the third generation, as is the case of the Judy family of Lee County. It is quite evident that the Judy family has genes for longevity.

John Judy says the original cropping program included pasture, corn, and hay. Timber was another crop of value to the first owner. Later, John's father, George E., who became the owner of the pioneer farm in 1914, added soybeans to the rotation.

A cow and calf herd has long been a part of the livestock enterprise on the Judy farm, along with the sale of Angus bulls.

Horses were used for power up until 1950, when a Farmall F12 was bought. (Incidentally that was also the first make of tractor bought by the father of this writer, and its steel wheels are still a rugged memory.)

Other tractors used by John Judy, evidently on the additional acres now being farmed, includes a larger Farmall, as well as a Case and a Ferguson.

As is true of most Iowa farmers with long memories, John Judy vividly recalls the year 1936, with its bitterly cold winter and its searing summer drought.

John Judy also has a right to remember World War II. He served four years and nine months and came out of it with five battle stars to show he was involved in five major battles in the European sector on the road to victory over Hitler.

THE BRITTON FARM OF WASHINGTON COUNTY

Settled 1842

Three hundred and twenty-one acres of Washington County land near the town of Kalona was bought for $1.25 an acre from the U.S. Government by William S. Britton back in 1842. The land has been in the Britton family's hands ever since.

A veteran of the War of 1812, William Britton married soon after that. In time, he became the father of five, which prompted him to work hard and save carefully. Thus it was that when the Indians were steadily moving westward by 1842, he was able to turn over $401.25 to acquire the 321 acres of good land, build a log cabin on it, and move his wife and family into it.

Rye and wheat, along with corn and hay land, were the first crops grown after the prairie sod was broken. During that first year, wheat brought 25 cents a bushel and rye a mere 10 cents. It's no wonder that rye was soon dropped from the rotation.

In 1897, Vernon Douglas Britton, one of William's sons, bought the farm; and then in 1924, one of Vernon's son's, William S. Britton II, became the owner.

Over the years, every generation of Brittons appears to have raised beef or dairy cattle, or both. Hogs have also been raised every year. Purebred Hereford beef cattle were once a major project.

Much happened to change farming those first 50 to 80 years. First, it was acquiring machines to alleviate the hand labor of the past. Once the early two horse drawn small equipment had proved its worth, larger machines, some calling for six horses, or larger, hitches, came into vogue. Next it was tractors displacing the horses.

In the Britton's operation, a Case tractor was the first mechanical power unit, followed by others, including Internationals, Fords, and John Deeres.

Chickens also were raised, mostly by the wives, during the earlier years.

During the William II occupancy, improved seeds, including hybrid corn, also became a major factor in the successful operation of the pioneer farm.

The 1936 drought occurred during William II's ownership and it was rough. However, during that same period, electricity was added, much to everyone's delight. At first, it was from the farm's own Delco plant, then later on in the '30s, Rural Electrification brought more brightness and comforts.

A John Deere mechanical corn picker was added to the farm's equipment line in 1935, spelling an end to the drudgery of hand husking, and speeding up the harvest considerably. Three years later, an Allis Chalmers combine came into the picture and that ended the handling of bundles of oats and other grain.

Today, Dale and Gerald Britton, great grandsons of William S. Britton I, own and operate the 260 acres, all of it part of the original 1842 purchase. Dale and Gerald bought the property in 1971. The farming is now done by the sixth generation of Brittons. They are Mark, who is the son of Dale, and Tracy and Tim, Gerald's sons.

Soybeans, along with corn, now are the crops raised, and hogs and cattle make up the livestock program.

Dale recalls a few interesting items about prices. He says when his great grandfather started farming, he spent some time splitting rails for which he received 20 cents for every hundred rails split. Hogs raised back then were $1.50 a hundred weight. Hog prices were hovering around $50 a cwt. during the Sesquicentennial, but Dale remembers his father selling them for as low as $11.10 a cwt in 1926 when corn was 68 cents a bushel, compared to up to $4.50 a bushel reached on farms in 1996. He also remembers buying a car for less than $550 in 1919.

Dale has been active on the school board, and the AAA government farm programs. The family formerly belonged to the German Lutheran Church, but are now Methodists.

DUCK HOLLOW ANGUS FARM OF THE FINN FAMILY OF JONES COUNTY

Settled in 1842

What is now known as the Duck Hollow Angus Farm in Jones County had an early beginning and has a long and interesting history of successful management and good husbandry of livestock.

It was John Finn, born in poverty in County Galway in Ireland in 1816, who emigrated to the United States in 1837 and who started it all. Finn first went to Boston, Massachusetts. There he found employment for four and a half years, saving almost every penny he earned, and marrying Alice Murray, an Irish lassie who had come to America in 1836.

Soon after their marriage, the young couple headed West, partly by rail, but mostly by ship through the Great Lakes, finally winding up in Jones County, Iowa. Once there, they found and bought 320 acres of wild prairie land near Cascade from a William Hutton. The purchase was made in October 1842.

John Finn lost no time in breaking part of the prairie, hitching a horse and an ox together to do it. He also built a log cabin, putting a clapboard roof on it. Soon thereafter, he started seeding hay land, sowing wheat and oats, and planting corn. Livestock enterprises also developed quickly. Horses, cattle and hogs were raised as were small flocks of chickens, turkeys, geese and guinea hens. By 1870, the energetic Irishman was already breeding and selling Belgian horses.

Not only was John Finn a good farmer and stockman, but he also was committed to help his community. A zealous Catholic churchman, he had much to do in the erection of the first Catholic church in his hometown of Cascade. He also helped establish some of the first schools in the area.

John and Alice had seven children, including sons Thomas and Michael, better known as "Tom" and "Mike". At their father's death in 1878, Tom and Mike took over the farm, which then totaled 240 acres.

A history of Jones County published in 1910 credits the brothers as being tireless workers and highly successful, who greatly expanded the cattle and swine herds, and for using six horse hitches in their field work. The partnership was so successful that they eventually increased their land holdings to 860 acres and were feeding up to 150 cattle and more than 300 hogs.

Tom did not marry, but Mike did. His bride was Mary Murray. She bore the same last name as that of her mother-in-law, but there was no relationship, although her parents had also been born in the "Emerald Island". Mike and Mary had three children. One was a son named John Clarence, who acquired the large farm in 1924.

John Clarence and his wife had a family of six. One of them was a son, Raymond, who is now the owner and operator of Duck Hollow Angus Farm, a name he applied to the property in 1970, the year he took over.

Duck Hollow Angus Farm is an appropriate name because a purebred Angus herd had been developed on the farm during John Clarence Finn's ownership. During that period, many other developments took place, including the introduction of numerous kinds of tractors after a Fordson had been bought in 1920. Included over the next 40 or more years were a Farmall F210, an "M", then a "Super M", as well as other International tractors, such as the 560 and 966, as well as an Oliver 1855.

Electricity was welcomed in the home and barns in 1939, and a corn picker in 1940, as well as several combines since then.

The farm now totals 430 acres and organic farming is stressed. Considerable land is in pasture for the purebred Angus herd. Corn, oats, and hay land make up the present rotation.

Working with Raymond on the farm is his wife, Mary, and two of their four children, Jeremiah and Emily.

Raymond is a Vietnam War veteran. All members of the family all through the years have been faithful St. Peters Catholic Church parishioners. T.J. Finn, Raymond's grandfather, was a Jones County Supervisor. Raymond has served as a 4-H leader, Extension Council member, Township clerk, Vice President of the Dubuqueland Angus Association, and President of the Iowa Natural Food Association.

THE HARDEE FARM OF PAGE COUNTY

Settled 1842

One of the first settlers in southwest Iowa was William Hardee, who bought 320 acres in Page County. He was the great grandfather of Phil Hardee, who bought what had been his mother's estate when she died in 1995. Phil's mother was the granddaughter of William Hardee. Phil, himself, had lived on the farm 59 years before it actually became his own property in 1996.

It is known that William Hardee and his family first lived in a log cabin, but there is little known about the family or the farm's first crops and livestock. Oxen are known to have been used first, followed by some good horses. Presumably corn and some kind of grain were grown. Cattle and hogs were probably also raised those first years.

Family records show that William and his wife had a family of 12 children.

William Hardee apparently held the farm in his name until 1902 when Phil's grandfather and great uncle, Ezra P. and W.D. Hardee got possession. Ezra and his wife had a family of nine, of which one of the sons was Estes J., who became the farm's third owner. Estes' wife's name was Agnes and they had only two children. Phil was their only survivor after both his parents had passed away.

Apparently Ezra and his wife, Mary, went through some difficult times. In any case, Estes J. is credited with saving the farm, which is now down to 120 acres.

Phil and his wife, Janice, and their son, James, who now represents the fifth generation, now operate the farm with a cow-calf herd and with the usual grains and hay along with pasture. Phil and Janice also have three other children.

In earlier years, some purebred Angus cattle were raised, along with an Angus-Simmental cross. In 1980, their fat cattle sold for $80.50 cwt., the highest price paid by the Omaha stockyards to that time. That was quite a contrast from the $50 and $60 cattle were selling for during the Centennial year.

The Hardee's first tractor was a 1935 Fordson. Since then Allis-Chalmers tractors have replaced as many as 16 to 20 horses on the farm.

Ever since Ezra and Mary were in charge, the family has embraced the Order of Eastern Star. Estes and Phil both belong to the NFO and Farm Bureau. Phil and Janice and their children are members of the Siam, Iowa, Church of Christ.

WALKER SETTLEMENT, INC. FARM OF THE POOL-VAN ORSDELL-WALKER FAMILIES OF DES MOINES COUNTY

Settled 1842

What may well be one of the most interesting and historic of all the features in this book centers on what is known as the Walker Settlement in Des Moines County. Few, if any, pioneer Iowa farm families can match the number of Walkers who settled in Iowa, or the longevity of their farming ventures.

To Dennis Walker, a fifth generation member of this family, who now splits his time between teaching in Scott County, Iowa, and helping operate the pioneer family farm near Burlington , and who looks back on many generations of the Walker family, goes credit for this feature. His research effort has been painstaking.

The story begins in 1775 when Joseph Walker was born in Virginia. In 1800, he married Barbara Taler, who had come to America from Germany. Shortly before her marriage, Barbara had been given a cow and calf, and a spinning wheel by her German immigrant father.

Joseph and Barbara became the parents of 13 children. They all married and had large families of their own, and almost all of them migrated toward the West shortly before, or soon after, their marriages. Some made the trip to such "westerly" places like Ohio and Indiana by covered wagon. Others traveled by horseback, but all headed toward country unknown to them.

Thus it was that some of the Walkers reached southeastern Iowa right after the 1832 BlackHawk War when the Indian chief had ceded to what was later the Michigan Territory. A few years later, it became known as Wisconsin Territory, but not until 1846 did it become a part of the State of Iowa.

To illustrate the number of Walkers who came here, the story is told about a boy riding to Burlington with his father. While sitting there on the slow-moving wagon approaching a farm, the boy asked his father whose farm it was. The father answered, "Walker's". After the boy had asked the same question as they approached farm after farm, and "Walker" was always the answer, the father finally said, "When we get to a farm that isn't a Walker farm, I'll tell you. " It is said they rode the rest of the way in silence.

In any case, there were so many Wal;kers, and they all lived close together, that the name, "Walker Settlement" was most appropriate and still prevails. As for the production of a large family, Joseph and Barbara had 88 grandchildren.

The farm where Dennis Walker is now a member of the fifth generation farming it originated on September 6, 1842, by his maternal great-great grandfather, Robert Pool, who paid right at $5 an acre for 327 acres of choice land. Robert and his wife had a family of six. One of them was a daughter who married John Van Orsdell soon after his discharge from the Civil War.

During the War Between the States, he served with the 25th Iowa Infantry through the Battle of Vicksburg and then re-enlisted, at only age 20, with the 45th Iowa Infantry for the battles of Chickasaw, Boyer and Arkansas Post.

John and his wife had three children, and it was one of their daughters who married Neal Walker, one of the many sons in the Walker Settlement, who was Dennis' grandfather.

It was during Neal's ownership beginning in 1911 that things became financially difficult in the '20s and '30s. One day in the early '20s, when banks were going under everywhere, Neal Walker met his bank's owner on the street right after the bank had just closed. With everyone's savings suddenly behind closed doors, the conversation was not the most pleasant, but the banker gave Neal a couple dollars so he could buy gas in order to get home.

From 1911 through the next four decades were years of change. Horses still furnished most of the field power through the twenties, but things were actually in transition as early as the early 1900s. A Port Huron steam engine and a Russell thresher, bought cooperatively with neighbors, began a threshing run by 1900. The first tractor, a Fordson, came in 1921. In the '30s, more tractors and other labor saving equipment was bought. Great effort was made to get electricity to the farm as early as the 1920s, but it was not until the REA was established that electric power actually became a reality.

Neal Walker had married Zora, one of John Van Orsdell's daughters. They had four children. Ray, one of the four, and his wife, eventually became the fourth of the Walker Settlement farm's owners.

However, before acquiring the property, Ray Walker, Dennis' father, served three years in WW II. He was with the 5th Air Force in the South Pacific, stationed in Australia. After returning home later, he used his veteran's preference rights to buy a $1600 John Deere "A" tractor.

It was not until 1956 that he became the actual owner of the Walker Settlement farm, which now totals 220 acres. In the meantime, he married and he and his wife welcomed Dennis and a daughter named Cathy.

The Walker family was one of the first families in Iowa to break the prairie. It is believed they were yoking up oxen for field power as early as

1832. Corn, oats and hay were the traditional crops grown by the early pioneers.

There is no record of the livestock raised during the 1800s. After oxen were used some years, horses furnished the field power. Shorthorn cattle, bred both for beef and milk, and hogs that were fed and bred several years were raised. Chickens, turkeys and geese completed the livestock and poultry program.

In the early 1900s, Percheron horses, Polled Shorthorn cattle and Poland China hogs came into the picture. By the end of WW II, Angus cattle and Hampshire and Spotted Poland China hogs were being bred and raised.

The farm is now incorporated as Walker Settlement, Inc. Ray and Dennis operate the 220 acres jointly and get occasional help from Cathy's son, Dan Anderson. Dennis splits his time between teaching in the Scott County Community school and working on the farm near Burlington.

Dennis' wife's name is Debra and they have two daughters, Anne and Emily, who represent the sixth generation to live on the farm. Both of the girls are adopted and now make for a happy family. However, getting Emily from Texas proved to be quite a challenge and somewhat costly as well. "But we'd do it all over again because it's really worth it many times over," say Dennis and Debra.

Dennis' interest in teaching comes as no surprise. His great grandparents were teachers as well as pioneer farmers. They helped open a large stone school house in 1868. Members of the Pool family taught as many as 50 pupils. In addition, they boarded the rural teachers. The VanOrsdell family also taught their own and other children in the school and boarded teachers as well. Interestingly enough, Dennis and his sister, along with several cousins, became the fourth generation in the old stone school his ancestors built some 128 years ago.

THE ROBINSON-PARROTT FARM OF DES MOINES COUNTY

Settled 1842

Despite a span of 154 years, the first owner of a Des Moines County farm and the fifth and sixth generations of that same farm family living on that same farm have had some things very much in common.

The first owner of the land in the family was Samuel Robinson, who gained possession of 160 acres on April 29, 1842. He was the great-great uncle of Roger Parrott who bought a portion of that original farm in 1955 and more of it in 1962, and whose son, Thomas, now operates the farm.

The first thing they have in common, of course, is the land itself , which Samuel operated with help of a yoke of oxen and which Thomas now farms with a late model John Deere tractor.

The second way in which five or six generations apart have much in common is the way they have answered the call for military service in wars in which the United States has been involved the past 160 years or more.

Ten years before he bought the land in 1842 from David Patterson for $1.47 an acre, Samuel Robinson was one of those early militiamen who fought in the BlackHawk Indian War. One hundred years later, his great-great nephew, Robert Parrott, who now owns the farm, was a four-engine bomber pilot in World War II.

When Samuel was in the Indian war, his enemies were using spears and bows and arrows, but some 135 or 140 years later, his great-great nephew, Thomas Parrott — Roger's son — was a helicopter pilot in Vietnam, flying low through jungle valleys to avoid being hit by sophisticated enemy anti-aircraft fire. Later, Thomas was flying a jet fighter, but the speed in which he was flying was quite a contrast from that of the horses Samuel was riding in 1832.

There apparently is no record of Samuel's family, nor any indication that he had a son to take over the pioneer farm. Evidently he had a daughter or niece, though, because a Robinson girl married Christopher Parrott, who

Harvesting soybeans on the Parrott Farm.

is shown as the second owner of the land. Christopher and his wife had seven children.

The next two names on the list of owners were William Sanford Parrott and Richard Parrott, but the years of their ownership were not given to those preparing this book.

Fifth person to own the farm was Everett Parrott, Robert's father, who bought it in 1945, right after WW II. Roger then acquired some of it in 1955, and the rest in 1962. He shares that ownership with his wife, Caroline.

In the very beginning, in the early 1840s, wheat, oats, corn and clover were grown, and Shorthorn cattle and Poland China hogs were raised. Chickens were also kept for egg and meat production.

Oxen were first used as power, and Roger Parrott still has one of the ox yokes used 150 or more years ago. Sandstone for a large basement barn was hauled to the farm in 1869 with yokes of oxen. That building is still being used.

In later years, purebred Angus cattle were bred on the farm, and alfalfa and soybeans were added to the cropping program.

Interestingly, the first tractor used on the farm in 1920 was a homemade machine cobbled together by Robert's father. Since then, John Deere, International Harvester, and Wallis tractors have been used.

Parrott says there has never been a mortgage placed on the farm in all those 154 years of ownership. Thomas, the son of Robert and his wife, now operates the farm. The family belongs to a local church and are members of the Farm Bureau and the Lions and Lionesses Clubs.

THE BRANDON-ULLEM FARM OF MONROE COUNTY

Settled 1843

James and Rebecca Brandon, said to have lived in Tennessee near the birthplace of Davy Crockett, apparently came to Iowa in 1842. Accompanying them were several of their children, including young Thomas Brandon, who in time would be another of Iowa's pioneer farmers, as well as a banker.

Not much is said about James and Rebecca, or about their family, but in published reports in the Chariton Leader, and in papers found in Lucas and Monroe Counties' files, it is said that they, along with their young son, Thomas, staked a claim of 160 acres in an unsurveyed area of Monroe County on May 10, 1843.

Soon afterward, the area was surveyed and given the hard-to-pronounce name of "Kish-Ko-Kosh", which apparently had Indian origin. Later it became established as Franklin Township in Monroe County.

In a paper reportedly written by Thomas Brandon, apparently some time in the 1860s, he said, "We had a team of oxen hired from a Missourian and by the middle of June, 1843, had broken nine acres of prairie land for ourselves and two and a half acres on William Moore's place. However, our plow got so dull we had to quit. We then planted our newly plowed land to corn."

A cabin was built near a good spring, which assured clean, fresh water for the family.

Thomas was only 17 when this took place. It is said the Brandons and Moores were some of the first white people seen in Lucas and Monroe Counties.

The account carried in the Chariton Ledger indicated it was very primitive living in the 1840s, and there was always a great yearning for more settlers to come in as neighbors. Indian trails were often traveled. To the Brandon's surprise and delight, they found the Clark brothers, whom they had first met while coming from Tennessee, had settled only a few miles away. Their other neighbor, William Moore, did not improve his claim in 1844, so John Ballard's family "jumped" the claim.

The article tells about the Mormons coming through in 1845 and '46. It also speaks of switching claims and of marriage in 1849. The next paragraph points out a rather amazing venture in which Thomas Brandon and his wife and two small children set out for California with two ox teams and a covered wagon, and reached San Jose six months later. It deals with other rather surprising things, including a journey to New York City before returning to Iowa.

After returning to Monroe County, Brandon farmed until nearing his 70s and then went into banking in Melrose, near Albia. Several of his daughters served as cashiers and tellers in their father's Melrose bank. Despite the rugged early years of his life, and the rigors of much early day travel, Tom Brandon did not pass away until 1923, at age 96.

Most of the material for this report has been supplied by Benjamin Floyd Ullem, the 92-year old present owner of the farm. He tells that the Brandon name on the land changed when Thomas' daughter, Laura, married a farmer named Ullem.

Their son, Benjamin Richard Ullem, was the fourth person to own the 160 acres and became Ben F. Ullem's father.

The farm now has been enlarged to 580 acres. Considerable livestock, including purebred Herefords were involved for many years. Corn and soybeans are raised on it annually now.

The current tenant is Maurice Sinclair.

Ownership is shared with a son, Benjamin Floyd Ullem, and his wife, Alice, and two daughters, Diane Rios of Davenport and Laura Cordell of Florida.

THE HELLMAN-RECKER FARM OF DUBUQUE COUNTY

Settled 1843

A deep faith in Divine Providence is credited with the founding of New Vienna in Dubuque County in 1843.

A publication called the "Saint Boniface Parish Centennial Souvenir Book", published in 1946, the year of Iowa's Centennial, tells about five families, all originally from Germany, leaving their Ohio homes for Iowa. The trip was made in six prairie schooners pulled by six yokes of heavy oxen.

Each of the six large wagons was covered by a triple layer of canvas, and was stocked with all the necessities for the 600 mile trek that took some 12 weeks of time.

Moving through Ohio, Indiana, and Illinois, they crossed the Mississippi River at Burlington and went as far west as Iowa City, then a struggling Johnson County village. Their first effort at establishing a settlement in Johnson County was not very appealing, and that is where Divine Providence entered the picture.

After reloading their wagon train, and not knowing where to go next, the 22 intrepid pioneers headed northeast and reached Dubuque County. There they met the saintly Catholic Bishop Loras, who, although French-speaking, could converse with the German-speaking group enough to welcome them and encourage them to settle.

To their delight, the immigrants found an area of rich farmland where there were streams that would furnish water power for a grist mill and a saw mill, with timber all around. That is where they ended their long search. They called the settlement New Vienna.

Although hardships almost beyond comprehension faced the sturdy group, they put their collective shoulders to the task with determination and zest. Each family acquired a quarter section of land from the government at a cost of $1.25 an acre. Then they used their axes, saws, and hammers to build log cabins. Next, it was clearing hazel brush the hard way. Then with oxen, crude plows, and even spades, ground was cleared and crops and gardens were planted.

One of those pioneers was Henry Hellman who bought 40 acres from the government in 1843 during the administration of President John Tyler. He and his wife, Agnes, had a family of six, and Henry was the great grandfather of Eileen Hellman, who with her husband, Ralph Recker, are the present farm owners.

One of Henry and Agnes' six children was a son, also named Henry, who inherited the land from his parents in 1887. Henry II and his wife had 12 children, one of which was a son named Lawrence who never married. Nevertheless, Lawrence inherited the farm in 1940.

Fourth persons to own the land, and who are the present owners and operators of what is now a 148 acre farm, are Ralph and Eileen Recker. Mrs. Recker, Henry I's great granddaughter, and her husband bought the farm from the Hellman Estate in 1977 for $1850 an acre for a total of $270,000.

Ralph and Eileen have six children and are now doing the farming using a soybean, corn, oats, and alfalfa rotation.

Eileen's father, Anthony Hellman, was a World War I veteran, and her husband was in the service in 1956-58.

The Reckers, whose address is now Dyersville, of "Field of Dreams" baseball fame, like all their ancestors, are staunch Catholics and very proud of their New Vienna community founded by those intrepid Iowa pioneers 153 years ago.

THE OAK GROVE FARM OWNED BY THE MEIER-LUERS FAMILIES OF WASHINGTON COUNTY

Settled 1843

Oak Grove Farm in Washington County is one of those Pioneer Family Farms where the founder came from across the Atlantic and where the fifth generation is now continuing a tradition of agricultural excellence, and a sixth generation now is bidding fair to carry it on in the 21st Century. It is a farm where much rural history has been written and more is likely to be in the future.

Johann Albrecht Meier and his wife, the former Anna Christine Luers, were both born and raised in Germany, but like so many others living under the Kaiser, emigrated to America in the early 1840s.

After the long ocean voyage, the young immigrants, who spoke no English, of course, reached Iowa's frontier in 1843. They came by covered wagon to Washington County, saw a 160-acre government tract near where Brighton is now, and bought it for $1.25 an acre.

Not only did they build a crude log cabin and a small barn right away, but Johann soon started breaking the sod and planting corn for food and feed, and also seeded timothy for hay. Thus, the first crop grown on the pioneer farm was harvested 153 years ago. Oxen were used those first years to haul supplies to and from Burlington.

It is said this farm is where Johann and Anna raised their seven children, learned to speak English, arranged to tan hides and make boots and harnesses for their own use and sell to neighboring settlers.

They also must have become premier pioneer hosts. Not only did they raise their own brood of seven, but through some of those early years, they also provided a home for three orphaned Miller family children, and for five Luers' grandchildren when their young father was killed by run-away horses. Moreover, they also provided hospitality for other family immigrants until they could find farms for themselves. To do this, another and larger cabin had to be built from hewed timbers. Eventually, in 1867, a large brick home was constructed. This is the home in which five generations of the family have lived these past 129 years.

God-fearing families that they were, the Meiers and other neighboring pioneer German settlers met in their homes for church services for a number of years. However, the need for a church building was soon evident, and to no one's surprise, Johann Meier's name was at the top of the charter petition.

Anna's 84-year old mother came in 1851 to live with the Meiers. Her voyage took three months' of ocean travel.

Johann and Anna were the great-great grandparents of R. Dean Luers and his wife, the present owners of the 153-year old farm. The farm is now 360 acres, and was named Oak Grove Farm in 1911.

Second owner was a great-great uncle of A. Dean Luers, Harmon Meier, evidently a brother of Johann.

Third generation to own the farm was Henry D. Luers, Dean's grandfather, who bought the property in 1899. Henry D. became widely known as an outstanding livestock man and breeder of Shorthorn cattle and Poland China hogs. His Shorthorn herd was headed by prize bulls like "Golden Aberdeen", a 1906 grand champion.

While her husband raised prize cattle and hogs, Dean's grandmother was busy raising a daughter, Ruth, and taking care of large flocks of chickens, ducks, geese, and turkeys.

Although they worked hard and were the best of farmers and animal husbandmen, the going was not exactly easy for some of Dean's ancestors. On one occasion, all the cattle had to be sold to pay off the mortgage on the land.

The H.D. Luer's daughter, Ruth, became the fourth owner of the farm in 1956. Ruth and her husband were the parents of six children, one of whom is R. Dean, who, with his wife, Rosemary, bought Oak Grove in 1966. They continue to have hogs and a beef cow herd and raise corn and soybeans.

Horses were used until 1942 when a steel-wheeled Farmall was bought, followed by seven other tractors in more recent years.

One of Dean and Rosemary's four children is a son, Dan, who is a gifted singer and who had a hard time deciding between pursuing this talent professionally or following in his parent's and other ancestor's agricultural path.

Finally, when he chose Bob Jones University in South Carolina for his college degree, he combined his two "dreams". He joined the noted BJU chorus and opted for a major in Agricultural Business.

A full-page color picture and a lead story entitled, "Corn, Cows, and Chords", in the BJU REVIEW, the university publication, tells how Dan deliberated and then chose agriculture in the end. "The Lord made me do it," was Dan's answer.

Throughout the years, the Oak Grove Farm families have been very active in their Evangelical Church, beginning with Johann Meier's signing of the charter and through to the sixth generations' college careers. And they have also been community leaders in Meservy, the Shrine, Farm Bureau, Beef Producers, and other organizations. However, when their country called, three brothers and two brothers-in-law donned uniforms to serve in WW II,

Korea, and Vietnam.

Rosemary Luers, in the Oak Grove Farm Report, concludes with an appropriate statement, saying, "We feel very fortunate to be the fifth generation to live and work on a pioneer family farm that has so much history."

THE PUMPHREY FARM OF JEFFERSON COUNTY

Settled 1843

Although they apparently did not get final possession of the land until 1850, the Pumphrey family actually first settled in Jefferson County in 1843. That is the year when Serene Pumphrey and his family, along with his mother, Edetha, came to Iowa from Ohio looking for farm land.

Family records indicate that they took out Land Patents on 245 acres near what is now Batavia in Jefferson County. Evidently Serene started his farming project with oxen as soon as the prairie could be broken. The Pumphrey family has been in control of that land ever since.

Soon after coming to Iowa, a log cabin was built, but after a couple of years, it was no longer satisfactory. Thus, about 1848 or 1849, two houses were built by Serene and some of his sons. One of the new homes was for Edetha, and the other was for Serene and his wife, Mary, and their children.

The walnut used for lumber came from a walnut grove located on some bottom land on the new farm and hauled to the building site by oxen. The doors, windows, and almost all other features in the two new homes were hand-crafted. Sandstone blocks were used in the basements.

There was a very short period when the farm was in an estate, but it was then bought by Frank Pumphrey, who was a son of Serene and Mary. Frank and his wife became the second owners of the property.

Frank Pumphrey not only was a good farmer and good custodian of the farm, but he also had a wealth of relics and remembrances of earlier years. Included were an ox yoke, pioneer church bell, early farm tools and farm equipment, a spinning wheel, flax wheel, and a wheel to measure yarn.

A coverlet made by those wheels is a special treasure, and has been handed down several generations to where it is now the property of the present owner of the farm, Phyllis Pumphrey, widow of the late Richard Pumphrey, who was a great grandson of the original owner. Richard and Phyllis' three sons — Robert, John and Jim — to whom Serene was a great-great grandfather, now share the management and ownership of the farm with their mother.

And that ancestor must have been quite a pioneer, because Serene Pumphrey is said to be the first farmer in the area to replace his oxen with a team of horses and apparently used the horses extensively. A family diary indicates he hauled supplies with the team to Keokuk on the east and Ft. Dodge to the north. The elder Pumphrey also operated a stage coach stop and had a mail collection postal station where the entire neighborhood got its mail.

There are 167 acres left of the original 245 acres homesteaded. The 78 additional acres have been sold to one buyer or another during the 153 years since they were first claimed. The three great-great grandsons now in charge of the farm probably are managing more than just the 167 acres, but no information is given in that regard.

One of Phyllis and Richard's sons has served in the National Guard. The family has held membership in the Batavia Methodist Church, Masonic Lodge, Order of the Eastern Star, and other organizations through the years. Among them was the National Farmers Organization and a Midget Racing Association.

THE RAILSBACK FARM OF LINN COUNTY

Settled 1843

One hundred and fifty three years ago — three years before Iowa became a state — Edward Railsback had a chance to buy 320 acres of land in Linn County in the year 1843.

The nation's President that long ago time was John Tyler, a member of the Whig Party, and his name is on the paper that proves that Railsback had bought the large tract from the United States. Cost was $1.25 an acre.

One of Edward Railsback's sons, John, took over the farm from his father well before the turn of the century, and one of John's sons, Gary, took possession in 1913.

The property remained in Gary's name for 60 years before the present owner, Gary L. Railsback, a fourth generation family member, and his wife, Helen, became the owners in 1973. Now the farm is being operated by still another generation, Clifford and Carlton Railsback, who are making it 153 years of continuous Railsback ownership and operation.

The farm now totals 287 acres, some 33 acres less than when Edward homesteaded it. Some years back, a utility company had to have 30 acres or so of it to provide additional service to customers.

The original home for Edward Railsback and his family was built from a combination of logs, stone, and sawed lumber. A barn was built soon thereafter. That building is still standing and is still being used to store hay.

The first crop grown, over 150 years ago, was winter wheat. Corn and oats soon followed, along with hay land. That was pretty much the pattern until the 20th Century got underway, when wheat production was largely discontinued and, in its place, a new crop — soybeans — became popular. Today, soybean acreage often is about equal to the corn acreage.

In the livestock department, cattle, hogs, and sheep have been raised and fed throughout these many years. Chickens were also a factor until some thirty or forty years ago.

Horses, of course, were important up until the late 1930s. In fact, their barn held ten horse stalls and they were always occupied.

In 1938, a Farmall F20 became the Railsback's first tractor. Fordson and several John Deere tractors have since been used on the 287 acre pioneer farm in Linn County.

The farm is located near Palo, a town of about 430 souls, in western Linn County.

ROTH'S RIVERSIDE FARM
owned by
THE ROTH FAMILY
Settled 1843

Roth's Riverside Farm is an unusual farm in that the land is on both sides of the Mississippi River. Three hundred sixty acres were bought in Iowa from the U.S. Government in 1843. That same year, 500 more acres were bought across the river in Illinois. This report will concern itself with the Iowa aspects of the farm.

The original farm home was of stone, and while it no longer exists, an ice house built in the early years of the farm is still standing. Presumably ice cut from the river was originally stored in the building, but it is now used as a storage shed.

The Roth farm is still growing wheat much like most Iowa pioneer farmers did soon after breaking the sod. Many of them continued to grow the crop until the year 1900 and beyond. However, when soybeans were introduced, virtually all Iowa farmers discontinued growing wheat, but John T. Roth kept on producing the milling grain. During Iowa's Sesquicentennial, disaster struck many of the nation's wheat producing areas, causing prices to soar over $6 a bushel by early summer.

Corn and hay have been grown on the Riverside farm from the beginning to this day. Soybeans were also added some 50 or more years ago. Hereford cattle and crossbred hogs are the types of livestock raised by almost all the farm's owners.

Information received from John T. Roth about the Riverside farming enterprise included a copy of an 1884 ledger sheet with some interesting figures.

Expenses included $5.99 for seed corn, $1.50 for a pair of shoes and 25 cents for watch repairs. Items sold included three cords of Maple and Ash wood for $10, six pounds of butter for $1.80, one Chester White boar, $5, and a Poland China boar for $7.50.

Second owner of the farm was John W. Roth, and the third was Lymond Roth.

John T. Roth, the fourth and present owner bought the land in 1958. He now has only a limited number of acres left of the original purchase made by his early ancestor in 1843.

Another generation of the family includes two sons of John T. Roth. Charles Roth, the older of the two, served in the Korean War. John A. Roth, the younger son, was in the war in Vietnam. It will be noted John A. is the fourth Roth to share that first name. He is one of the three John Roths who had middle names and used middle initials in their signatures. However, the 1843 member of the family, and originator of the farm, was just plain John Roth, with no middle name or initial.

VALLEY VIEW RANCH, INCORPORATED and THE ZANGMEISTER-SINGMASTER-FLANDERS FAMILY OF KEOKUK COUNTY

Settled 1843

Lagos, undefeated World Champion Percheron Stallion.

To veteran horsemen and thousands of long-time farmers the nation over, as well as many in Europe, the name Singmaster is legend. However famous the Singmaster name may have been to so many over more than a half century, it was not the family's original name.

Going back to Memmingen, Germany, to the year 1415, Keota, Iowa's Singmaster ancestors spelled their name "Zangmeister". And it was spelled that way all through the 15th, 16th, 17th, and most of the 18th centuries.

In 1749, Johan Zangmeister and his son George Frederick, came to America on the good ship "Patience". Not long after their arrival in Philadelphia, they sensed the Colonists' dissatisfaction with their mother country, and when the Revolutionary War broke out, both George Frederick and his son, Phillip, joined in the struggle against King George.

All through the long Revolutionary War, the Zangmeisters went by that name, but soon thereafter the spelling was Americanized to Singmaster. Proof of that is found in the records of the War of 1812, when a son of George Frederick's enlisted as Jacob Singmaster.

All of the foregoing information has been carefully documented by family genealogists, and has been provided to this book's author by James F. Flanders, a great-great-great-great grandson of Johan Zangmeister, the first in the family to emigrate to the United States.

Charles Singmaster, son of Samuel, one of the Singmaster Brothers who imported thousands of horses from Europe for Iowa farmers to buy.

Flanders writes, "My great-great grandfather, John Adam Singmaster, another of George Frederick's sons, was married to Lydia Van Buskirk, and they had eight children, one of whom was Samuel, my great grandfather who was born in 1807. He grew up in Pennsylvania, where he worked in a tannery for $6.00 a month before he joined his brother, Jacob, the 1812 War veteran, in a tannery. A few years later, he became a sheep buyer, riding on horseback from farm to farm."

It is at this point that the Iowa angle of the story begins.

About 1838, Samuel made a prospecting trip to Iowa. Evidently he liked what he saw. In any case, he came back to Keokuk County in 1843 to claim a sizable parcel of land. In the meantime, he had married, so he went back to Pennsylvania in 1844 to get his wife, Mary.

Indians were still plentiful in the area at that time. A log cabin was built, and Samuel resumed his livestock marketing business. Soon he found himself handling 100 or more cattle and many more hogs at a time, so three of his sons — Charles, Thomas, and William — joined the business, called Singmaster and Sons.

The business prospered, but not without difficulties. There was no railroad to Burlington, 65 miles away, so droves of 600 or more hogs had to be driven six to seven miles a day. They sold for $1.50 per hundred pounds.

It was a time when corn had to be ground by hand and sorghum molasses was made. A storm took the cabin. To replace it and build a larger home, lumber had to be hauled from Iowa City. Their barn also burned, destroying all their machinery. Cattle and hogs were raised on the pioneer farm. Oats, corn, and hay were the main crops. Officially, the firm was licensed as a cattle broker. Cost of the license was $8.33.

It was a period of time when oxen were still being used for much of the field work. It was obvious there would be a growing demand for horses, so in 1875, William, the youngest son, persuaded his father to send him to Europe to purchase good quality horses. His first importation was only a few horses, including three Percheron stallions for which there was a ready market. On July 3, 1876, William went back to Europe with $16,000 and took

A horse auction at Singmaster Sale Barn in Keota.

Joseph Mounts, one of the best horse judges in Iowa, with him. William returned from Europe with six Clydesdale stallions and one Percheron. One of the Clydesdales, named "Baron Kier", never failed to take first place wherever he was shown.

The Singmaster and Sons partnership continued until 1889. At that time, Thomas stayed on the original home place with his father, Samuel, and continued in the livestock business. In the meantime, Thomas' brothers, Charles and William, formed the partnership of Singmaster Brothers. William continued making yearly trips to Europe to re-supply their stables.

One of Charles' sons, J. Omer, soon became involved in the business. He made his first trip to Europe with his Uncle William in 1897. It was the first of 56 such trips he would make. His biggest importation was in 1909 when 200 head of top Percheron, Belgian, Clydesdale, and Shire stallions were brought back to Iowa from France, Belgium, and England. Cost of importation's sometimes exceeded $100,000. Over the years, a number of famous, prize-winning stallions were obtained, including "Merry Monarch", "Honorable", "Cabrillion", and "Lagos", an undefeated world champion.

In 1914, J. Omer and his family found themselves stranded in London during a buying trip at the beginning of WW I. That ended the importation of European horses to Iowa.

As for the 320 acre farm Samuel Zangmeister started in 1843, it is now 768 acres and is incorporated as the Valley View Ranch.

The farm was owned by Samuel Zangmeister from 1843 to 1899, when his son Thomas took over until 1915, when Lillian, daughter of Thomas, and widow of the late Frank Flanders, became the owner. She was James Flanders' mother. The incorporation took place in 1980.

It is interesting to note how many men in the family have answered the call of their country as far back as the Revolutionary War, in which George Frederick Zangmeister and his son, Phillip, served. In the War of 1812, Jacob Singmaster, along with George Seisholtz, both great-great uncles of James Flanders, served. And in a much more recent time, James himself enlisted in the U.S. Navy during the Korean War, serving nearly four years.

In the spring of 1955, after his discharge from the Navy, James joined his father and has worked the ranch ever since.

Two of James' sons, Murray and Randy, who are the eighth generation in the Zangmeister-Singmaster-Flanders family, now have much to do with operating the ranch with their father.

THE CAMPBELL ORCHARDS OF VAN BUREN COUNTY

Settled 1844

The Campbell Farm, now owned by Robert and Margaret Campbell, was bought on May 22, 1844, by Robert's great grandfather, Archibald Campbell, from the Barret family for $3.25 an acre. It was a 320-acre tract.

One of Archibald's sons, Bethel Campbell, was the farm's second owner. He and his wife had a family of three, one of whom was a son, Charles Campbell, Robert's father. Robert, or Bob, as he was usually called, was one of five children, and is the one who, along with his wife Margaret, now owns the 152-year old Campbell family farm.

Almost from the beginning, fruit production was a major goal for the Van Buren County family. As a matter of fact, by 1890, when Bethel Campbell was the owner, 50 acres of the farm was already in apple orchards. By 1905, it became known as the Campbell Orchards. During the time Robert's father, Charles, was the owner, he was winning a great many blue and purple ribbons in statewide fruit competitions sponsored by the Iowa Horticultural Association in Des Moines and elsewhere.

At the outset of the family's ownership of the 320-acre farm with its home made of logs and sandstone, and as fruit trees were being planted by the hundreds, wheat, corn, oats, flax and hay made up the cropping program.

Large gardens also were tilled, but the emphasis was on the fruit trees, mainly apples, peaches, and pears. Flowers also were grown profusely, along with all kinds of vegetables.

Robert says the 1934 and 1936 drought years were a near disaster, as were the floods of 1935 and 1947. That three-year period with its two droughts and one flood, were exceedingly tough. He also recalls corn selling as low as nine cents a bushel, quite a contrast from the $4.80 a bushel paid at one time during the Sesquicentennial year of 1996.

Well-bred livestock was raised by the Campbells through the years, including Belgian horses, Jersey dairy cattle, cross-bred cattle, Corridale sheep and purebred Chester White hogs.

Poultry also was a factor on the farm for many years, including chickens, turkeys, guinea hens and geese.

Lowest price ever received for hogs was a mere 2-1/2 cents a pound.

Up through the 1930s, horses furnished the power in the fields, but in 1944, a John Deere tractor was bought and put to use.

Records show that the first corn planter was purchased in 1905, while the first grain combine came onto the farm in 1940, and the first corn picker in 1946. Electricity, with all its benefits, was also welcomed in 1944.

Robert was a close friend of the late Iowa Secretary of Agriculture, L.B. Liddy, who started out his career as a successful cream station operator at Keosauqua.

Through the years, the Campbells have always been active in their church and in Masonry. Robert has been president of the church board. and is a 32 degree Master Mason, serving as secretary of his Keosauqua Lodge #10 for 26 years. Mrs. Campbell is active in the P.E.O. and is a member of the Daughters of the Revolution. They also belong to the Farm Bureau, Iowa Horticulture Society, and Farmers Institutes.

By virtue of her membership in the D.A.R., it is obvious that way back in the 1770s, an ancestor served in the Revolutionary War. Henry Campbell, a brother of Archibald, the farm's first owner, spent three years in the Union Army during the Civil War. Dan Campbell, Robert's brother, was a member of the famed 101st Airborne Division in World War II.

THE NEDROW-TAUDE-GATES FARM OF VAN BUREN COUNTY

Settled 1844

Way down in southeastern Iowa, in Lick Township in Van Buren County, there's a farm tract homesteaded by George Nedrow back in 1844 — two years before statehood came to Iowa. It was 120 acres at the time it was acquired from the government on June 29 of that year. Cost of the land was $1.25 per acre.

Although purchased and claimed in 1844, it took until January 1, 1846, when John Tyler was President, to get the deed that had been signed by Mr. Tyler.

George Nedrow was the great-great-great grandfather of Randy Gates, the present owner, who purchased the property in recent years.

Second owner was one of George Nedrow's sons, Simon Peter Nedrow, who was Randy Gates' great-great grandfather. One of the sons of Simon Peter and his wife, Anna Belle, was Irvin Nedrow who was the next member of the family to gain possession of the pioneer family farm. Irvin and Anna Belle were Randy's great grandfather and grandmother.

One of Irvin and Anna Belle's children was a daughter, Donna. She was listed as Randy's great aunt. She married Don Taude. They owned the farm for a time before Randy's mother and father, Mr. & Mrs. Duane Gates, took over.

The present home in which Randy and his wife, Elizabeth, live was built in 1896.

The 117-acre farm, now operated by Randy, who is the sixth generation in the family, is very intensively farmed. Grown are corn, oats, and hay. Raised over the years have been cattle, hogs, sheep, and chickens.

THE SEYB FARM OF LEE COUNTY

Settled 1844

Peter Seyb and his wife, Katherine, together with their eight children, migrated from Rhein-Platz, Bavaria, in southern Germany, to America in 1835.

They first settled some 14 miles east of Buffalo, New York, near an Indian town called Tonawonda, not far from a village known as Townline. One more child, another son, was born on their New York State location. Two of the oldest of their nine children, Michael and Christian, lured by tales of golden opportunity, left the New York State home about 1842 and came to Iowa. Evidently their letters home were enticing. In any case, in 1844, Peter and Katherine and six of their brood climbed on a covered wagon pulled by a yoke of oxen and made the long, tiring trip that finally wound up in Lee County, Iowa.

It did not take them long to settle on an 80-acre parcel of virgin soil near a village called Franklin. There they built a two-story log cabin with two rooms below and two more above. It was well enough built that it was still intact near the home of the sixth generation to follow Peter and Katherine.

While Peter and his wife and children were the original settlers on the farm in 1844, 152 years ago, they did not own it long.

In 1846, two of their oldest sons bought it and soon had changed the prairie and the virgin soil to very productive crops of wheat, corn, oats, and hay. A fruit orchard and vineyard, reminiscent of what the family had known in Germany, was also planted.

Livestock entered the operation later, and a barn was built in 1875. The barn is still in use.

One of Christian Seyb's sons, also named Peter, became the third owner following his father's death.

Peter, II, had a son named William, who was next to own the land, and although none of William's children ever owned the land, his grandson, Garry Wayne, a great-great-great grandson of the Peter Seyb who homesteaded the property 152 years ago, now is the owner. The original 80 acres have now been supplemented by the purchase of additional land.

In sending in an application to the Iowa Department of Agriculture for the pioneer family farm recognition, Garry Wayne Seyb also sent a number of pages of published material about the Seyb family.

Christian had a son named Peter, II, who was a member of the third generation of Seybs. He married Magdalina Blaufuss, nicknamed "Lena". They had a son named William Frederick and a daughter, Teresa, representing a fourth generation. William had a family of five — Leota, Merle, Maurice, Eulilia and Kenneth — all of whom lived on the Seyb homestead.

Kenneth Wayne, the youngest son, was mechanically inclined and was often found in his father's machine shop, or racing his motorcycle. In 1942, he enlisted in WW II and served three years in the European Theatre, where he participated in the battles of Normandy, and those in France, the Rhineland, and the famed Ardennes. He served as a Staff Sergeant with five medals, including the Victory medal.

After the war, he married Laura Margarette Lewis. They had one son named Garry Wayne Seyb, who is a sixth generation member of the Seyb family and is now the fifth and sole owner of the 120 acre Seyb pioneer farm. He is listed as Garry Wayne Seyb, Sr., which suggests there is a Garry Seyb, Jr., who would be a seventh generation of the family interested in the land originally settled by Peter and Katherine Seyb when they sailed the ocean blue for America in 1835.

Included in the material sent to the Department of Agriculture is a rundown of the members of the six recorded generations of the Seyb family and also the picture of a large granite marker on the grave of Peter Seyb, founder of the Seyb family in America.

The marker was dedicated on June 19, 1949, with over a hundred of Peter Seyb's descendants present for the impressive ceremony.

THE WHITNEY - STRONG FAMILY TRUST FARM OF BUCHANAN COUNTY

Settled 1844

It was on October 1, 1844, when Mark Whitney, a native of Kane County, Illinois, purchased 40 acres of Buchanan County, Iowa, land and received official papers to verify his claim. The purchase was made directly from the United States Government. Undoubtedly, the cost was the customary $1.25 per acre for the original 40 acres purchased.

After homesteading the original 40 acres, Whitney added 161.44 more acres to his operation. The second 40 acres was obtained on February 1, 1846. Third purchase was for 41.44 acres on May 1, 1854, followed soon thereafter, on June 1, 1854, with another 40 acre tract.

Final of Whitney's pioneer farm land acquisitions was still another 40 acres bought on May 1, 1856, making for a total of 201.44 acres, the amount of land that has remained in the same family's hands for no less than 140 years. The cost per acre of the four last acquisitions was not given .

Mark Whitney had a daughter who married Church Strong. Evidently she had inherited the 201.44 acres. Subsequently, the farm has been passed on to the children of Church and his wife which would have included a son, Howard Percy Strong. However, Howard Percy Strong is now deceased, so his widow, Harriet L. Strong is now the Trustee of the Howard Percy Strong Trust, which includes the 201.44 acre farm.

Names of the fourth generation members of the family, if any, were not listed in the reference to the Trust.

In any case, it would seem the farm is now in the hands of the fourth generation and, as indicated, is now in the form of a Trust.

There is no home left on the property, indicating that the land is now rented out either on a cash or crop share basis, because the application to the Iowa Sesquicentennial Pioneer Farms Committee reports that corn, soybeans, oats and hay are crops now being raised, but nothing is said about livestock.

No further information about the 152 year old Whitney farm was provided.

THE ADAMS-BROWN FARM OF MUSCATINE COUNTY

Settled 1845

The Ronald Brown Farm, located in Wapsinonoc Township in Muscatine County, has been owned by the same family since 1845.

Preston Brown, born in 1812 in West Virginia, moved to Madison County, Indiana, with his parents when a child. In 1843, he married Jane Adams of Portsmouth, Ohio. In 1845, Preston and his father-in-law, Jacob Adams, came to Iowa looking for good farm land. Enoc Lewis owned a strip of land near the Cedar County line that appealed to Adams. He bought the southern portion, which is the site of the present farm, for $3000. The next year, Preston Brown and Jacob Adams brought their families to Iowa to make this their permanent home.

The first house built on the farm was a very small one. As their family increased, they built a ten-room house on the south side of the road.

Jacob Adams died in 1850 and is buried in the North Prairie Cemetery. Preston Brown then became the owner of the farm. Preston and Jane became the parents of eight children, one being Alfred Able, born in 1857. In 1866, Preston Brown became a member of Mt. Calvary Masonic Lodge. He died in 1888. At that time, Alfred bought the farm of 345 acres. He paid for the land by selling wood in town from a large nearby wooded area of around 200 acres. He also raised Percheron draft horses and had sales that attracted buyers from other states. He was married in 1892 to Corena Houser of Liscomb, Iowa.

Alfred and Corena built a new home on the north side of the road in 1899, but had only lived in it for six years when it was destroyed by fire. During the rebuilding, they returned to the old house.

The farm land was rented out when Alfred retired from active farming. Then in 1922, one of their two children, Preston Walter, started farming the land. In 1924, he was married to Dorothy Birkett. They were the parents of four children, the oldest being Ronald Preston. Part of the farm was sold to Ronald in 1955, and the rest in 1968.

Ronald Brown and Zoe Mantor were married in 1948 and are the parents of four children and are the present owners of the farm. Two sons, Steven and Thomas assist with the farming at this time.

As is true of most pioneer Iowa family farms, corn, oats, and hay were raised from the outset, along with horses, cattle, hogs, and chickens. Soybeans were added to the cropping program by Preston Brown.

Records show that in the late 1890s, crops were very poor due to droughts and grasshopper infestations. Other years when drought or other difficulties made for short crops were 1934, '36, '47, '54, '58 and '88. On the other hand, the best crop years were 1933, '48, '77, and '94. During 1994, corn yields averaged over 200 bushels an acre.

The early generations on the farm were very fond of their Percheron horses. Even Ron's grandfather was dead against tractors for a long time. In fact, he told his son, "Don't ever buy a tractor." However, in 1937, Preston Brown did buy a tractor and that spelled the finish of horse power in the fields. Since then, the 338 acre farm has had no less than eight tractors, six of them International, one Ford and one Allis Chalmers.

However much the elder Brown was against tractors, he was one of the first Muscatine County farmers to accept electricity. He paid for one city line to bring electricity out to the farm as early as 1916.

He also was a leader in use of a farm elevator. While attending Iowa State College, he came across plans for an inside bucket-type elevator, powered by an electric motor, capable of elevating 4000 bushels into a new double crib in 1920.

Corn, however, was picked by hand until 1939, when a 2-row mounted mechanical picker was bought, and used for 20 years. A combine was added to the machinery line in 1949.

Ron Brown is the fifth generation member of the Adams-Brown family to own the farm and has hopes future Brown generations will carry on. He says the land is close to West Liberty, and he repeatedly gets offers to sell, but it is the wish of the family to keep the property.

Brown's youngest son and his family live in a home close to where Ron and his wife live. The son has a ten year old daughter, who represents the sixth generation, and who can rightfully say she lives in a house built by her great-great grandfather.

ELM HILL FARM
OWNED BY THE GOODENOW FAMILY
OF JACKSON COUNTY

Settled 1845

J.E. Goodenow
and
Mrs. J.E. Goodenow

John Elliot Goodenow, the great grandfather of the family now in possession of land purchased in 1845, was the pioneer who bought 160 acres of timberland from the government 151 years ago. A U.S. Government Patent made the transaction official.

Mr. Goodenow was born in 1812 in Vermont and moved with his parents to New York State when only eight years old. There he grew to manhood and organized a militia of which he was Captain. He also owned a canal boat and taught school.

In 1837, he decided to go West. He equipped himself with a 4-horse team, covered wagon, and stock of food and supplies for the nine week trip. He made the trip in the dead of the winter of 1837-38 at a time when he could cross rivers on ice, including the Mississippi. He went on to just north of where Maquoketa is now in Jackson County; and, with an earlier settler, Alfonzo Gowen, built a cabin. Unfortunately, it was on low ground so a second cabin had to be built higher up on the 160 acres he had acquired.

That done, he made the long journey back to New York State to marry his long-time sweetheart, Eliza Wright. After the wedding, the young couple got another team and covered wagon and came back to Jackson County where the new cabin he had built was waiting for them.

Enroute on their wagon train "honeymoon", they saw few people and no one that they knew. The bride became very homesick, but hid that fact from her new husband. At night, wolves were heard howling along the way.

Forty acres of land were broken as soon as the weather permitted. John

Elliot built a horse-powered mill called the "Corn and Wheat Cracker". It was so popular with neighboring pioneers that he sometimes had to run it day and night.

He also opened a stone quarry. A "lean-to" built on the cabin became Maquoketa's first "hotel".

John Elliot Goodenow later became Maquoketa's first postmaster and first mayor, and was also a member of Iowa's first Legislature. In addition, he gave land for a Methodist Church, and also for where the Maquoketa Junior High School is now located.

Friendly, but greedy, Indians frequently came to the Goodenow cabin in the early years to open the cupboard and help themselves. Once, a couple of Indians picked up the family's first baby boy from his cradle. To the horror of his mother, they took him to their village to show their squaws what a white baby— the first one born in Jackson County—looked like. They then brought him back and tenderly tucked him back in his cradle.

Another time, after the boy had grown up to four years, his mother prepared doughnuts for an Indian hunting party and had the boy pass them out. The boy did so, but skipped by every Indian that carried a gun. To him, bows and arrows were one thing, but a gun was quite another.

There were many other interesting stories about the pioneer homesteader, such as carrying little pigs under his arms all the way from Belleview, and of selling a load of wheat in Dubuque and loading the cart with supplies for his wife and family, only to have the oxen go off the trail and upset the cart and watch all the precious supplies go down the river.

John Elliot Goodenow had quite a heritage. He was a great-great-many times removed grandson of Peregrine White, the first white child born after the Mayflower had landed at Plymouth.

Second generation to own the farm was Osceola and Fannie Goodenow. The husband's name was an Indian name given him because when his father was in the first Iowa Legislature, Osceola County was added to Iowa.

Third to have the pioneer farm was John E. Goodenow and his wife. Now the farm is in a trust provided for in John E. Goodenow's will.

Those sharing in the trust now are John Elliot Goodenow III, his sister, Dorothy, and his son (who is John Elliot Goodenow IV) and daughter, Marie Irene Koob.

The original farm was 160 acres, but now totals 320.

During its existence, purebred Shorthorn cattle and Chester White hogs, as well as Plymouth Rock chickens and Shropshire sheep were raised. Crops grown included corn, oats, hay, potatoes, soybeans, and wheat and pasture.

The Goodenow Family Trust farm is now farmed by a tenant on a cash rent basis. It has long been known as the Elm Hill Farm.

THE HADLEY-MILLER-WEISS FARM OF JEFFERSON COUNTY

Settled 1845

Several persons are now the owners of a tract of land in Jefferson County purchased from the U.S. Government in 1845 — one year before Iowa gained statehood.

For six generations, members of the Hadley family were the only ones to do the farming or have their surname attached to any patents, deeds, abstracts, or other official papers connected with the Jefferson County farm, beginning with John Hadley who homesteaded it in 1845.

However, the farm now is owned by no less than six persons. They are Randall Hadley, Rick Hadley, Gary Hadley, Stuart Hadley, Mrs. Wilma Weiss (whose first husband was the late Kenneth Hadley), and Lynette Miller, the daughter of Kenneth and Wilma.

In an application submitted to the Iowa Sesquicentennial Commission and Iowa Department of Agriculture and Land Stewardship, sponsors of a contest to determine the oldest Iowa farm continuously held by the same family, the present owners of the 135 acres have listed their ancestors as follows:

John Hadley, great-great-great grandfather who was the original buyer of the government land;

Ira Hadley, the great-great grandfather and second owner of the property;

Owen Hadley, great grandfather and the third owner.

Lawrence Hadley, their grandfather who was a member of the fourth generation of the family to be involved in the farm;

Kenneth Hadley, their father, who was the last to own the land before it was purchased by the afore-mentioned children and Kenneth's widow and daughter.

Randall Hadley, one of the six current owners, in submitting the application, pointed out that John Hadley had lived in North Carolina before coming to Iowa in 1845. He also indicated that his great-great-great grandfather bought the land for the purpose of farming it, and did actually farm it, rather than buying it for speculation.

Presently, the farm is 148 acres in size and is devoted to growing corn, oats, and hay and raising hogs. Now doing the farming of the land is a cousin's son, Dennis Louk. The property remains listed at 160 acres.

In a questionnaire filled out by Keith Hadley, uncle of Randall Hadley, he remembers that at one time their father did not have the money to pay taxes, and even had to borrow money to replace one of the horses that had died. "Yet," says Keith, "we never went hungry, and never felt poor."

Keith says he and his brothers worked on the farm with their father and that all three went to college and won their degrees. He adds that all five of his children are also college graduates. All five of the late Kenneth Hadley's children also graduated from college.

As for the farm, in the 1840s, '50s, '60s, and beyond the year 1900, crops were largely corn and hay for livestock, and grass for stock grazing. Soybeans came in the rotation after 1930.

1932 with its drought and chinch bugs was a disastrous year. Oil poured in furrows around the fields was used to try to stop the chinch bugs from getting to the crops.

A Ford tractor was bought in 1941. Prior to that, eight horses were used in the fields. Polled Shorthorn cattle, hogs, and chickens constituted most of the livestock over the years.

Farm Bureau membership has been held over many years, and 4-H programs were important to the youngsters, including showing 4-H calves.

Kenneth Hadley, who was the fifth owner of the farm before he passed away in 1976, served in the Navy in WW II, and his brother, Keith, was a U.S. Air Force Pilot.

HADLEY-STEWART-STUART-ZEAR FARM OF KEOKUK COUNTY

Settled 1845

In their application submitted for the Iowa Sesquicentennial Pioneer Farm Family Contest, Jerry and Dan Zear listed eight names of persons who have held ownership of all or part of the 160 acre farm in Keokuk County obtained from the U.S. Government in 1845. Cost of the land shown on the application was only $1.07.

The application shows eleven names, but does not list the years of ownership. The list includes the names of the buyer as well as the seller, and the relationship, one to another. Shown on the entry for the contest are the following persons, all members of the same family in succeeding generations.

William Hadley, who purchased the land from the U.S. Government;

Joseph Hadley, a son of William Hadley;

Ruth Stewart, a daughter of Joseph Hadley;
Josephus Hadley, a brother of Ruth Stewart and son of Joseph Hadley;
Sarah Hadley, widow of Josephus Hadley;
Joseph Gurney Stewart, shown as a son of Josephus and Sarah Hadley;
Mary Lutitia Stuart, sister-in-law of Joseph Gurney Stewart;
Joe T. Zear, son-in-law of Mary Lutitia Stuart;
Raymond Zear, son of Joe T. Zear; and
Jerry and Dan Zear, sons of Raymond Zear.

The original purchase by William Hadley in 1845 was in the form of a homestead.

William Hadley farmed the land himself, as did most other homesteaders, and did so confronted by many frontier hardships. There are no longer any of the original cabins or other buildings, assumed to have been on the farm at one time, left on the property now.

Only 40 acres of the original 160 are now in the hands of the present owners, Jerry Zear of Algona and Dan Zear of Winfield. Corn and soybeans are the only crops now being grown on the remaining land.

THE HOGAN FARM OF DELAWARE COUNTY

Settled 1845

Just one year before Iowa became a state, Patrick Hogan became one of Delaware County's early settlers. In 1845, he managed to buy 80 acres from the U.S. Government for $1.25 an acre, and a Hogan family has lived on that land ever since.

Patrick Hogan gave the family a good start. He was the father of ten, and the great grandfather of Philip Hogan, who is the present owner of 120 acres, two-thirds of which was the original farm.

Soon after buying the farm, Patrick started putting up buildings. A cabin was made of logs. Stone went into the large barn. Proof of how well that barn was built some 150 years ago is seen in the fact that cows are still being milked daily in the same stone structure.

In those early years, as many as 12 horses were stabled in the barn. All field implements were powered by teams of horses until 1942, when a McCormick "H" tractor was bought.

One of those ten children born to Patrick and his wife was named Roger.

He became the second owner of the property, but not until the early 1900s. Roger and his wife had five children, one of whom was Raymond, who was Philip's father.

Raymond gained possession of the farm in 1933, and held ownership for nearly forty years, until Philip and his wife bought it in 1970.

During the first years he owned the farm, Raymond came near losing the land. It was a rough period for all farmers. The Depression struck deeply. Hogs sold for as low as $3 per cwt. Drought in 1933 and 1934 spelled disaster to crops. 1936 was a year of both record cold and record heat. Somehow, the Hogan family and their farm survived.

Philip was one of a family of five and, along with the help of his wife and four children, has operated the farm the last 25 or more years.

Various breeds and types of livestock were raised over the years. Included were both Holstein and Guernsey dairy cattle, as well as Hampshire, Duroc, and Chester White hogs. Laying flocks provided income by way of their eggs. Philip continues to have dairy cattle and hogs on the 151 year old farm. The cropping program now is corn, oats, and hay.

Philip belongs to the Farm Bureau and the Colesburg Creamery. His four children make the fifth generation of Hogans who have lived on the Sesquicentennial farm. For many years, the Hogans have been members of St. Patrick's Church in Colesburg.

THE MASON-HUNT-GOODHUE FARM OF POLK AND WARREN COUNTIES

Settled 1845

Although the first to be named as a central Iowa pioneer by Warren County, Iowa, historians was John D. Parmelee, he was not the first homesteader in the area. That distinction belongs to William Mason, whose five generations of descendants tell some interesting stories about their long ago ancestor.

William Mason was born in England, and after migrating to America, first settled in New Jersey. Evidently a man of adventurous spirit, he left New Jersey some time in the early 1840s; and, on learning about the midwestern frontier, managed to get to Iowa, apparently some time in 1842.

He first stopped in Wapello County where he must have heard about the Dragoons planning to build a Fort in a place called Des Moines. Intrigued by this, he came to the Des Moines area in 1843, found where the

Dragoons were at work building a Fort at the junction of the Des Moines and Raccoon rivers, and found work cutting shingles for a Dragoon building. Not only that, but, according to the "History of Warren County", he learned about the Parmelee Mill on the Middle River and got some work there, too.

For reasons that are not clear, Mason left the area in 1844 and went back to some eastern Iowa friends for the better part of a year. There can be no question, however, that his brief stay in central Iowa left a lasting and favorable impression. The result was that he came back in 1845 to what later became Warren County, and this time it was for "keeps".

It was in April 1845, more than a year before Iowa became a state, when William Mason became one of the area's first permanent settlers. Family history tells that he staked out a claim on 860 acres, which must have been one of the biggest claims of the area. Part of the land was in what became Warren County and the rest in what is now Polk County.

Apparently, Mason did not have cash for so large a claim, but he was able to pay for it by constantly working "in kind" on the Government's Fort Des Moines barracks, as well as the Parmelee Mill. Whatever the case, he was able to gain the necessary patents or other official papers to prove the 860 acres was his.

Moreover, after all his wanderings, that farm became the permanent and final home for him, his wife, and their six children.

The home in which the children all grew up was built in the fall after the claim was filed in April.

One of Mason's special claims to fame is that he plowed the first furrow in what is now Warren County. And he obviously plowed a lot. Wheat, corn and oats were the first crops raised.

Moreover, Mason is credited with having planted the first apple, peach, and other fruit trees in the area.

The 860 acres was eventually divided among his six children. The 212 acres of the original farm, which is now owned by the Goodhue family in Polk County, was first inherited by William Mason's youngest son, James Mason. James had a daughter, Ermila, who married Carl Hunt. The Hunts, in turn, had a daughter, Lucille, who married Wilbur Goodhue. Wilbur became an Iowa Master Farmer and was Polk County Farm Bureau president, and was a grain producer and stock farmer.

Wilbur and Lucille started farming in the 1930s and had three children—two daughters and a son, James, better known as Jim. Jim married Nadine Fowler and they have three sons—Mark, Michael (Mike), and Steve.

Two of Jim and Nadine's sons are now in a highly diversified farming partnership with their wives and parents, involving the raising and feeding of cattle, hogs, and sheep, and raising corn, soybeans, and hay on what is now a

1007-acre operation.

All three of the sons and their wives have children, adding up to Nadine and Jim's six grandchildren, who are the seventh generation on the farm and are the great-great-great-great grandchildren of the William Masons who homesteaded the land 151 years ago.

THE SCHENCK-COXON-MARINE FARM OF JOHNSON, CEDAR AND MUSCATINE COUNTIES

Settled 1845

Unusual as it may seem, there is a 151-year old pioneer farm in eastern Iowa established by James Findley Schenck in 1845 on which taxes must be paid in three different counties — Johnson, Cedar, and Muscatine.

Schenck's Great-grandparents

The strange taxing arrangement has come about because Mr. Schenck would not allow a Johnson and Muscatine County Line road to go through his sugar maple grove. As a result, when that part of the road had to be curved around the trees, it put a half acre of the farm in Johnson County. The rest of the land was partly in Cedar County and partly in Muscatine County.

Mrs. Mabel Marine of Lone Tree, the great granddaughter of the 1845 pioneer, reports some interesting facts about her ancestor. Born in Franklin, Ohio, he first came to Iowa the hard way when he was only fourteen — by helping drive a large flock of sheep to the Mississippi River and then ferry them over the raging stream.

Some time later, he was accompanying his uncle, Woodhull Schenck, on an ill-fated trip to California, probably in connection with Gold Rush Fever. However, near Ft. Leavenworth, Kansas, the uncle contracted cholera and died. Young Schenck then accompanied the body back to the uncle's home in Ohio.

The tract of land Schenck purchased in 1845 was 160 acres in the very corner where Johnson, Cedar, and Muscatine Counties come together.

Grandpa Schenck, as he is referred to by all in the family, was a lover of trees and as soon as his claim was assured, he set forth to plant the sugar maple grove, as well as catalpa trees to be used as fence posts, along with mulberry trees, shade trees, and about every kind of fruit tree.

Nine years after the farm was purchased, James Schenck married Maria

Schenck-Coxon-Marine farm, 1920's

Bell, who had come to Iowa in 1850 from Ohio. Seven children were born to them, and all were raised in a two-room cabin that their father had built with whip-sawed lumber and using hand-forged nails. Then, as the family grew, those two rooms became part of an eight room two-story home in 1873.

The second of those seven children was a son, John Bell Schenck. He and his wife took over the farming some time in the late 1800s, and bought the farm in 1912. They had only one child, a daughter, Margaret.

Margaret remembers her father, who was Mrs. Marine's grandfather, as being a hard working farmer, producing crops and livestock, and always taking a deep interest in the productive orchard planted by his father. She tells that in the fall, her father would pick apples by the wagon load, then take them to Iowa City, where he sold them door to door.

She also reveals that her grandfather, James, had planted a second orchard featuring Snow apples and Wealthies and Grimes Golden varieties, as well as plum trees and rows of grapes.

In the fall, her father and grandfather made enough cider and vinegar to provide for the winter. They also put several barrels of Snow apples, and a few bushels of Wealthies and Grimes Goldens in the basement for winter enjoyment.

Margaret, who became Mabel Marine's mother, married Walter Coxon, and they became the farm's operators in the 1920s. Then, in 1932, Mrs. Coxon inherited the farm.

The Coxons were active in the National, State and Pomana Grange organizations. They were strong on producing livestock with Holstein Friesen dairy cows, hogs, and chickens, as well as crops of corn, oats, and alfalfa hay. During WW II, they also produced several acres of tomatoes for the canning factories. They farmed with Percheron horses until 1936 when a John Deere "A" tractor was bought.

The farm was inherited by Mabel Marine in 1988, but Mr. & Mrs. Marine operated it for many years before that, growing corn and soybeans much of the time, and maintaining a Holstein dairy herd, as well as raising hogs, sheep and chickens. It is now rented to Roger and Jerry Hote.

Mabel became the mother of five children — Mary, Pat, Dwight, Wendell, and Leonard.

One of the sons, Wendell, must have inherited his great-great grandfather's love of fruit trees. He has planted apple, peach, cherry, and plum trees where his early ancestor had his original apple orchard, and has transplanted lilac and mock orange bushes in the farm yard where they can flourish. In addition, he is following in his great-great grandfather's steps with several rows of grapevines.

As for military service, James Schenck, who purchased the land 151 years ago, served in the Quartermaster Corps during the Civil War, and his brother-in-law, George Bell, was taken prisoner in a battle during the War Between the States while in the 22nd Iowa infantry.

THE TENER FARM OF WASHINGTON COUNTY

Settled 1845

One of the briefest of all the applications for pioneer farm recognition to the Iowa Sesquicentennial Commission and Iowa Department of Agriculture and Land Stewardship has come from John Tener of Iowa City.

Mr. Tener points out that a Certificate of Entry was granted to his grandfather, Frederick Tener, on June 24, 1845, for a claim, and that on March 1, 1846, he received a Patent for 80 acres of land.

Frederick Tener was a native of Maryland and evidently was one of many Easterners who was lured to Iowa soon after the Indians ceded much of eastern Iowa to what was then known as the Iowa Territory of the United States of America.

In any case, by the time he got through with his claims and purchases, Frederick Tener owned 240 acres of land. Cost of some of it was reported as up to $12.50 an acre for that which he had to buy from pioneer land speculators who had paid only $1.25 an acre. The application goes on to say that Frederick Tener's son, John W. Tener, and a nephew, William Tener, became the next owners of the land, but no date was given as to when it was sold, or passed on, to them. They were the father and uncle of John Tener.

Corn, oats, hay and soybeans have all been raised on the farm, and hogs and cattle have been fed and fattened.

John E. Tener provided no further information, but it is assumed he is now the owner of the 200 acres currently remaining in the farm.

WASSOM-WEHRLE-WANDERS OF MAHASKA COUNTY

Settled 1845

Moses Wassom, born in Tennessee, came to Mahaska County in 1843 and first lived near Duncan's Mill by the Skunk River. Then, in 1845, with his wife, Elizabeth, and the start of a family, he moved to northwest Richland Township and homesteaded the farm that still exists today.

Moses held the office of school director, constable, township trustee,

With Iowa Secretary of Agriculture, Harry Linn, (standing at upper right) and other state officials and family members looking on -- Mrs. Laura Wassom Wehrle receives an Iowa Centennial Farm Citation from Herb Plambeck during a special 1946 Centennial broadcast over Radio Station WHO.

and justice of the peace. He selected for his homestead one of the best pieces of land in the county. He was a lover of good stock and his farm was always stocked with the best grades of hogs, Shorthorn cattle, and especially Roadster horses. Moses was the owner of Monarch, the best race horse in the county during his time.

Wassom was credited with being "a good farmer, a broad-minded, public-spirited man ever willing to help his neighbors and friends. He was a good neighbor who always stood by his friends." (Quote taken from his obituary.)

The youngest child of Moses and Elizabeth Wassom, Laura, carried on the family farm. She bought the land from the family heirs and with her husband, William Tell Wehrle started their family. "Tell" farmed 205 acres. He and Laura had five children. Tell added the east side second story addition to the house in 1917, after the twins were born.

Mr. Wehrle also served as Justice of the Peace for the small town of Peoria. He raised crops and livestock until ill health forced him to quit farming. He passed away in March, 1936.

In 1946, the Wassom farm was honored at the WHO Radio Banquet for

Centennial farms held on December 28, 1946. At that time, Laura was the only second generation owner of a Centennial farm in Iowa. For this honor, she was seated at the speaker's table and was selected to cut the Iowa Birthday Cake.

Upon the death of Laura in 1947, Tell and Laura's son, Lyal, bought the farm from the other heirs. Lyal and his wife, Fran, had three children. Lyal lived on and farmed the homestead of 125 acres and also farmed for the other heirs an unconnected 80 acres, raised Shorthorn cattle, sheep, and Chester White hogs. Lyal was a life-long prominent farmer. He had a deep love of nature and especially enjoyed fishing. He passed away in October, 1971. His three children became the heirs of the farm. His wife, Fran, continued to live on the farm until her death in March, 1992.

The great-great-granddaughter of Moses and Elizabeth Wassom, Lana Wanders, moved to the family farm in April 1992, with her husband, Gary, and their four children. Gary and Lana have recently purchased the family

1900, Eva Wehrle and Van Dee farm home.

Lyal Wehrle on binder and Ed Stoner on tractor in 1936 harvest field.

farm from her mother and the uncle and aunt who co-owned it with Lana's mother. Their dream is to one day be able to farm this land like their ancestors did and to build barns similar to those that used to be on the homestead. Most of all, they want to uphold the integrity of this 150-year old family farm.

Moses Wassom built most of the buildings that stood on the farm through several generations while living in a log cabin house. Among the buildings that exist today are a granary, the first building built, and a sheep shed.

The house that was completed in 1862 by Moses still stands. It is a two-story farm home with large rooms and a screened back porch that overlooks a three-acre pond. The unique feature of the house is the four-foot wide open stairway. No one has yet to figure out why Moses built such a wide stairway. The foundation is of limestone rock brought from the small town of Peoria just two miles to the west. The house has seen minimal changes throughout its life. The outside still looks similar to what it did in the past.

THE ALBAUGH-CALLAHAN FARM OF LINN COUNTY

Settled 1846

It was about nine months before Iowa became a state back in 1846 that Daniel Albaugh, son of a Pennsylvania Dunkard preacher, came to Linn County to buy an 80 acre tract of land from the United States Government, The price was $1.25 an acre.

The land was located about six miles north of Cedar Rapids near Robbins, and has been known as the Old Albaugh Farm for many years. It is presently owned by Leona Callahan, a fourth generation member of the Albaugh family.

Right after the land was bought, a small log cabin became the first dwelling place. However, Daniel Albaugh and his wife had a family of eleven children, so the log cabin became decidedly over-crowded.

A larger frame house was built a few years later as soon as lumber became available, but even that was not sufficient. Therefore, in 1867, twenty-one years after the farm was homesteaded, brick manufactured on a nearby farm was used to construct an attractive and spacious ten-room house that still exists and is still being used as a home.

Things were very different in the early years of the farm. Prairie sod had to be broken so that wheat could be sown. Corn and hay land came later.

Although horses were replacing oxen on many of the earlier pioneer farms, the Albaughs believed that mules worked better and were less likely to be stolen. It was at a time when horse thieves were still a menace.

In an article written in the Cedar Rapids Gazette by the popular Iowa farm writer, Rex Conn, it was pointed out that in the early years of the farm, Indians frequently came along with their bows and arrows to shoot deer. Occasionally, they also begged food from the settlers.

Not long after he acquired the land 150 years ago, Daniel, a very religious person, gave two acres of his property near Robbins to the Brethren Church to which the family belonged, and to a school. Later, after the church was built, it was moved to the town of Robbins, where an active congregation found it more convenient.

In writing about what kind of livestock and poultry her ancestors raised, Leona Callahan, the current owner, tells about Holstein and Guernsey cows, Chester White hogs, goats, and Buff Orpington and Leghorn chickens, as well as the mules and a few horses. As was indicated earlier, horse thieves were still very much "in business", and once when Daniel was at a church meeting in the East, thieves made away with one of his horses.

Second owner of the farm was Leona's grandfather, William Albaugh, followed by his son, Wilbur, who was Leona's father. He acquired the farm from his father's estate in 1937.

The farm is now 91 acres in size and is now a sod farm.

THE STRONG-BILLINGSLEY FARM OF JEFFERSON COUNTY

Settled 1846

The first 150-year Pioneer Family Farm sign to be displayed in Jefferson County, Iowa, is to be seen on the Don and Lois Billingsley farm located near Lockridge. The sign is being provided by the Iowa Sesquicentennial Commission and the Iowa Department of Transportation to all Iowa owners of farms that have been in the same family's hands 150 years or more.

In the case of the Billingsleys, a great uncle named William E. Strong became the first owner of the land in 1844 and apparently sold it to Elijah Billingsley in 1846, the year Iowa became a state. Elijah Billingsley was the great grandfather of the present owners.

Lillian Theda, a popular and able columnist for the Fairfield Ledger summarized some fascinating history about the Billingsley family in the au-

1846, Billingsley Farm Lois and Don Billingsley with their Sesquicentennial Farm sign located on Billingsley Road.

tumn of 1995, shortly before the Lockridge couple were announced as recipients of the 150 year recognition and the farm sign which celebrates Iowa's incredible progress in Agriculture a century and a half.

In her column, Theda wrote in part:

"The history of the Billingsley farm begins with Elijah Billingsley who was born in Ohio on January 28, 1818. He moved with his parents to Harrison County, Ohio, in 1824. On Christmas Day, 1841, Elijah was married to Prudence Strong. In 1842 they moved to Iowa with Prudence's recently widowed mother, Prudence Elliot Strong, and five of her brothers and six of her sisters. Their journey took them by boat from Wheeling, Virginia to Keokuk, Iowa. They finished their trip to Jefferson County by team and wagon.

"Elijah entered a claim to 40 acres of land in Round Prairie Township and soon after claimed another 40 acres. The patents were issued in Burlington in 1842, but it wasn't until a land office was moved to Fairfield that the Billingsley patent was issued on January 1, 1846. They had settled on the land in the spring of 1843. Part of the 120 acres now owned by Don Billingsley has remained in the Billingsley family all through these 150 years. The owner now is Elijah's great-grandson, Don."

In information received from Don and Lois Billingsley early in the Sesquicentennial year, it is noted that the original purchase was 40 acres and that Elijah and Prudence, the first of the Billingsley couples to own the land, were the parents of eight children. As was true of so many early pioneer farm families, their first Iowa home was a log cabin.

One of those eight children was Samuel, Don's grandfather, who eventually became the farm's owner in 1895. Samuel and his wife were the parents of ten; and one of them, Samuel C. Billingsley, gained ownership of the property in 1942. He was Don's father, who turned the farm over to Don and Lois in 1976. They continue to actively operate the 150-year old pioneer holding.

Through the years, family members kept adding to the original 40 acres to where it has become a total of 400 acres, a ten-fold increase.

And through those many years, the crop program has been largely corn, oats, wheat and hay, while horses, cattle, sheep, hogs and chickens were raised. For a period of time, prize Morgan horses were bred and Angus cattle were emphasized. More recently, the horses, sheep and hogs apparently have been replaced with a cow-calf herd.

Following the many years when horses provided power in the fields, a Massey-Harris tractor was purchased in 1942. Since then, Allis-Chalmers and Deutz tractors have also been used.

It is interesting to note that the 1856 census shows Elijah Billingsley had 14 acres producing a ton of hay on each, 50 acres of spring wheat producing a little over two bushels per acre, 25 acres of corn averaging 50 bushels an acre, while one-half acre of potatoes yielded 156 bushels. In addition, the family sold 140 pounds of butter at 18 cents a pound that year.

On a pioneer community level, Elijah was a township director, county commissioner, and school board director. Don and Lois are members of the Mennonite Church. They also belong to the Farm Bureau.

The Billingsley family knows much about the price of war. Don's great uncle, William R. Billingsley, served and died in the Civil War, and his brother, William H. Billingsley, was killed in the Battle of the Bulge in WW II. Earlier, Elijah, the first of the farm's owners, had also been in the Militia.

THE COLLINS-ROMKEY FARM OF HENRY COUNTY

Settled 1846

Earnest Collins was a Quaker, and in order to escape military conscription in his native country of Germany, he migrated to the United States in the early 1840s. So it was that he came to Iowa exactly 150 years ago and bought 85 acres from Jesse Pease, who had originally purchased the land from the government. Collins paid $300 for the 85-acre tract.

The farm now totals 150 acres and is owned by Mabel Collins, Earnest Collins' great granddaughter.

As was almost universally true of those who bought virgin land in the year 1846, a log cabin was erected soon after the purchase.

Western mustangs were used for field work by the pioneer Henry County farmer. Corn, oats, and clover were the first crops to be grown. Hogs were fed and marketed. A flock of chickens was kept to provide the farm kitchen with eggs.

Earnest and his wife had eight children. One of them, a son named John, bought out his siblings and became the owner of the pioneer farm in 1861, just before the Civil War started. None of the Collins family served in the War Between the States, but John Collins' father-in-law, S.J.Woodson, was a Captain in the Union Army and fought in the Battle of Shiloh and was also on Sherman's March To The Sea.

John Collins and his wife had a family of eight and one of their sons, John Harvey Collins, and his wife became the third owners in 1898. They had seven children, and one of them is Mabel, who is now the farm's co-owner. The other co-owner is Helen Romkey, Mabel's partner and business associate. During WW II, Mabel was Secretary to the Army Inspector at the Iowa Ordinance Plant.

During John Harvey's ownership in the 1860s, there was a tax sale ordered by the state for a paltry $3.35 that should have been paid in 1859. John Harvey Collins quickly reclaimed the property by paying $5.45 to satisfy the tax authorities.

Duroc and Poland China hogs were fed for market when John Harvey did the farming. Soybeans also were added to the cropping program. Electricity came to the farm by way of the REC in 1939.

Today, livestock is no longer raised on the pioneer farm, which is now rented by Howard and Jerry Mabru, who concentrate on corn and soybeans.

THE DUENSING-LORTZ-VICK FARM OF KEOKUK COUNTY

Settled 1846

The Duensing Farm of Keokuk County was established in 1846, the year Iowa was admitted to the Union. It is one of many pioneer farms with a fascinating story about an immigrant family coming to America to settle, and succeed, in Iowa.

Ruth Duensing Lortz, great granddaughter of the German pioneer family, and her daughter, Joyce Lortz Vick, the present owners of the 150 year old Sesquicentennial farm, tell the interesting story of their ancestors' activities and adventures. However, limited space will permit retelling only a small part of the story.

As was true of so many immigrant families, Christian and Dorthea Duensing and their four children were lured from Germany to the "New World" by letters from family members and friends who had preceded them here. Invariably, those letters told of endless opportunities opening up in the Mid-west. Seldom were hardships and difficulties mentioned.

Two of those who had written so enticingly were David Voltner,

Christian and Dorthea Duensing

Dorthea's brother, and Karl Backhaus, a family friend. Both had left Germany for America and both had staked out land claims in Keokuk County. There they not only found fertile prairie soil, but also an area rich in wild life and timber. Deer, wild ducks, prairie chickens, and wild turkeys were plentiful. Clear streams were loaded with fish. Oak, hickory, elm and walnut trees abounded in the timber.

Both had built log cabins on their claims, but in the winters, Voltner would go to St. Louis to earn additional money, while Backhaus stayed in Iowa to look after the cabins and claims.

One winter day, a terrible blizzard developed and for some reason, Backhaus was caught in it and could not find home. To stave off cold and deadly sleep, he kept circling around a tree through the night. This is where friendly Indians found him the next morning. They took him to their village where food and warmth revived him. For much of the rest of the winter, he stayed with them.

Then came 1845, and the Duensings decided to leave Germany and come to America. At that point, Dorthea's sister, Sophia Humpka, and her husband, Fritz, and their children asked to join Christian and Dorthea in the venture.

After a long ocean voyage, they reached New Orleans and immediately started up the Mississippi for Iowa. Ultimately, they made it to Voltner's cabin. For several weeks, that one room cabin, with its deerskin flap to keep out the elements, was a very crowded place for twelve people.

Early the next spring, Christian was able to establish a 40 acre claim and build a cabin for his own family. Meanwhile, Fritz and Sophia Humpka hired out to a farm family, but a few months later, during the hot summer, Fritz died of a sunstroke in a harvest field.

A grieving Sophia continued to serve as a housekeeper, but later married Karl Backhaus, thus reuniting the three families who had all come from the same area in Germany.

The next year there was a "barn raising" on the Backhaus farm. During the event, Dora, Sophia's little golden haired girl, and her dog set out for the Duensing farm, but became lost on the way. Search parties were unsuccessful in finding her, but Sophia and her dog continued the search day after day until its tragic ending. One day the dog started whining heavily at the edge of some woods and then some of the little girl's remains were found where wolves, or wild boars, had killed her.

This was also a period when medical help for the pioneers was almost non-existent. Instead, home remedies had to be relied on. Thick salt pork for cuts. An onion poultice for pneumonia. Honey or elderberry syrup for colds. Goose grease and skunk oil for other troubles. It was a trying period for many pioneer families.

Christian had started farming with only two oxen, but soon switched to horses. After four years of intense work and carefully hoarding his savings, he was able to buy another 40 acres from the government. Cost was $1.25 an

The Duensing Farm

1846, Duensing-Lutz, Plowing with steam engines and six-bottom plows.

acre. A few years later, the same thing was done, and then again.

When Christian had acquired 160 acres, a larger, more modern, home was built. Good crops of wheat, corn, oats and hay were raised, as well as sheep, cattle and hogs. To grind the wheat into flour, they had to take it all the way to a mill in Amana.

In 1867, 16 year old Adelheide Bruns and her 14 year old sister also left Germany. Somehow they managed to get to Iowa to the home of their uncle, Henry Bruns, of Sigourney. Soon thereafter, Adelheide found employment in the Duensing family's home.

One of Christian's sons, a hard-working youth named Henry, soon took notice of the pretty, young immigrant girl. The friendship blossomed into romance and, in time, to marriage.

Realizing the young couple needed a home of their own, Christian built them an 8 room house. It's a good thing he did because in the next 15 or 20 years, twelve children were born to Adelheide and Henry.

Henry took over the pioneer farming responsibilities long before his father died. He was highly successful, and by 1881, was able to buy 160 acres of his own. Then, when his mother passed away a few years later, he inherited Christian's 160 acres as well. Now, with a 320 acre enterprise, he could raise more wheat, corn, oats, flax, and other crops, but also feed out large numbers of sheep, cattle and hogs.

John and Fred, two of Henry and Adelheide's sons, took over the operation; and after their parent's deaths, bought their sibling's shares, and farmed in partnership until John's death in 1952.

John and his family had lived in the old house all those years, but Fred had built a new, modern home for his bride, Rosa Kleinschmidt, where they lived with their family of three. Homer, Fred's son, farmed with his father until Homer's unexpected death.

After John's passing, part of Christian's original 160 acres, plus the 160 Henry had added had to be sold, but 140 acres were retained. A trust was established and the tillable land was put into CRP while the pasture land and hog buildings were rented to Tom Webb, a neighbor.

In 1993, the 21 year old trust was broken and Ruth and Joyce became joint owners. Joyce now hopes her sons, Chad and Ryan, the sixth generation in the family, will some day own the farm.

Members of the family have belonged to various organizations through the years. Included are Farmers Union, Odd Fellows, Farm Bureau, 4-H, and local clubs. Association with the Evangelical Country Church started as early as 1857.

THE GROUT FARM OF JOHNSON COUNTY

Settled 1846

One of the 80 acre Johnson County homesteads established exactly 150 years ago this Iowa Sesquicentennial year on which the same surname has appeared on every official document this past century and a half is the Grout farm.

It started when Zenus Grout, great-great grandfather of Gary Grout, the present owner, obtained an 1846 land patent and deed from the U.S. Government. Cost was $1.25 an acre. Five generations of Grouts have now owned the land.

Zenus Grout and his wife had six children, and one of their sons, Loren Grout, was the next to own the property. Loren and his wife had a family of seven. They acquired the farm in about 1890. Loren was in Iowa's Civil War Attachment and fought in several major battles in the War Between the States.

One of that family's sons, Lucius, grandfather of the present owner, was the third to occupy the farm. Evidently he had no family. His ownership began in 1900.

In any case, the fourth owner was Childon Grout, one of Lucius' nephews, and an uncle of Gary. He took over the farm in 1968. Childon served overseas in World War II. Then Gary bought the pioneer farm in 1985.

Gary and his wife have three children so there is a sixth generation "in the wings".

Incidentally, Gary continued in the Grout tradition of answering his country's call to service. He was a member of the U.S. Army Reserves during the Vietnam conflict.

When Zenus started the homestead back in 1846, one of his first tasks was to build a log cabin for his wife and children.

Over the years, the traditional crops of wheat, corn, oats, and hay for livestock were grown. Horses, cattle, sheep and chickens were raised. Conventional crop rotation of corn and soybeans was begun about 1930. Now all 77 acres of the Sesquicentennial family farm are in the Conservation Reserve program.

The first tractor, a Case, arrived in 1920. Since then a Ford, a Farmall, an International, and an Oliver tractor have been used.

All generations of the family have belonged to the South Sharon Methodist Church, known locally as the "Grout Church". It was moved to the Kalona Historical Village in 1985.

THE HITCHCOCK FARM OF MUSCATINE COUNTY

Settled 1846

Although John Pugh Hitchcock was the successful owner and operator of three fine brick companies in Portsmouth, Ohio, back in 1846, he must have wanted to become a farmer in Iowa pretty badly. In any event, he saddled up a good riding horse and rode — or occasionally walked — all the way to Muscatine County in the Hawkeye State in the early fall of that year. His purpose was to find some of that good land he had been hearing about from travelers going by his brick plants.

He must also have been pretty ambitious as a would-be farmer and must also have had some fairly deep pockets. When he finished looking around, he laid claim to 540 acres of Muscatine County soil with enough clay hillsides to enable him to make bricks for his family's future home.

After staking out his claim, he rode back to Portsmouth to wind up his business affairs. That done in late 1846, he then brought his wife, Emily, and their nine children to their new surroundings in Iowa in early 1847. Shortly after his return, he settled with the government for the 540 acres, presumably at the going rate of $1.25 an acre.

Some makeshift housing was arranged right away, and some of the prairie was broken as soon as the spring weather permitted, followed by some corn planting. Major project, however, was beginning the construction of a large brick home. Hitchcock's experience with bricks was put to good use at once. Bricks were made from the clay in one of the nearby fields, and then fired.

The brick house, like the size of the farm, was a remarkably ambitious three-year project. When it was finished, it was a far cry from the log cabins still in use by some of the Hitchcock family's pioneer neighbors.

The completed home, all built by Hitchcock and some of his older sons, had six rooms on the first floor, plus a hallway, and pantry, and an adjacent summer kitchen. Upstairs were five large bedrooms. It had a three-story open staircase that led to an observatory above the second floor. The outside walls were four bricks wide. All the rooms had 10 foot high ceilings and there were seven fireplaces, two with marble tops.

That house must have been the show place of the entire county. It served several generations of the large family well for 99 years, when it was finally destroyed by fire in 1948.

As for the farming, it was also a huge undertaking. As time went on, a five-year corn, oats, hay and pasture rotation was perfected.

Horses were emphasized from the beginning with as many as 18 draft horses used in a single year. Registered Hereford beef cattle and purebred Poland China hogs, as well as flocks of sheep, were also raised through the years. Chickens were always raised for eggs and fried chicken dinners.

Second owner was one of John Pugh and Emily's sons, John S. Hitchcock, and his wife, Abbie. They did not acquire the farm until 1898. They had only one child, a son, Bion Henry. Logically, he and his wife Marguerite, became the third owners in 1937. Four children were born to them, one of whom was Burdette, who, with his wife Louise, bought 240 acres of the pioneer farm in 1968. Each of Burdette's two sisters owns 80 acres of the land homesteaded by their great grandfather 150 years ago.

Burdette and his wife have three children, accounting for the fifth generation of Hitchcocks on the Muscatine County farm.

In 1927, when Burdette's father was starting to take over

the farming, a John Deere "D" tractor was bought. John Deere tractors and other Deere machines have been used exclusively on the farm since then. In 1937, the REC brought electricity to the Hitchcocks.

Harking back to the first years, Indians used to come to the house to enjoy Emily's mince pie, but always spit the raisins into the fireplace.

During the Civil War, one ancestor, Henry Hitchcock, served in the 35th Iowa Infantry and was in the Battle of Vicksburg.

Burdette and his family are members of the High Prairie Methodist Church, the Farm Bureau, and County and State Cattlemen's Associations, and Burdette is a 50 year member of the Elks Club.

THE MILLER-LONG-SMITH-GILTNER FARM OF WAPELLO COUNTY

Settled 1846

Berl Giltner of Ottumwa has provided information on a Sesquicentennial Wapello County farm that has been in his wife's family's hands under four different surnames.

In the fall of 1846, just 150 years ago this year, Caleb Miller bought 160 acres from the government. Caleb was Berl and Marjorie Giltner's great-great grandfather.

One of Caleb's daughters, Mary Catherine, married George Long, and they became the second owners. They were Marjorie's great grandparents; and it was their daughter, Eccie, who had married Harry Smith. Eccie and Harry were the next couple to occupy the 1846 farm. They had a nephew, Charles Smith, who followed his uncle and aunt on the farm.

The Charles Smith's had a daughter, Marjorie, who is Berl Giltner's wife. Berl and Marjorie now own the property, which has increased from the original 160 acres to 337.52 acres.

The original small house built by Marjorie's great-great grandfather is still intact.

Like most other pioneer farms, corn, oats, and hay were first raised. Soybeans have come later. Angus cattle have also been an important factor in the success of the Wapello County Sesquicentennial farm.

A Wapello County historical publication printed many years ago has some interesting information on the founder of this particular pioneer farm. The following appeared in the publication:

"Caleb Miller was born in Union County, Indiana, on October 15, 1815, and followed farming throughout his entire life. In 1839, he moved to Darke County, Ohio, where he resided seven years before he located in Dahlonega Township, Wapello County, Iowa, in the fall of 1846. Entering a claim, he followed farming until his death, which occurred in 1874. He was a Republican in politics, served as justice of the peace for some years, and was on the school board of Dahlonega Township for a number of years. Religiously, he was a member of the Methodist Episcopal church. He was united in marriage with Mary Bedell, who was also born in Indiana. They reared six children: W.H., Sarah E., John B., B.F., Mary C., and Clarence B."

It was Mary Catherine and her husband, George Long, who first assured that the land would remain in the same family all these 150 years.

Iowa's Heritage of Pioneer Family Farms

Section Three
Farms 149 to 132 Years Old

DUCK CREEK FARMS OF THE BLATTNER-BRINNING FAMILY OF WASHINGTON COUNTY

Settled 1847

Among the many German immigrants to come to Iowa in the 1840s were George Blattner and his wife, Christina, and their two oldest children. The Blattners had relatives who had come to America and settled in Washington County several years before George and Christina came in 1847.

Evidently those earlier settlers painted a rosy picture of what life was like in America, and particularly in Iowa. In any event, they persuaded the Blattners to come, and actually selected some land on which the new arrivals could settle as soon as they arrived.

Interestingly, it was Christina's parents who had come to this country ahead of the Blattners, and who had established a homestead in Washington County. They were the ones to prevail on their daughter and son-in-law to come, too. It would seem they were delighted they had made the move.

The 160 acres of choice land selected for the Blattners, 40 acres of which was in timber, cost $700. They started farming it right away. The purchase included a good house, some brood sows, and some corn to feed them.

George Blattner, who could speak no English on his arrival, quickly resolved to become an American citizen. He applied for a certificate for U.S. citizenship as soon as possible, only to learn he could not get naturalization papers until he had lived in our country at least five years. While waiting to become a citizen, he learned considerable English . He got his U.S. Citizenship in September, 1852, the earliest opportunity he had to do so.

In the meantime, he wrote a fascinating letter to his parents, brothers, sisters, and other relatives and acquaintances in Germany in which he elaborated, in glowing terms, about his experiences in Iowa, and his happiness about coming to America.

Excerpts from the letter described Iowa as a "fine country and Washington County as highly productive." The letter points out there was a pioneer farm about every half a mile, that rail fences were necessary to keep out animals and stock from running wild, that weeds were burned off and plowing was shallow, that the soil was rich and produced abundantly, that wheat was shipped down the Mississippi and was worth about a dollar a bushel, but hogs were only worth 2 cents a pound.

The letter went on to say most homes were made of logs and were quite comfortable. He said a one-story, two-room cabin cost about $200 and a 60-

foot long barn, $350, and that nothing was built or bought unless for cash and that money borrowed cost 7 per cent interest. He added that church services with an itinerant preacher were being held every three weeks and that every township supported a school and teacher from the proceeds of the sale of 640 acres of land.

The German pioneer closed his letter to the folks back in Darmstadt, Germany, by saying, "I'm very glad we came here to Iowa."

Second owner of the farm was Henry Blattner, one of the sons of the pioneer immigrant couple. Henry and his wife had a son, named George after his grandfather, and a daughter, Dorothy, who married William Brinning. William and Dorothy became the third owners of the farm.

William and Dorothy continued crop rotations of corn, hay, and oats, and raised cattle and hogs. Clay tile was dug in the ground two spades deep for $1.00 per rod. In 1920, farming changed with the purchase of a Fordson tractor. Other equipment such as corn pickers and cultivators would be purchased later.

They had one son, Merle, who farmed with his dad and later married Margaret Anderson in 1940. Five children were born. However, twin girls died at birth. The farm passed into Merle's hands in 1961 and he continued farming with one of his sons, Lanny, until his death in 1986. Grain bins had been built to begin storing the soybeans and combined corn on the farm rather than using corn cribs to store the ears of corn. He continued to raise Hereford cattle as well as hogs. Tile was now put in the ground with a machine and was plastic, not clay. Cost of 4 inch tile would now be about 75 cents per foot.

Twin sons, Lanny and Larry, as well as William, presently own the farm, with Lanny and his wife Margaret (Huber) currently living in the farm home.

Land stewardship and conservation practices remain important to help preserve the soil. Several terraces have been built on the land and no-till farming has been practiced since 1984.

THE GARDNER FARM OF VAN BUREN COUNTY

Settled 1847

Robert Gardner had quite a few miles to cover before he finally settled on an 80 acre farm in Village Township in Van Buren County on October 5,

1847. He was born in Ireland, came over to the "New World" while still quite young, and then first settled in Kentucky.

In 1847, he was one of many from the more easterly states to come to Iowa, then the nation's newest state, to look for land. He found an attractive 80 acre tract not far from where the town of Douds is now located.

Richard Gardner, a great grandson of the Irish-born immigrant, in making his Sesquicentennial farms application submitted to the Iowa Department of Agriculture and Land Stewardship, writes that there was no cost in obtaining the land from the U.S. Government.

If that is correct, it was probably the only homestead of its nature. In any case, Mr. Gardner must have had some extremely good Irish luck, or some generous government friends, because all other pioneer homesteaders paid from a dollar to $1.25, or more, for government land.

One of Robert Gardner's sons became the second owner of the farm. He was Thomas Gardner, Richard's great grandfather.

Third proprietor was Dale Gardner, who must have been one of Thomas' brothers because he is listed on the application as Richard's great uncle.

There is no information as to the dates that Thomas and Dale gained possession of the property, nor was the date when Richard and his wife, Nancy, acquired the pioneer farm. The farm now totals 220 acres.

The legal description of the location of the original 80 acres is East 1/2 of Southwest quarter Section 9 Township 70 North Range West.

Crops now being grown are corn and alfalfa. Cattle and sheep are now being raised on the farm that first came into the Gardner family hands in 1847.

THE BAKER FARM OF MAHASKA COUNTY

Settled 1848

The Baker Farm near Oskaloosa is commonly believed to be the oldest farm in Mahaska County. It has been under the Baker name generation after generation.

Willis Baker, the great grandfather of the current owner, Ivan Baker, started it all back in 1848. Willis Baker had first come to Iowa in 1844. Two years later, he married Lettitia Sewell of Jefferson County. That same autumn, the newlyweds claimed a plot of ground where they set up housekeeping. However, they were so low on money, they made no attempt to purchase the land.

Eunice and David Baker

There were very few other families living in the area at the time, so the next year Willis decided plans should be made for a village to accommodate future settlers. Accordingly, he laid out a tract near where he and Lettitia were living and named it Indianapolis.

In 1848, Willis and his wife purchased his first 40 acres of Mahaska County land from the U.S. Government for the traditional $1.25 an acre. The original purchase included the village of Indianapolis.

Two yokes of oxen were used on the farm and in laying out the village.

Land was available on all sides. A few other homesteaders settled in the area, but not many, so between 1848 and 1859, when Willis was doing well with his pioneer crops and with the cattle, sheep, and hogs he was raising, he made frequent trips to the Federal Land Office, amassing no less than 600 acres to firmly establish the Baker Farm.

Included in those 600 acres was a quarter section that Willis was able to acquire with the help of his father-in-law's military bounty awarded him after he had served in the War of 1812. That purchase was made in 1850.

During this period, eight children were born to the Willis Bakers. However, Willis' health failed and he died in 1862, leaving Lettitia with eight minor children and 600 acres of farm land to worry about.

In 1876, David Ashbury Baker, oldest son of Willis and Lettitia, was able to buy out his seven siblings' share of their father's estate, enabling him to farm the large farm, and to eventually acquire 200 acres for himself, just south of the village of Indianapolis.

David's wife was Eunice. They married in 1878.

David and his wife had a family of six, one of them a son, Arthur. He had worked with his father on the farm until his father's death in 1912. Arthur then borrowed money to buy out his five brothers' and sisters' shares of the David Baker estate.

It was a $6000 loan and was incurred during a rather trying period that was followed by World War I and then the 1921 plunge in land values. (The author of this book is well aware of that disastrous period when he saw the land his father had bought two years before for $400 an acre plunge to a value of less than $150 an acre.)

Nor was that all. Before there was much recovery from the 1921 debacle, the 1929 stock market crash took place, followed immediately by the early 1930's Depression and the droughts of 1934 and 1936.

President Roosevelt said all we had to fear was fear itself, but there was a great deal of that in farm circles.

Nevertheless, Arthur managed to pay off the farm loan in 1936, enabling him to own 175 acres of his grandfather's original homestead. Meanwhile, a portion was left to his widowed mother.

Arthur and Laura Baker, Wedding, 1908

Arthur and his wife had three children. One of them was a son named Ivan. In 1948, Arthur and his wife deeded the 175 acres to Ivan and his wife, who are now the present owners of the pioneer farm. A few years later, Ivan and his wife were able to buy a neighboring 200 acre farm, thereby making their holdings total 375 acres.

Two children were born to the Ivan Bakers, thus making a fifth Baker family generation to live on the 148-year old farm. The farm has been in the Conservation Reserve Program (CRP) since 1986.

Jerry D. Baker, Ivan's son, now shares ownership of the farm with his father.

Although oxen were first used by Willis, he had switched to horses by 1850. David used as many as eight horses, and was one of the first to use a trip wire corn planter in 1910. Allis-Chalmers tractors were used on the farm beginning in 1939, when Arthur was still the owner. A two-row corn picker and a combine were welcomed in 1950, soon after Ivan had taken over.

The Bakers have been active in farm organizations over the years. Arthur

Baker was a member of the Farmer's Union in the '20s, and later of the Farm Bureau. Ivan served as Mahaska County Farm Bureau president one year.

The Baker family helped establish the Indianapolis, Iowa, Disciples of Christ Church in 1954, but now belong to a Disciples Church in Oskaloosa.

Ivan's brother, Samuel Ward Baker, served two years in WW II and Ivan's son, Jerry, was in the U.S. Army in the 1960s.

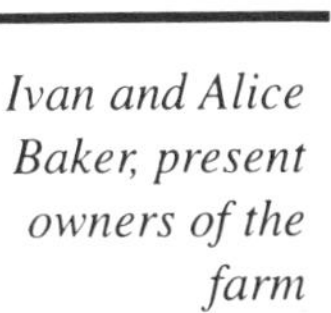

Ivan and Alice Baker, present owners of the farm

Baker farmstead and another farmstead along a road that was once a winding Indian trail.

BURKE FARM
OF
JACKSON COUNTY
Settled 1848

Michael J. Burke of Jackson County is the great-great-great grandson of David Burke who was born in Ireland and came to America, along with many other European immigrants. He first settled in Dubuque, but in 1848, came to Jackson County to establish a 40 acre claim, and purchase it from the U.S. Government.

The property became a homestead and David farmed it as best he could, in addition to serving as a school teacher in the area.

One of his sons, John Burke, followed his father on the farm, and one of John's sons, also named John, was the third owner. He was Michael Burke's great grandfather. Apparently none of his sons owned the land.

Next to own the land was Earl Burke, the grandson of John II, and Michael's father.

During those four generations of ownership of the original 40 acres, more acres were added from time to time, and now that Michael has succeeded his father as owner, the farm consists of 145 acres.

It is now in the Conservation Reserve Program.

THE MALLORY FARM
OF
CLAYTON COUNTY
Settled 1848

The Mallory Farm, now owned by Elsie A. Mallory and her children, Bruce J. Mallory and Judith Mallory Holthaus, was purchased in 1848.

Original owners were Horace A. Mallory, the great-great-great grandfather of the present owner, and his brothers, Amasoc and Allen Mallory, great-great-great uncles of Judith Mallory Holthaus. A good neighbor, Algernon Martin and his wife, Sarah, made the then long trip to Dubuque and secured the farm for the Mallorys in order to save them the long trek.

There is no record of whether there was any fee paid the Martins for their effort, but it is known that 160 acres were purchased from the U.S. Government for $1.25 an acre, and that it was deeded to the Mallory's on the first day of July, 1848.

Horace Mallory was born in the state of New York and came to Iowa in 1838. The land he and his brothers acquired was in what was originally platted as Township #91, but later renamed Mallory Township in recognition of the family's sizable purchases.

Second to own the property were Augustus and Rose Mallory, great-great grandfather and grandmother of the lady who owns it with her children now.

The third owners were Samuel Mallory, the great grandfather, and his brother, Horace, a great uncle.

The fourth generation owner of the pioneer farm was Mrs. Elsie Mallory's grandparents, Dean and Edna Mallory, who, of course, were the father and mother of Clarke Allen "Bob" and Elsie Mallory, and grandparents of Bruce Mallory and of Judith, who furnished the information for this pioneer family farm application.

Horace Mallory and his sons made several trips out to California to take part in the Gold Rush years of 1848, '49 and '60. It is not known whether that was for the purpose of helping pay for the farm or not, nor is there any information as to whether the Gold Rush adventure by those three "Forty-Niners" was successful.

Present home on the farm was built in 1881. The farm remains at 160 acres in size.

After the death of Clarke Allen "Bob" Mallory, Judith's father, the farm was put in the government's "set aside" acres.

The address of the farm is Route #1, Garber, Iowa, in Mallory Township in Clayton County.

THE SQUIRES FARM OF LINN COUNTY

Settled 1848

Milton Squires was born in Virginia and came to Iowa by way of Kentucky where he had farmed with his father for several years, and where he was married to Esther Gilbert of Kentucky in 1841. Whether it was in childbirth or for some other reason, Esther died in 1844. Subsequently, Milton married Elizabeth Mounts, who was born in Illinois, but the marriage apparently did not take place until after Milton had homesteaded in Linn County, Iowa, in 1848.

The journey to Iowa from Kentucky was made on horseback, and the Mississippi River was crossed at New Boston. Milton then rode on until he got to Linn County, where he eventually homesteaded 40 acres near what was then the little village of Cedar Rapids. A subscription school had provided Milton with limited education, which he was soon able to put to good use.

At the time he bought the barren 40 acres of prairie, Indians were still camped all around the few pioneer families who had settled in the area.

In the beginning, the milling of his grain had to be done in Muscatine, which was 45 miles away. One of the unique projects Squires undertook was to raise potatoes and ship them by flatboat down the Cedar River, a project that netted him a good sum. In time, he was able to buy more land until his farm totaled 271 acres.

Early on, most travel was by oxcart. One such cart had wheels made by sawing off the butt, round end of large logs. A 75-mile trip in that conveyance must have been quite an experience.

The 14' x 12' cabin in which Milton and his family first lived was made of logs, but was given a more aristocratic appearance by a covering of clapboard.

His second wife also died rather young, but not until Milton Squires had become the father of eleven children from his first two marriages.

Nor was life easy for the family some years. The family history tells how the mills were frozen one winter and the family had to subsist on what they had in the cabin—mostly hominy—and on wild game they could hunt or trap. The family diary tells that they had to go nearly two months before more milling could be done and bread could be tasted once more.

After his second wife passed away, Milton Squires was married a third time, when he married another Elizabeth, the widow of Phillip Neighbor, and herself also a mother of eleven, thereby making for a total of 22 children in the combined family.

The Pioneer Iowa Family Farm application received by the Iowa Department of Agriculture shows that one of their sons, Smith Squires, was the second owner of the pioneer farm. One of Smith Squires' sons, named Milton II, represented the third generation on the property.

Fourth owner was Roy Squires, a WW II veteran, who started farming soon after the end of the war. He was the father of the present owner, Robert Squires, of what is now a 125-acre farm. Robert, with the help of his wife, Katherine, and their daughters, Breanna and Melody, now has a corn, bean, and hay rotation, and raises cattle and chickens.

In the application he made to the Sesquicentennial Commission, Robert Squires tells that his great-great grandfather obtained the farm by land grant, although he was not able to actually purchase the land until 1848, after he had farmed it several years. Moreover, by stint of hard work, unique marketing endeavor (such as the potato project), frugality, and shrewd buying, he increased his farm holdings from 40 to 271 acres.

The pioneer farmer apparently was highly regarded. An 1888 Linn County publication stated, "Among the representative farmers in Linn County, the name of Milton Squires stands out prominently as a good citizen, enterprising business man, and farmer of the first class."

He was an early member of his Masonic Lodge and held in high esteem by the Brotherhood. Politically, he was a Republican. In 1887, he contributed land for the building of a community church. Small wonder, then, that the 1888 publication suggested Milton Squires was "in the front ranks in building for his community and the county."

The present home on the pioneer farm was built in 1978, and is quite a contrast from that first 14' x 12' cabin and those that followed when the family grew to eleven, and then to twenty-two.

Corn and hay has been grown by all five generations of the Squire family, and cattle and hogs have been raised through the years. Today, the emphasis is on corn, soybeans, and cattle.

THE CURTIS-BEAUCHAMP FARM OF IOWA COUNTY

Settled 1849

An 1849, homestead was established on February 9, of that year in Iowa County by George Curtis.

While there is only limited information on this venture of 147 years ago, it is known that it consisted of 80 acres purchased from the U.S. Government at the cost of $1.25 an acre and that it was located in Section 29 in what was listed as Township 86.

George Curtis was born in England, but there is no information provided on when and how he came to the new world. Nor is there any notation on his age or where he was located in the United States before coming to Iowa.

Once he had the official deed in his hands, Mr. Curtis proceeded to farm the 80 acres himself, presumably with a yoke of oxen to break the prairie. Corn and hay apparently were the first crops grown.

George Curtis was the great grandfather of Charles W. Beauchamp of Maquoketa, who now owns the farm along with his wife, the former Veronica Millius.

Second owner listed is Saul Beauchamp, who presumably married a Curtis daughter, the grandmother of Charles.

Next to be shown as owner was an uncle, Leo Beauchamp. Charles and Veronica are recorded as the fourth, and current, owners of the 1849 homestead.

Several additional acres have been added to the property through the years.

It is not known what type of lodging George Curtis and his family experienced, but in all likelihood, it was a log cabin.

The Sesquicentennial family farm application shows that the present home was first built in 1885 and enlarged in 1916.

THE DUROW-SEE-SMYTH FARM OF JOHNSON COUNTY

Settled 1849

Louisa Durow and her husband, David, purchased the 160-acre farm in Big Grove Township in Johnson County, Iowa, from Joseph and Mary Fisher on January 25, 1949. The 160 acres were purchased for the sum of $200, which came to $1.25, the same figure that homesteaders were paying for land purchased from the Government.

David and Louisa and their children, along with Gottfried See, had come to America from Germany in the early 1840s. Mrs. Durow held a licensed diploma issued to her in Germany giving her the right to practice as a midwife, and to help with the dead. Many are the tales told of her experiences.

Unloading corn on the Charles See farm in 1939.

The Durow's daughter, Mary, and Gottfried See, were married in the bride's log cabin on the farm near the creek. Indian Burial Mounds were found nearby. Mr. See farmed with a yoke of oxen, but he was also an experienced shoe maker.

An additional 40 acres were purchased on January 11, 1853, from Frederick and Henrietta Borghart by the Sees, and then they purchased the original 160 acres from Louisa Durow on October 2, 1857.

Gottfried and Mary became the parents of seven, all of whom attended school held in a sheep shed on a neighbor's farm.

The See's had a few problems along the way. In 1868, a railroad went through a corner of the farm; and then, in order to get to the road, the family had to go under a railroad bridge which was built over a creek. They had to travel right along side the creek and when the water was high, it was impossible to get to the farm except by foot.

In 1856, the two oldest sons, John and Christian, helped hew logs and build a basement barn on the present building site. It took two years to complete the task. The two boys also dug three wells by hand. The wells were four feet across and over twenty feet deep. The excavated ground had to be pulled up with buckets as they dug. One well was full of water by the next morning and had to be dipped out with buckets before they could continue walling it up.

Some years later, tragedy struck. Gottfried See was killed in January of 1871 when he was run over by a team of horses at a neighbor's farm.

Eight years later, Christian, one of the See's older sons, purchased the farm from his mother. A crop rotation of corn, oats, and hay had been carried out by Gottfried most of his life and was continued by Christian. However, the livestock program seemed to need enlarging. In answer to that, a large cattle barn was built in 1890 and a combined corn crib and hog shed were built three years later. Still another barn was erected in 1904.

Nor were the home facilities neglected. A large summer kitchen was added to the house. The structures apparently were all well built. All are still standing and all remain in use.

Fourth owner of the farm was Charles See, son of Christian and Mary. Charles bought the farm from his parents on March 3, 1919. He was only 19 years old at the time. Charles and his wife, Myrtle, farmed all of the land, including raising a lot of livestock, until the U.S. Government purchased 35 acres of the farm in 1951 for the Coralville Reservoir.

Charles died some time after that, but his widow continued to manage the operation. Then, just two years before the Sesquicentennial, she and her daughter, Lena, sold the farm, but made sure it stayed in the family. The buyers were Ruth Ann and Roy Smyth. Roy is the great-great-great grandson of Louisa and David Durow who started it all with that 160 acres they bought for $1.25 an acre 147 years ago.

Charles See and daughter, Trula, bringing in a load of hay from the field.

THE FELDERMAN FARM OF JACKSON COUNTY

SETTLED 1849

Roots of the Felderman family, one of eastern Iowa's pioneer families, go back to Germany.

John H. Felderman was born over in the "Old Country", but, like thousands of other German citizens, wanted no part of the Kaiser and his ways for the rest of his life. Accordingly, John was one of a countless number who came to America and who eventually settled in Iowa.

Unfortunately, in an application sent to the Iowa Department of Agriculture and Land Stewardship, there is no mention when Mr. Felderman came to this country, which part he entered, or his age, or whether or not any other family members came at the same time.

It is known that John H. and Mary Felderman purchased 40 acres in 1849. Those 40 acres were a part of a 680-acre tract that the Felderman family had evidently procured from the government at an earlier time, but no year was mentioned in the information provided those writing this book.

The material submitted tells that the original home for the family was a log cabin. It was replaced by a larger home in 1862 and enlarged several times before it was destroyed by fire .

Ever since its inception in 1849, the farm has been owned and operated by a member of the Felderman family. Following John and Mary, the original owners, their son, Herman L. and his wife, Augusta, were the owners. Next, Erwin, Sr. and his wife, Leonora, gained possession of the property, and now, Erwin, Jr. and his wife, Mary Jo, own the farm. The farm now comprises 194 acres, 40 of which John H. and Mary homesteaded in 1849.

In submitting their application for the Sesquicentennial contest, Erwin, Jr., and Mary Jo, make the statement, "Great Grandma Felderman would tell how, after the men would leave for the field, Indians would come to the pioneer home seeking food. Fearful for the safety of her children, and for her own life, she always gave the natives some food."

THE HORNBAKER FARM OF VAN BUREN COUNTY

Settled 1849

November 26, 1849 is the day the Hornbaker name first was introduced in Van Buren County farm annals, and it has been associated with the southeastern Iowa county ever since.

First to settle in the Farmington area were Benjamin and Elizabeth Hornbaker, great-great grandparents of Joyce Hornbaker, who now lives at Newton and who submitted the Iowa Sesquicentennial Iowa Pioneer Family Farms project application. Ms. Hornbaker reports her great-great grandfather was a native of Kentucky, and her great-great grandmother was born in Ohio.

The great-great grandparents came to Iowa in late 1849 to buy 40 acres from a man named John Sinnard. Good farmland in the Bonaparte community had already increased in price significantly since Statehood took place only three years earlier. In 1846, the government was selling land to pioneer settlers and investors for $1.25 an acre, but when the Hornbakers were ready to buy in November, 1849, they had to pay $10 an acre.

First crops grown by the new settlers were wheat and corn.

Second owner of the land was a son of the original owner, Martin Hornbaker, great grandfather of Joyce.

One of the children of Martin and his wife was a son named Clarence Hornbaker, Joyce's grandfather. Clarence and his wife had a son, also named Martin Hornbaker, who was the fourth owner of the Van Buren County land. Martin in turn sold it to his brother, Ardella Hornbaker, the fifth member of the family to acquire the property.

Corn and soybeans are now the two major crops.

All the original buildings on the farm are gone now except a stone smokehouse built by the original owner and now used for storage. A new home was built in the 1920s.

No information was provided about the family or dates of farm ownership.

THE JAMISON FARM OF CLARKE COUNTY

Settled 1849

During the 150 years Iowa has been recognized as one of our nation's sovereign states, there have been many times when Iowa farmers, or their sons or grandsons, or their brothers or others in a family, were called upon to bear arms. From the start of the Civil War in the early 1860s through two World Wars and on through various other major conflicts, all the way to helping with the Peace Keeping in Bosnia mine fields in 1996, the total number of Iowan's who have enlisted or been drafted is into the many hundreds of thousands.

A countless number have given several years of their young lives to the nation's defense. Many thousands have been wounded or taken prisoner. Thousands more have paid the supreme sacrifice.

First Generation,
Robert and Christina Jamison

One Pioneer Iowa Farm Family whose men have responded to the country's calls as early as the Civil War, and through several other major conflicts, is the Jamison family of Clarke County.

During the Civil War, Ashton Hall, great grandfather of Raymond Jamison, current owner of the farm founded in 1848, was an Illinois infantry sergeant who died of wounds suffered in the Battle of Fort Donelson, Tennessee. Meanwhile, John Jamison, a great uncle, was a corporal in the Iowa Infantry and was wounded in a battle in Georgia.

In WW I, Raymond's uncle, Charles Jamison, served overseas.

Then came WW II, when the Jamison family, like thousands of others, went all out to provide the food to "Help Win The War and Write The Peace."

Not long after WW II, the United States became embroiled in the Korean conflict, with two members of the Jamison family in it. Raymond, himself, was in the U.S. Army 86th Infantry, and his brother, Russell, was in the Marine Corps.

After Korea, it was Vietnam, with the same brother, Russell, serving two terms of duty with the Marines.

Turning now to the family's pioneer farming venture, Robert Jamison and his wife's brother, John Kyte, left their home in Indiana in 1848, went by boat on the Ohio River to St. Louis, then up the Mississippi to Keokuk. They had only $14 left. However, it was enough to get them by ox cart to Albia, Iowa, where they staked a claim in Monroe County that fall.

The next spring, they found they could not get clear title to the Monroe County land, so that autumn, Robert and his brother-in-law headed west on the Mormon Trail and found an area in Clarke County with fertile soil, water, and woodland. Almost immediately, they staked out a 160-acre claim, before returning to Christina, Robert's wife. Then, in the spring of 1850, they came back to Clarke County and paid for the land they had claimed the year before, paying the government $1.25 an acre. In so doing, they became the first permanent settlers in Clarke County.

Second Generation, Tom and Ella Jamison

A small log cabin and a crude barn for oxen and other stock were built right away.

By this time, Robert was very low on money, so he started swinging his ax to split hundreds of rails to be used as rail fencing and sold to other early settlers. As soon as conditions permitted, he started to break the prairie sod and planted corn. A favorable growing season followed, and he was able to harvest an average of 40 bushels an acre from several acres.

Meanwhile, Mormons seeking their "promised land" farther west, and other pioneers, some even destined for California, kept going west on the Mormon Trail, first established in 1846. The trail ran close to Robert and Christina's cabin. Frequently, the travelers would stop, anxious to purchase foodstuffs and glad to get a few bushels of the 1850 corn crop, even at the price of a dollar a bushel or more. Sometimes, Mormons camped overnight.

By 1855, the original log cabin would no longer suffice, so a house was built of raw lumber. It was a period of turbulent times, so the new house was frequently used as a stop on what became known as the "underground railroad".

During those first years, Indians often roamed the area. Jamison ancestors told of an Indian chief and his squaw dying near the early settler's new home and being buried, with all their weapons and colorful personal effects, near that new house.

Soon after they were permanently settled on the Clarke County land, Robert and Christina started raising their family of six boys and three girls. A large orchard was started early on, and more land was acquired. A larger barn was built shortly after the end of the Civil War.

Robert became the first school commissioner in the county and was also elected to the Clarke County Board of Supervisors.

The farm did not change hands until 1901 when Tom Jamison, one of the nine children, and his wife, Ella, gained ownership. By then, many things had changed drastically, although corn, oats, clover, and timothy were still the major crops, but horses had replaced oxen long ago.

Third Generation,
Robert Ashton and Neva Jamison

In the livestock area, some fine stud horses, along with registered milking Shorthorn cattle, started getting special emphasis. A second large orchard was planted. Eggs from the large laying flock were also an important source of income. Land improvement continued.

Amazingly, a new telephone line was built at the turn of the century, to become a source of much pride. A Case tractor was bought before the 1920s. Their first auto struggled through the dirt roads in 1916 and the first radio was enjoyed as early as 1924.

Tom and Ella, who were the present owner's grandparents, had two sons—Robert Ashton and Charles S.—who farmed with their father until his death in 1936, at which time Robert and his wife, Neva, became the third set of Jamisons to own the farm. Robert and Neva were the parents of the present owner.

Robert and Neva had a family of five. They lived in a new home built in 1924. A year after buying the farm, a new John Deere tractor was purchased, marking the beginning of the end for horses on the farm. Ponds were constructed during that period, and new corn cribs, grain bins, hog sheds, and poultry houses were built.

In 1958, Raymond, the fourth child in Robert and Neva's family, and his wife, the former Shirley Moore, became the fourth generation on the Jamison homestead. In 1964, they purchased 280 acres to become the present owners. They raised hogs, had a herd of Holstein dairy cows, and did general grain farming. Their success enabled them to buy more land until the farm totaled over 700 acres.

Raymond and Shirley raised a family of three—Gary Roy, Raymond D., and Penny Sue. The farm now totals 720 acres, and the owner is quick to acknowledge his son, Raymond D., a fifth generation member, and grandson, Jeffery D., representing a sixth generation, are the ones "doing the job" now. A cow-calf operation, along with the corn, soybeans, and alfalfa hay crops, keep them and their modern machinery mighty busy.

Fourth Generation,
Raymond and Shirley Jamison

All the Jamisons have belonged to the United Methodist Church and to the Republican Party. Many community responsibilities have been undertaken, including Under Ground Railway Director, County Supervisor, School Commissioner, World War Bond Chairman, telephone company officer, ASC Township commissioner, REC board member, County Zoning Committeeman, and Masonic Lodge officer.

Raymond D. also reports an interesting family treasure. When Robert Jamison and his wife came to Clarke County by ox cart and covered wagon , they carried a corner cupboard as one of their prized possessions. Since that long ago day, it has been used by each succeeding generation and is now proudly used by the present farm owners.

THE JENKINS-DICE-KINRADE FARM OF CLINTON COUNTY

Settled 1849

Sketchy details on an application for Pioneer farm family recognition sent to the Iowa Department of Agriculture and Land Stewardship during the Iowa Sesquicentennial show that Alexander Jenkins, the great-great grandfather of Bruce Kinrade, purchased 160 acres from the U.S. Government on April 10, 1849.

The application shows that Mr. Jenkins was a native of Essex, New York, and lived in Michigan before coming to Iowa. It is assumed the lure of good land available for homesteading, and priced at only $1.25 an acre, brought him to Iowa.

Corn, oats, and wheat were the early crops grown. Cattle and hogs were the livestock raised.

There is no further mention of Alexander Jenkins or his wife, but a daughter, Harriet, who was Bruce Kinrade's great grandmother, is listed. She was the second person to own the farm, along with her husband, Bruce Dice.

The Dice couple had a daughter, Helen, who married Bruce Kinrade's father. They were the next generation to own the farm, and their son, Bruce Kinrade, is the present owner.

Bruce now grows corn, soybeans and oats, and raises cattle and hogs.

The original home was built in 1877 and is still being used.

No further information about the farm or any of its owners was received.

THE JOHNSON FARM OF LEE COUNTY

Settled 1849

One of the largest pioneer land purchases made in Lee County in 1849 was made by Aaron and Mary Wilson Johnson. It was a 416-acre tract purchased from David and Polly Wilson, believed to be Mary's parents. Cost was $1.25 per acre, probably the same amount paid by the Wilson's in purchasing the land from the U.S. Government in the first place.

Aaron and Mary Johnson were the great grandparents of Kenneth Johnson, who, with his wife, Eunice, purchased 80 acres of the original tract in recent years.

Preceding Kenneth and Eunice in the acquisition of the farm were Kenneth's grandparents, Edward and Adeline Turner Johnson, who were the second owners. Their son, George, became the third owner.

George was Kenneth's father, but before Kenneth and Eunice gained possession of a part of the farm to become the fifth owners, one of George's sisters, who was Kenneth's aunt, Florence Johnson, was the owner.

In 1946, Iowa's Centennial year, the Johnson farm was one of many Iowa pioneer farms to receive a Century Farm Certificate signed by Governor Robert Blue.

Wheat, corn, oats and hay were the first crops grown on the farm. Cattle, hogs, and sheep, along with chickens and turkeys, were also raised by several of the first generations to own the land.

Through the years, various acreages of the original 416 acres were sold to family members and others. Kenneth and Eunice now own 80 acres of those original 416, and rent an additional 100 acres.

Some of the land has also been devoted to pasture land all through the years, and continued to be under the ownership of Kenneth and Eunice. One of their main enterprises was a cow-calf herd whereby good pastures are absolutely essential.

Horses, of course, had to furnish the power for field work through the first 75 or more years of the farm's operation. However, in 1922, a Fordson tractor was bought, spelling the beginning of the end of horses. Once there were as many as ten horses at a time being used on the farm.

Other tractors purchased after 1922 included a John Deere, an Allis-Chalmers, a Ford and a Duetz. The first combine was purchased in 1935 and a two-row corn picker in 1961.

Because of an injury suffered by Kenneth from a fall earlier in the 1996 Sesquicentennial year, the cow-calf herd had to be dispersed.

ANOTHER OF THE GROUT FARMS OF JOHNSON COUNTY

Settled 1850

An unusual, and almost unbelievable, pioneer era "Believe It Or Not" story has come to those preparing this book from the owner of one of Iowa's older farms. She is Mrs. Marilyn Grout of Riverside, Iowa.

It is a story of a frontier period family reunion that would seem more unlikely to take place than finding a needle in a haystack.

It speaks of Zenus Grout, who is mentioned as a pioneer Iowa settler in another section of the book, looking around on horseback, hoping to stake out 40 acres somewhere, possibly in Johnson County. He suddenly noticed a trickle of smoke rising out of a woodland not far away. Because he had been led to believe he would be the first white settler in the area, it startled him and fear of Indians gripped him.

Nevertheless, he dismounted from his horse and slowly and cautiously made his way toward the origin of the smoke, his heart beating faster by the minute. To his amazement, he found the smoke was coming from a log cabin, not a wigwam or wickiup.

Barn across the road from the Grout home. Included are Harry, Loren, Emma & Neta with stroller.

Greatly relieved, and realizing another white settler was in the area, he decided to learn more. He walked toward the cabin, and then got the surprise of his life. Not only was it a white settler's cabin, but its occupants were his own wife's father and mother, four younger sisters, and a brother with his wife and child.

There is no way of adequately describing the unrestrained joy on all sides when the full impact of the discovery was realized. Of course, Zenus sped back to his wife to give her the electrifying news.

Although the Zenus Grouts had known of Margaret's parents and siblings leaving Ohio for unknown territory across the Mississippi, they had no idea where. The chances of finding themselves settling in the same immediate area were about as remote as finding a needle in a haystack. The touch of Divine Providence seemed to be the only answer.

Originally, Zenus and Margaret had considered exploring farther west, but after the amazing discovery of Margaret's family, and finding a spring, good land, much timber, and flocks of wild turkeys nearby, they lost no time in settling down then and there.

Forty acres were claimed the next day.

The story continues with many strange and confusing developments. Space permits only brief references following that amazing discovery of immediate family members instead of an Indian village.

The Zenus Grouts had made the long trip from Ohio by prairie schooner. There was only one child, two year old Melissa, but there would be six more brothers and sisters welcomed later.

One brother was named Loren, whose name also appears in the other Grout family featured in this book as a veteran of the Civil War and as the second member of the family to own the pioneer farm.

However, at this point, confusion of two separate mid-1800 Grout farms begins. Evidently, Loren and his wife, Emma, had five sons and three daughters.

In any case, the Grout family feature of 1846 deals with a different longtime Grout farm than this report does. In the 1846 feature, Lucius Grout is listed as the third owner, whereas Harry Grout is the third owner of the farm with which this report deals. Obviously, Lucius and Harry were brothers or cousins and each had a farm of their own.

Harry married Neta Southwick, and they had a family of six -- Lloyd, Earl, Mae, Daisy, Doris, and Edwin. It was Edwin who became this Grout farm's fourth owner, as compared to Childon being the fourth to own the other Grout place.

Edwin married Marilyn Strickler in 1949, and they also had six children, as well as 13 grandchildren and three great grandchildren.

House on Grout home place - 1919. Pictured are Neta, Daisy, Harry, Lute, Loren, Earl, Mae, Lloid, Emma, clendon.

Edwin passed away in 1987 and Marilyn, who provided all of this branch of the Grout family farm's history, now owns the 179 acre farm and still lives on it, although a neighbor now rents the land.

Marilyn had made a careful study of her late husband's family history. She tells that Zenus and Margaret Grout arrived in Iowa with a team, a prairie schooner, one child and $20. Their nearest market was Muscatine, 37 miles away, and their only sweetener for the first year was a gallon of molasses.

They had a family of six daughters and one son, but Margaret's parents had ten children and 70 grandchildren, all of them living in Johnson County.

Marilyn Grout adds that the farm has produced all the usual crops -- corn, wheat, oats, soybeans, hay, etc. -- and all the common livestock and poultry - cattle, hogs, sheep, chickens, and turkeys -- plus one more exotic livestock project-- raising buffalo.

Zenus purchased land in 1867 to build a church which became a Methodist church. It was later remodeled, and in 1984 was moved to the Kalona Historical Village, where it stands today as the Grout Church.

Memberships of family members have been, and are, many. Included are Masonic Lodge, Eastern Star, Farm Bureau, Civil War veterans, and many others, as well as the Methodist Church.

THE MATHER FARM OF CEDAR COUNTY

Settled 1850

The Mather Farm in Cedar County first came into the Mather family's hands on November 6, 1850. Samuel Mather I paid Moses Butler $1271 for the original 160 acres. Samuel Mather I was the great grandfather of Anders Mather, Jr., who is now the farm's owner.

Records show that Samuel Mather I was born in Pennsylvania in 1805, but had lived in Ohio for a time before coming to Iowa to establish a pioneer farm.

Second member of the Mather family to own the land was Samuel II, Anders Mather's grandfather.

Third to own and operate the farm was still another Samuel Mather, who apparently shared ownership with a brother, Anders U. Mather, Sr., the father of the present owner.

The application is signed by Janice Mather. It tells that the present home on the farm was built in 1951, and that corn and soybeans are the crops now being grown.

There is no information about other family members, dates of ownership, livestock, or other pertinent information about the 146-year old Cedar County farm.

THE MORGAN-SNAKENBERG FARM OF KEOKUK COUNTY

Settled 1850

Dennis Snakenberg of near Webster, Iowa, is the owner of the land his great grandfather bought from the government for $1.25 an acre back in 1850. The great grandfather's name was Thomas Morgan, and he acquired 40 acres near what later became the town of Webster near where the English River goes through Keokuk County. It was one of the earlier acquisitions in what had been Indian territory only a few years earlier.

Thomas Morgan was followed on the farm by his son, Thomas A. Morgan, who bought it from his father in 1867, shortly after the end of the Civil War.

From the beginning corn, oats, and hay were the crops grown on the small farm. In the livestock area, cattle, hogs, and sheep, as well as chickens, were raised.

None of the original buildings are still to be found on the farm, although it is known that the first home was of hardwood boards instead of logs.

In 1929, the name of the owner and operator of the farm changed from Morgan to Snakenberg when Byron Snakenberg, a son-in-law, bought the land. He was Dennis' father, and he owned the property until 1942, when Dennis took over.

Both dairy and beef cattle were raised on the farm. The dairy cows were Holsteins, while the beef stock was Angus. For a period of years, the Angus cattle were purebreds.

At the time Dennis' father took over, six Percheron horses were providing the power on what had become an 80 acre farm by then. Prior to that, horses had also apparently always been used, or at least there is nothing in the family records to show oxen ever were yoked up.

However, when Byron took over in 1929, the era of horse power ended. He bought a McCormick-Deering 10-30 tractor that year to become one of the earlier tractor users in the county. Subsequently, a Farmall F-20 and an Allis-Chalmers tractor were also used in the Snakenberg fields. A mechanical corn picker was added to the machinery line in 1935, and a combine in 1945.

Interestingly, in 1942, when Dennis acquired the 80 acres, another meaningful development took place. Electricity came to the area and to the farm, with much rejoicing by all concerned — but especially for the wife in the home. It was a fond good-bye to lamps and lanterns, and a warm welcome to the lights and appliances in the house and in the barn.

There are many memories on the farm, but not all are happy ones. Corn sold as low as 14 cents a bushel in 1953, and drought hit hard in 1934 and 1936. Hogs once brought only $2.50 a hundred weight.

The Snakenberg farm is now in the Conservation Reserve Program.

Dennis has served on the County Board of Health.

He and his wife have a son who is now the fifth generation to have lived on the 1850 farm.

WARD-MOELLER FARM OF CLAYTON COUNTY

Settled 1850

Ronde and Donna Moeller live on a 200-acre farm in Cass Township in Clayton County that first came into the family in 1850. Mr. & Mrs. Moeller are the fifth generation to own the land.

Giles Ward, who was born in Ohio, and who had migrated to Illinois with his parents before coming to Iowa, was the first owner of the 200 acres that had been bought in two lots. The first tract was only 40 acres and was acquired on March 1, 1850. Some six months later, an adjoining 160 acres became available and he was able to buy that, too.

All of the property was purchased from the U. S. Government, presumably at the traditional $1.25 an acre.

Giles Ward was the great-great grandfather of Ronde Moeller. Giles had a son, George, and a daughter, Nellie, who are listed as the second owners. George Ward's family included a son who was named Giles Lavern Ward. Giles Lavern became the third owner, and was the grandfather of the present owner.

Giles Ward had a daughter whose name was Leonana Betty. Leonana, who would become the fourth owner, married a man named Moeller. They were the parents of Ronde Moeller, who with his wife, Donna, now have possession of the pioneer family farm.

Crops now grown on the Ward-Moeller land include corn, oats, peas, and hay. Dairy cows and feeding cattle make up the livestock program.

Cass Township, where the farm is located, is in the extreme southwestern corner of Clayton County. It was named in 1847 in honor of General Lewis Cass. It is an area of rich soil that had both timber and undulating prairie, which had great appeal to early settlers.

However, the first white settler in the township was Joseph Hewett, who arrived from Kentucky in 1844 to trade with the Indians. It was at a time when that area of Iowa was still a part of the Winnebago Reservation.

Hewett stayed there until the Indians were moved west in 1851, just a year after Giles Ward purchased the 200 acres. Five white families, including Ward's, had settled in Cass Township by 1850. James Tracy and family arrived in 1846. Harrison Boggs and his wife from Virginia and Josh Betts and family from Ohio arrived in 1847.

Giles Ward did not actually buy the Ward-Moeller land until 1850, but he and his family came from Illinois and settled temporarily in the township in 1848 so he could scout around before buying. Thus the Wards were the fifth white family to put down roots in Cass Township in Clayton County back there in the days of sturdy pioneers.

THE DAVIS-WILLIAMS FARM OF JOHNSON COUNTY

Settled 1850

The Williams family of Johnson County is one of many pioneer families with an interesting story to tell, but it is one that has a somewhat different pattern than most. It is a story in which the pioneer wife and mother figures very prominently.

She was Phebe Davis Williams. Her story begins in Tennessee where she was born Phebe Wilson in 1808. She was married to Josiah Davis when she was 22. Three children were born during the first eight years of their marriage.

In 1839, Phebe and her husband and the three small children made the long trek from Tennessee to Johnson County, Iowa, where they settled and where their fourth son was born soon after their arrival. However, the following year, Josiah died, leaving Phebe with the four small children and all the challenges of sudden widowhood.

During about 1841, Phebe filed a claim for a land grant of 40 acres, thus enabling her and the children to at least have a home.

Four years after Josiah's death, Phebe was married to Edward Williams, who had come to the United states and to Iowa from across the Atlantic in Wales.

During the next five years, two daughters and a son were welcomed by Phebe and Edward, making for seven children in the home. And it was not until 1850 that President Zachary Taylor signed the land grant for which Phebe had filed in the early 1840s.

Thus it was that the William' s pioneer farming project was not started on the 40 acre claim until 1850. The next year, another child, Robert McCrary Williams, was born to complete the family.

In submitting the Pioneer Farm application in February, 1996, Edward R. Williams, who with his brother, Robert, now own and operate the farm, reported that the farm has grown to 340 acres. That makes it nearly ten times larger than when their great-great grandmother filed for the 40 acre land grant more than 150 years ago.

Edward also listed his great grandfather, Robert McCrary Williams, Phebe's last child and youngest son, as the second to own the land. Robert's son, Carl E. Williams, who was Edward's grandfather, became the third owner. He was followed by Herbert Williams, Edward's father, as the fourth generation to own the farm.

Evidently it was during Herbert's ownership that the farm was incorporated as the Herbert Farms.

It is, and has been, a highly diverse farming venture. Wheat was probably the first crop grown, followed through the years by corn, oats, prairie grass pastures, hay land, and soybeans.

The Williams farm's livestock program has been no less diversified, beginning with sheep, a few cows, chickens, and some pigs. Eventually, it branched out to include blooded stock — Holstein dairy cattle, an Angus beef herd, Hampshire and Duroc hogs, and Suffolk sheep.

Up to twelve horses were stabled and used annually until 1922 when a Waterloo Boy tractor was purchased, followed by a Huber, McCormick-Deering, Case, Ford, John Deere, Massey-Harris, and Allis-Chalmers tractors.

The present home on the farm was built in 1953, but there is also a barn still in use that was built more than 100 years ago.

Still helping their sons with the farming now are their father and mother. During the Vietnam war, Robert S., the youngest brother, was a Navy pilot.

There is now a sixth Williams generation involved in the pioneer farm. Edward and his wife have two children, and Robert and his wife have three.

During the great-great grandmother Phebe's lifetime, she was a devout Presbyterian and her husband belonged to the Welsh church. Members of the family have continued church interests, as well as serving as District Soil Commissioner, and on school and other boards. They have also been members of Kiwanis, the Shrine, the Elks Club, Moose Lodge, and Iowa Farm Bureau.

THE BERTHOLF FARM OF MADISON COUNTY

Settled 1851

Linda Bertholf Johnson of Winterset, Iowa, provided the author of this book with enough material about a Madison County pioneer farm to fill the pages of several books. Space will permit using only a small fraction of it. The material includes everything from the ancestors homeland in Holland, through ten generations of Bertholfs in America, beginning with a Revolutionary War drummer boy to the mid-1800s pioneer farm and rattlesnake hunts in Madison County, on through an 1875 grain reaper catalog, and on to the Japanese bombing of Pearl Harbor, and everything in between and beyond.

Mrs. Johnson tells about her family's many years in the U.S. following their departure from the Netherlands. The great-great-great-great-great-great-great grandparents first settled in New York City. Several generations later, the great-great-great grandparents moved to Ohio and Indiana, then Illinois, and finally the great grandfather, Andrew Bertholf, came to Iowa and bought a farm in Madison County in 1851.

The family has owned the 160 original acres ever since. The grandfather, Alexander Bertholf, one of Andrew's ten children, bought it in 1855. Alexander and his wife had twelve children. One of them was Ellis Bertholf, who became the third owner in 1907. He was followed by his only child, Halden Starr Bertholf, father of Mrs. Johnson, in 1936. In 1991, the farm went into a trust shared by Geneva (Halden's widow) and their two children, Mrs. Linda Bertholf Johnson, and her brother, Halden Clair Bertholf.

No one in the family lives on the farm now, but Mrs. Johnson's husband, Daryle, manages it for the Trust. In addition, he handles the American Turf Beauty Lawn Service he and Linda own. The farm now totals 205 acres. The Gibson Brothers are now farming the land.

In establishing his farm in Madison County in 1851, Andrew Bertholf found himself in a unique neighborhood where neighbors shared everything from bolts to a welding shop.

In 1920, Linda's great grandfather, Alexander Bertholf, built the house now on the farm, and her father wired it for electricity from a wind charger.

Linda's grandfather, Ellis Bertholf, was one of the first farmers in the county to build terraces and assume other soil-saving practices. He grew corn, soybeans, hay, and had pasture for his Hereford cattle and his sheep. He also raised Berkshire and Yorkshire hogs.

Oxen furnished the field power when the great grandfather started farming, but horses soon replaced them, and horses were a mainstay on the farm until about 1940, when a John Deere "Johnnie Popper" tractor first entered the scene, followed by more John Deeres.

Much of the material sent by Mrs. Johnson came from files, cigar boxes, and special metal safe boxes her parents had carefully preserved.

Included were Co-op and Odd Fellows membership certificates and dozens of financial records. Also found were five cent I.O.U.s the great grandfather had gotten when he had a general store. Also included are post office records kept by him and the grandfather when they served as community postmasters before Rural Free Delivery was established.

Also of special interest was a report on the Madison County Rattlesnake Hunt when the county was divided into a north and a south competition, resulting in the annihilating of more than 3000 "rattlers" in that single day. A handbill announcing an 1882 circular wolf hunt was also found in the tin box of "treasures".

An impressive printed 1875 catalog with clear pictures depicts the advantages of the Champion Reaper's dropping drag bar and lever. Going all the way back to the Revolution, one account tells about a Bertholf youth serving as a drummer boy in George Washington's army.

The records also show that three of Halden Berthoff's cousins were in WW II with one of them serving as a messenger for General McArthur, and another one — Chenny Bertholf — at Pearl Harbor when the Japanese bombs fell.

There are dozens of xeroxed family pictures and letters in the material provided your author, and some diary excerpts, including one that indicates he had husked corn three days and gotten married, all in the same four-day period.

THE GREEN FARM OF WINNESHIEK COUNTY

Settled 1851

Not many Iowa pioneer family farms can claim maple syrup as one of their major products, but one that can do so is the farm now owned and operated by Dale Green of near Castalia in Winneshiek County. The very address of the farm — Maple Valley Road — indicates it is in the heart of "Sugarbush Country."

In making application for his farm to be considered by the Iowa Sesquicentennial Pioneer Farm Family project, Mr. Green did not hesitate to include maple sugar in the list of farm products. The fact is, the original owner of the Green Family Farm had grown up in New York State in an area where maple sugar trees abounded. It is entirely possible that, in choosing an Iowa farm, he selected the Winneshiek County property because he saw sugar maple trees growing there.

That first owner of the farm was Gudeon Green, Dale Green's great-great grandfather, who was born and raised in upstate New York. His early ancestors had come to this continent from England long before we became a nation. Records show that the Greens arrived in Jamestown, Virginia, in 1635. That was less than 30 years after three British ships — the Susan Constant, the Godspeed, and the Discovery — sailed into Chesapeake Bay and disembarked 105 adventurers to form the first permanent settlement in North America, and to call it Jamestown.

Gudeon Green was a carpenter by trade, but evidently he had an adventuresome spirit. After leaving New York State, he first tried his hand at farming in Wisconsin. However, his main goal was to own land of his own, so he came to Iowa in 1851 to an area which, up until that year, was known as Winnebago Indian country. On looking around, Gudeon found a 160 acre tract that had been given to James Simpson by the government for his army services. On learning it was for sale, Mr. Green bought it on July 10 of that year.

Undoubtedly, his carpentry skills were put to good use when it came time to build a cabin for his wife, Dorcas, and their children. One of those children was a son named Melvin, Dale's great grandfather. Melvin became the second owner of the farm. His family included a son named Stephen Allen, who was the next to own the farm, and who was Dale's grandfather.

By the time Dale's father, Clarence Green (Stephen's son), gained possession of the farm, the acreage had increased somewhat and tractors and more modern machinery had made quite a difference in the fields.

First crops raised on the farm back in the early 1850s included oats, corn and hay.

Through the years, those crops were maintained. Soybeans were added during Dale's father's ownership. Beef cattle were also a source of income throughout the farm's nearly 150 years.

The farm now totals 188 acres.

As for the maple sugar production, Dale is certain that his great-great grandfather started that unusual production that has continued through all five generations of the Green family's tenure in Iowa. Dale says, "It's the most interesting aspect of our production and continues to this day."

HOWIE FARM, LTD.
OF
JONES COUNTY
Settled 1851

In Jones County, one of the oldest farms to be held by members of the same family is the Howie Farm, Ltd.

Robert Howie, who was born in Scotland, was the first to own the land. He was the great-great grandfather of Mike Howie, who is the son of Kenneth and Margaret Howie, the present owners. The land purchase was made in 1851. The acreage and the cost per acre was not given. It was bought from what was then known as the School Fund Commissioner.

Second owner was Frank Howie, Mike's great-great uncle. Frank was followed by James Howie, the great grandfather, who was the third to own and operate the farm.

Listed as the fourth owner was Robert Howie II, the grandfather, whose son, Kenneth, is the applicant whose name is shown on the form sent to the Iowa Department of Agriculture and Land Stewardship. Kenneth is the father of Mike, who is listed as the sixth generation on the farm.

Interestingly, the present home on the farm was built back in 1880, and the barn that is still being used was built in 1882. The first home back in 1851 was a log cabin.

Whatever the acreage was when it was bought 145 years ago, the farm now totals 470 acres.

THE JONES FARM
OF
APPANOOSE COUNTY
Settled 1851

There's not much doubt about the "Jones Boys" taking things over on a 200-acre farm near Plano in Appanoose County.

The Joneses started taking over in December, 1851, when William Jones was able to acquire 160 acres from the U.S. Government. Although it is not documented, it is virtually certain the cost for the homestead farm would have been $1.25 an acre.

The pioneer farmer and his wife had a family of eleven children. One of them was a son, Nathan, who was the second of the Jones family to own the land. Nathan and his wife bought the farm in 1855, only four years after it was homesteaded by William Jones.

Nathan and his wife had three children, one of whom was a son named John, the third owner of the farm, John and his wife had only one child, a son named Merle. Merle was the fourth of the "Jones Boys" to take over.

Merle and his wife had a larger family. They were the parents of six children, one of them a son named J. Neil Jones, who along with his wife, Ielene, are the parents of J. Neil Jones. J. Neil and his wife purchased the farm, which has now grown to 200 acres, in 1971.

Cattle and hogs have been raised on the farm many years, as well as corn and other crops. The cattle were Angus and the hogs were Duroc Jerseys.

Oxen were first used for farm power, but horses handled all the field work from the beginning in the year 1851 through the early 1920s, when a Minneapolis-Moline tractor was purchased. Other tractors used since then include Allis-Chalmers, International, and John Deere.

Organizations in which the Jones family was involved include the Farm Bureau and the Appanoose County Beef Producers.

Neil Jones also served in World War II.

THE McARTHUR-YATES FARM OF LINN COUNTY

Settled 1851

When Richard Yates of Linn County looks over his farm, he recognizes he is already the fifth generation to own the land, and that it all started with his great-great grandfather, who was a storekeeper and surveyor as much as he was a farmer.

The great-great grandfather who originally got a U.S. Land Grand on 160 acres was James McArthur. He helped survey land for the town of Palo and ran a drygoods and grocery store, in addition to breaking the prairie for crops.

The McArthur name also applied when the second and third set of owners took over the property. They were Richard Yates' great-great uncles, Alden McArthur, who was the second buyer, and Earl McArthur, who was the third owner of the farm.

Earl's daughter, Jane, was the fourth in the family to own the land, but she had married Benjamin Yates, thereby making a name change in ownership that has been evident ever since. Benjamin and Jane, Richard's great grandfather and grandmother, must have been a highly successful farm couple. Records show they owned three farms with clear titles.

Early in the McArthur period of ownership, a house was built using rough sawed lumber, ax-hued timbers, and square nails. Amazingly, the building, although often remodeled and modernized, has been home to five generations.

Harry Yates, the son of Jane and Benjamin was the next to own the farm. He and his wife were Richard's grandparents and the father of Ben B. Yates, the sixth generation member of the family. Ben and his wife had three children. One of those three was Richard, the seventh and present family representative to own the farm. Richard and his wife have two children, a daughter and a son. Douglas, the son, may very likely become the eighth owner, or co-owner, of the 145-year old pioneer farm.

Crops grown over the years include corn, oats, hay, and soybeans. Livestock raised included dairy cattle and hogs. The first tractor was an Allis-Chalmers bought in 1937. The home was electrified in 1940 by Olen and Don Hepker just before Don entered WW II where he was later blinded by enemy fire. Richard, himself, was in the Korean conflict two years.

The Yates family has been active in the Palo Methodist Church, Farm Bureau, and the American Legion. Richard has also served on the ASCS committee.

THE OLSON-REIERSON FARM OF CLAYTON COUNTY

Settled 1851

Ole Olson, a proud son of Norway, where his name was spelled Oslien, served in a U.S. Army unit with considerable distinction. In 1850, the U.S. Government was rewarding men who had served in the military with 40 acre land grants. However, Ole Olson was awarded 160 acres, four times the usual size grant. Presumably, after coming from Norway by ship with his wife, Berget Holsdatter, and four of their six children, Ole served in one or another Indian war. The grant was signed by President Fillmore.

Ole and Berget were the great-great-great grandparents of David Reierson, who now owns the land with his wife.

In any case, the Norwegian family came to Clayton County, Iowa, to settle on Ole's 160 acre grant, where two more children were born.

Their oldest daughter, Gunild, who was born in Norway and had come to America with her parents, married Lars Reierson in 1860. Lars, also born in Norway, had come to this country in 1852. In 1860, Lars and Gunild purchased the farm from Ole and Berget. Lars and Gunild had four children. Reier, the oldest of the four, became the third owner of the property in 1891.

Lars Reierson, first Reierson family member to settle on the Pioneer Farm.

Reier married Maren Olson and they also had a family of four. The oldest of the children was also a son, named Cornelius. Like his father, grandfather, and great grandfather, Cornelius grew up on the pioneer farm and dreamt of the day it would be his.

That day came in 1916 when he was able to buy the farm from his father. In the meantime, Cornelius was married to Millie Skarshaug. They welcomed two children, both sons. Millie passed away when still young. Cornelius then married Martha Tollefson. They had a son, Joseph, who became the fifth owner of the farm after buying it from his father, Cornelius. That took place in 1964.

Joseph married Helen Eberling and became the father of five — Dixie, David, Ronald, Mark and Dean. However, it wasn't until 1996, Iowa's Sesquicentennial year, that David, the oldest son, who was the logical person to become the sixth owner of the 145 year old farm, and his wife, the former Debra Hagensick, actually gained possession. They have two children, Lauren and Mathew, so there is a seventh generation "waiting in the wings".

It is interesting to note that from the day Ole Olson received the land as a military grant, it has always been farmed by owners, first himself and since then by five generations of descendants, usually an oldest son. Not once has a single inch of the property been rented.

It is also interesting to note that all through these 145 years, livestock and about every kind of poultry has been raised at one time or another. The livestock included hogs, dairy cattle, beef cattle, and sheep; and the poultry included chickens, geese, ducks, guinea hens, hundreds of turkeys, and even peacocks — probably about the only Iowa farm to raise those attractive birds.

When Reier Reierson had charge from 1891 to 1916, he also had an unusual crop growing on the Clayton County farm for a while. It was tobacco — one of the few Iowa farms to undertake production of that crop.

The conventional crops grown, however, were, and are, corn, oats, and

Joseph and Helen Reierson, fifth owners of the six generation pioneer farm.

hay land on a five-year rotation.

Horses provided the field work power from Ole Olson's time through the first part of the 1900s. When Cornelius took over, as many as 16 horses were used annually. However, that started to change when a Waterloo Boy tractor came onto the scene as early as 1916, followed by five different makes of tractors — Parrot, 1920; Farmalls, International Harvester, Allis Chalmers, and Massey-Fergusons since 1929.

In about 1916, a hard freeze struck on August 12th, so Cornelius turned 300 pigs into the corn fields to salvage what they could, then sold them at 90 pounds for $2.50 cwt. In 1934, the drought also caused a crop failure.

In 1941-45, Cornelius' brother, Louis, served in WW II, and in 1954-56 Joseph served in the military.

The families apparently almost all belonged to the Lutheran Church. Membership is also held in the Farm Bureau and the American Legion.

Although the original home was a log cabin and has been long gone, a granary built of stone and a barn, both built in the 1870s, are both still standing and being used.

THE PAPE FARM OF DUBUQUE COUNTY

Settled 1851

When Jerry and Ramona Pape sent in an application to have their farm considered for the Iowa Pioneer Farm Family Contest, they not only told about the five generations of Pape family members who have owned and prospered on the 176 acre farm they now own near Dyersville of "Field of Dreams" fame in Dubuque County, but they also told a fascinating story of how Iowa's oldest mutual insurance company, the New Vienna Insurance Company, was started.

As for the farm, Jerry's great-great grandfather, who was born in Germany and had worked in St. Louis before coming to Iowa, bought the land in 1851. Twelve years later, a large house replaced the family's log cabin. Even today, that house, modernized several times, of course, still serves as the present generation's comfortable home.

Second owner was a son of the German-born pioneer, Conrad Pape, who bought the land in 1882 and passed it on to his son, Louis H. Pape, Jerry's grandfather, in 1906.

Fourth to get possession of the farm was Lewis C. Pape, Jerry's father. That was in 1949, and then Jerry and Ramona took over in 1987.

Dairying has been a main enterprise on the farm many years, along with growing corn, oats, and alfalfa hay.

Regarding the fascinating story of the origination of the New Vienna Insurance Company, Jerry and Ramona explain that pioneer weddings, like other momentous occasions of the pioneer age, were occasions which were celebrated by the whole community. Invitations would be delivered a month before by a "gallant" youth on horseback.

When the eventful day arrived, the bride and groom proceeded solemnly to the church in an elaborately decorated wagon drawn by oxen, mules, or horses, and were escorted by young men on horseback.

Such a wedding took place on April 14, 1863. All was going well when the merrymaking was suddenly interrupted by a call of "fire".

The wedding guests rushed outside and saw a cloud of smoke rising from a neighboring farm a few miles away. They made a valiant, but useless, attempt to subdue the flames, but there was no water supply, or hoses, or fire fighting equipment, so in a matter of minutes, another settler was left destitute.

The farmer whose property was destroyed was Conrad Pape, a close friend of the bride and groom, and the son of the pioneer who bought the farm in 1851.

When it became obvious the barn would be a total loss, one of the wedding guests who had rushed from the church took his hat, went among the crowd that was gathered at the scene and took up a collection for the stricken farmer and his family. Thus it was that the oldest farmers mutual insurance association of Iowa had its inception.

The next Sunday the priest who performed the ceremony took up a collection for the Pape family, and then called a meeting on May 25, 1863, to officially form the insurance society. It had only 22 members, but they were a dedicated group. After that, whenever there was a loss by fire, collections were taken up in church. Each member of the association paid a flat rate of $1.00.

Despite its strange and climactic beginning, the New Vienna Mutual Insurance Society became a popular farm protection organization and continues to be to this day.

As for the young couple whose nuptials were so rudely interrupted, they were duly married and "lived happily ever after".

THE RIEDESEL FARM OF CLINTON COUNTY

Settled 1851

The history of the Riedesel farm and of the St. Paul's German Lutheran Church of Wheatland is about as closely intertwined as any two entities could possibly be, and their beginnings make for a rather remarkable story.

Two young brothers - George and LaHenry Riedesel - having heard about the good land opening up in Iowa, left their Ohio home in 1850 and walked all the way to Clinton County, Iowa, to see for themselves. It must have taken many weeks to walk through much of Ohio, all of Indiana and Illinois, and then find a way to cross the Mississippi River, but they did it. And what they saw of rich soil in the Wheatland area quickly convinced them that "this was the place" for them and for others back home. They lost no time in staking a claim.

That done, they again set out on foot for their home in Gallion, Ohio. The walk was just as long, but they were in such high spirits, it seemed to take less time.

Once back home, they gave such glowing accounts of the rich, black soil in Clinton County that other families bearing German names like Acker, Duerr, Homrighansen, Schneider, Schmidt, and others, quickly decided they also would make the move, and did.

The result was that before the end of 1851, LaHenry Riedesel was firmly established on 160 acres and his brother also had acquired land, while the other new families were doing likewise. Almost before they knew it, there was a German settlement near Wheatland, and the need for a church was very obvious.

Both LaHenry Riedesel and Ludwig Duerr had studied some theology under their Ohio pastor, Reverend Max Stern, so these two conducted services in settlement homes every Sunday, thereby laying the foundation of the St. Paul German Lutheran Church that would soon be built.

So pleased were they that they invited Reverend Stern to come visit. The Ohio pastor did so, and while exulting over what members of his former flock had accomplished in Iowa, he also baptized babies and other children that had been born to the new settlers since coming to Iowa.

LaHenry Riedesel and his wife had six children, and the family prospered in their new Iowa surroundings. Cattle, hogs, and sheep were raised, and good crops of corn and hay were grown. Their log cabin was soon replaced by a larger house made of sawed lumber, and that house is still in use today.

In 1885, Theodore Riedesel, one of LaHenry's six children, took over the farm. Four children were born to Theodore and his wife. One of them, Reuben, bought the farm in 1937, followed by Paul Riedesel, one of Reuben's three children, who gained ownership of the farm in 1976. Paul and his wife also have three children, and their son, William, is now doing the farming on what has now grown to 200 acres.

In earlier years, the cropping rotation was corn, oats, hay and pasture. Angus and Shorthorn cattle, Poland China hogs, and sheep were raised.

Today, the cropping program is limited to corn and soybeans, Livestock is no longer raised.

Western horses furnished all the field power until 1935 when an Oliver 70 tractor was purchased. Case, White, and Oliver tractors have been used since then.

Paul says 1934 and '35 were drought years, and 1924, '44, '47 and '93 were flood years.

Paul served in a Medical Detachment in WW II. He is a member of the Farm Bureau. His family continues to be active in the German Lutheran Church, just like all of his ancestors have been.

THE KITTELSON FARM OF FAYETTE COUNTY

Settled 1852

One hundred sixty acres of the 197-acre farm now owned by Clarence Kittelson of near Clermont in Fayette County was first owned by Clarence's great grandfather, Hans Kittelson, a native of Norway. It was obtained in 1852 by a land warrant from the government.

Clarence's grandfather, Kundt Kittelson, was the next to take it over, after which, Henry Kittelson, Clarence's father, became the owner.

A crude cabin was built in 1853 and served the Norwegian family a number of years.

Much of the land was kept in pasture and hay land to provide for the beef cattle herd which has been the farm's main enterprise through the years.

The present home on the farm was built in 1953.

THE MOLSBERRY FARM OF WORTH COUNTY

Settled 1852

A Worth County report submitted in connection with the Iowa Pioneer Farm Family contest indicates that a 135 acre farm near Plymouth has been in the Molsberry family's hands since 1852.

Marcel Molsberry, who sent the report, says she and Jesse Molsberry purchased the land from a relative in 1930 and still own it today. The farm now totals 169 acres.

The early years of their ownership were not easy years. These years were marked by the nationwide Depression and by two years of drought, plus record heat and cold, chinch bugs, grasshoppers and other problems, including 10 cent a bushel corn.

Holstein dairy cattle and hogs were raised many years. Crops grown included potatoes, corn, oats, and soybeans. Chickens were also produced. Belgian horses provided the power in fields until a Fordson tractor was purchased during the World War I period. One of the first mechanical corn pickers was used in the 1920s. Electricity came to the farm in the 1930s.

No further information was provided regarding previous owners and their families, other than the fact a Molsberry ancestor first purchased the land in 1852 and members of the family have owned it ever since.

THE NUTTING-BURNETT-SPEAR FARM OF WARREN COUNTY

Settled 1852

A Warren County farm family has much to be proud of about their 144-year old farm established by their great grandfather back in 1852. They are the C.D. Spear family, and they can relate many fascinating activities, events, and happenings associated with their 280-acre holding, even though they are only one of three families to own the property.

The great grandfather was David Nutting, born in Connecticut; and after an arduous trip to Iowa in 1852, bought 160 acres by way of a School Grant from the State of Iowa. He then went to St. Louis to earn money so he could send for his family, who was living in Massachusetts. His wife, Mary, and their two sons came by boat down the Ohio River to Missouri. There, the father joined them, got a team of oxen and a wagon, and with all their belongings and a cow and a calf, came to their new Warren County farm.

A large log cabin was built right away; and then, for protection against prairie fires, furrows to a width of 50 feet were plowed around the cabin.

Mr. Nutting was called to serve in the Civil War, but was given sixty days' time to replace the log cabin with a three room house for his family, now including his wife, two sons, and a daughter.

Corn was first planted by hand and hay was cut with a scythe. Small grains were also harvested by hand with the use of a tool called a cradle.

After the war, the first four-foot Buckeye mower was bought and used by this pioneer farmer and all his neighbors. The next purchase made to ease up on the hand labor was a reaper.

In the livestock area, Shorthorn cattle and hogs were raised, and breeding of Percheron horses became a major enterprise for many years.

There were no schools when the Nuttings first came to Iowa, so Mary, an Amherst College graduate, set up and taught classes for her own and the neighboring children right in her own home. Later, a public school called Bluebird Academy was established in Indianola, where Simpson College is now located. David and Mary's sons walked several miles daily to attend the Academy. One of those sons, William Porter Nutting, later became a teacher.

The farm changed hands in 1907, when the Nutting's daughter, Sadie, and her husband, Smith Burnett, bought it. They had no children. Then, thirty years later, C.D., a great nephew, and Mable Spear, became the third and current owners.

The Spears have four children, three daughters — Edith (now Mrs. Merrill Henry), Edna (Mrs. Larry Lester), and Janice (Mrs. Bob Goode) — and a son, Marvin, who now farms with his parents.

The Spear Farmstead

All were active in youth groups and 4-H clubs.

The Spears also have eleven grandchildren and 14 great grandchildren.

Registered Angus cattle have been raised on the farm for more than 50 years. In 1946, Edith showed the Iowa State Fair's Grand Champion steer.

The first tractor was an Allis Chalmers bought in 1938. Numerous Allis Chalmers' models have been used since then. The first corn picker arrived in 1940, the same year a combine was purchased. Electricity was welcomed in 1948.

The Spear family is active in the Methodist Church, Farm Bureau, State and National Angus Associations, 4-H leadership, and the Warren County Historical Society. Mrs. Spear was chosen one of five Iowa Master Farm Homemakers in 1963, the highest recognition a farm homemaker can attain.

PEARSON FARM PARTNERSHIP OF LINN COUNTY

Settled 1852

The Hertz Farm Management Firm, Inc. is responsible for providing information about the Carbee-Pearson farm in Linn County, which is now being operated under the name of Pearson Farm Partnership.

John F. Carbee bought 400 acres in 1852 for $1.25 an acre from the U.S. Government. Apparently 240 acres of that original purchase is still being farmed under the present partnership. However, the total number of acres now being farmed is 400, the same number originally purchased.

Mr. Carbee was born and raised in New Hampshire, but after settling in Iowa, found himself not only handling a large farm, presumably with oxen to begin with, but also called upon for much community service. He was first chosen for the school board, then named Justice of the Peace, and then elected to the State Legislature.

Although not stated in the Pioneer Farm application form, it is assumed the first home was a log cabin. However, a sturdy, well-built home was built in 1866. Part of this home remains in use, as does a barn established in 1854.

Second family member to own the Carbee farm was George J. Pearson.

Listed as the Pearson farm owners since George Pearson are Thomas Pearson, great-great uncle; George Pearson II, great grandfather; Isaiah Pearson, grandfather; and George J. Pearson, father.

According to the information provided by Hertz Farm Management, George III and Warren Pearson, who apparently are brothers and the sons of

George J. Pearson, now are in charge of Pearson Farm Partnership. They are Mount Vernon residents, but the farm is located near Springville.

No information was provided as to the years of ownership, nor was there any mention given of the great grandmother, grandmother, mother, aunt or wives involved in the Carbee and Pearson families.

THE VINZANT-GORDAN FARM OF APPANOOSE COUNTY

Settled 1852

William Vinzant was able to buy a 320 acre Appanoose County farm for a total outlay of $700 in 1852. The farm is now owned by R. Katherine Vinzant of Hannibal, Missouri, and her sister, Dorothy Vinzant Gordon of Florida. After several generations of ownerships, the farm now has 214 acres. Katherine Vinzant and Mrs. Gordon are great-granddaughters of the pioneer buyer of the land in 1852.

Second owner of the farm was also named William Vinzant, a son of the original buyer of the land. William Vinzant, Jr., was one of ten children. He and his wife had three children. Alice Vinzant was one of them and was the grandmother of the present owner. One of her three children was a son named Harley Vinzant who took over the farm in 1944. He and his wife had a family of four, of which R. Katherine was one. Her sister, Dorothy Gordon of Clear Lake, Florida, shares ownership of the farm with Katherine. Their brother, William III now farms the land. Corn, oats, soybeans, and hay are the crops currently being grown.

Through the years, hogs, Shorthorn and Angus cattle, and chickens were raised.

At one time in 1909, there were 26 horses and ponies on the farm. In 1946, an International Harvester tractor marked the beginning of the end of horses in the farm's fields.

R. Katherine has traced her ancestors back to a great-great grandfather, James Vinzant, who was born about 1776. The great grandfather, William, was born in Kentucky. He and his first wife had five children before she passed away at a young age. He then married Judith Ratcliff, who became Katherine's great grandmother. William and Judith also had five children.

Incidentally, the great grandfather, William, walked from Indiana to Iowa to buy the 320 acres and then turned right around and walked back to Indiana.

On one occasion when William was bringing his wife Judith from Indiana to another Appanoose County farm he had acquired, they sewed the money they were carrying into her dress.

The Vinzants have been involved in many community organizations, including 4-H, County Fair Board, Beef Producers Association, Soil Conservation Service, Farm and Home Administration, County School Board and Board of Health, Masonic Lodge, ASCS, and the United Methodist Church. William H. Vinzant also served in WW II.

THE GREGG-KISTER-WAGNER FARM OF CLAYTON COUNTY

Settled 1852

Tom and his father with some of their horses.

Several years ago, the Dubuque Telegraph Herald listed a number of farms that had been in the hands of the same Clayton County family for well over 100 years. One of those farms was the Wagner Farm near Monona that was established in 1852.

This year, when the Iowa Sesquicentennial Commission announced its search for the oldest farm in Iowa, Steven and Paul Wagner submitted an application in the Pioneer Farm Family Contest. Although they did not win, they found it fascinating to trace the farm's 144-year old history.

Delores and Thomas Wagner with their six children, Norma, William, Donald, Mary, Steven and Amy.

First to acquire the 140 acres were Mr. and Mrs. John Gregg, Steven's great-great grandparents.

The farm next went into the hands of a great uncle, A.B. Kister, whose nephew was Herbert Wagner, who became the third owner and the first Wagner to gain possession of the

The Wagner Farmstead.

farm. He, of course, was Steven's grandfather. Herbert Wagner's son, Thomas, was the next to own the property, and was Steven's mentor.

In an interview conducted by Brent and Brad Grinn, who are grandchildren of Thomas Wagner, some interesting facts were brought out.

Some of the things that interview brought out were all the hand work that was still being done during Thomas Wagner's ownership of the land, and costs of those days.

Overalls, for instance cost no more than $1.80 a pair. Pop was 5 cents. Bread was 10 cents a loaf. Three rings of bologna could be had for 25 cents and going to a movie only cost a dime.

There was no electricity, of course, and water was pumped by hand. A wood stove did the cooking and wood furnaces provided heat.

There was not much leisure time in those days; but if there was some, horseshoes were often played, and baseball was already a popular Sunday sport.

Steven Wagner points out that hay land, oats, and corn have been the cropping program throughout the years, and dairying the main livestock project.

THE ELLIS-BESWICK FARM OF DELAWARE COUNTY

Settled 1853

Back in 1853, William Barber Ellis purchased a 240-acre tract of Delaware County land from the U.S. Government.

The 240 acres had been left unclaimed from an 1848 Mexican War Grant, and then reverted back to the government, so Mr. Ellis was able to buy it on August 13, 1853, for $1.25 an acre.

An example of how Iowa farmland has increased in value over the ensuing years is shown in the 1980 contract signed by Mr. & Mrs. Burton Ellis, third generation owners of the farm, and Mr. & Mrs. John Beswick, the buyers of the property. Mrs. Beswick is the great granddaughter of the original owner, and the daughter of Burton and Dee Ellis. In those 127 years, the per acre cost of the land had gone up from $1.25 per acre to $3000 per acre. Thus, the Beswicks agreed to pay the Ellises a total of $720,000 for the land at the rate of $60,000 a year until the year 1991, in addition to the original down payment.

William Ellis, the pioneer buyer of the land had been born in Genesco County, New York, and had lived and farmed in Crawford County, Pennsylvania, before coming to Iowa.

After buying the farm, William was able to open a charcoal pit on nearby Elk Creek.

Second owners of the land were Kittie and Ella Ellis, daughters of William Barber Ellis and his wife. Third to claim the land were Burton French Ellis and his wife, who sold the land to John and Mary Lou Beswick for the $720,000 in 1980, very close to the peak period of Iowa land price highs.

A house to replace the crude homes on the farm in the 1800s was built in 1912.

Corn and hay were the main crops raised on the farm, along with herds of beef cattle.

John Beswick has passed away, so the 240 acres is now owned and controlled by his widow, Mary Lou Beswick, whose home now is Greeley, Iowa.

THE JOHNSTON FARM OF POWESHIEK COUNTY

Settled 1853

John G. Johnston was one of the many who "went West" to seek his fortune in the early 1850s. Before he got through with his "seeking", he owned more than 1000 acres of good Poweshiek County soil, most of it contiguous, and most of it now owned, or farmed, by descendants.

Born in the state of New York as John Johnson, he started his westward trek as a young man, but got only as far as Ohio on his first move. Then in late 1853, he went through much of Ohio and all the way across Indiana and Illinois before reaching Iowa.

Once across the Mississippi, Johnson kept going until he reached Poweshiek County where he was able to get a 40 acre land grant from the government. It was near the end of the year on December 20, 1853 when he actually acquired the land.

By then, Johnson found he was only one of many with the name of Johnson searching for good land. Even before he came to Iowa, his mail often became mixed up with others who had the same last name. Accordingly, when he signed the grant, he drew a red circle around Johnson and added the letter "t" so that from that time on his last name would be spelled Johnston, and it has been carried that way by everyone in the family ever since.

While the original purchase was only 40 acres, John G. Johnston continued to add another 40, or 80, or whatever amount of nearby land he and his family could afford. In time, he had increased his holdings more than tenfold and before he was finished, he was the owner of over 1000 acres, and one of the largest land owners in the county.

When his great grandson, John G. Johnston, II, of Belle Plaine submitted an application in the Iowa Sesquicentennial Pioneer Family Farm contest, he added a note pointing out that 840 acres of the senior John Johnston's original holdings remain in the hands of his descendants.

Second to own the land was Frank Johnston, John II's father, after which Wallace E. and John II acquired the land in a brotherhood partnership. Since then, John II has become the principal owner of the large homestead farm located in Jefferson Township in Poweshiek County.

THE KLINSKY FARMS, LTD. OF LINN COUNTY

Settled 1853

The Klinsky Farms of Linn County, now owned and operated by Robert and Kenneth Klinsky, are quite a different enterprise than when the two brothers' great-great-great grandfather started it all with a 40-acre purchase of land back in 1853. He was H. Henry Vornholt, who paid Morgan Reno $2.75 an acre for the small plot of ground back then.

H. Henry's son, Henry William Vornholt, became the second owner, but no date is given as to when that, or any other land, changed hands.

One of Henry William's daughters, Anna Caroline, married Frank Klinsky and became the third owner of the property with her husband. They were Robert and Kenneth's great grandparents, and they were the ones who changed the name on the farm's ownership records.

Anna and Frank had a son named H. William, who married a lady named Stella. H. William and Stella became the fourth generation to own and farm the property, which had been constantly growing in acreage for a number of years. They had a son, Glen W., whose wife's name is Darlene. Glen and Darlene are Robert and Kenneth's parents.

There is no information as to exactly when the farm was incorporated, or which year it reached its present size. Evidently, it has been since the fifth generation that is now in charge, took over.

Corn, oats, and hay, along with beef cattle, are the major projects on the Klinsky Farms, LTD. now.

Diane Klinsky now serves as the farm's efficient treasurer.

THE KUBLER-EDEN FARM OF CLINTON COUNTY

Settled 1853

On his Iowa Pioneer Family Farm application, Richard Minor of Clinton County has listed a goodly number of ancestors that have preceded him on a farm on which six generations have now lived and worked, or have been owners and operators.

First on the long list were his great-great-great grandparents, Leanhart and Agnes Barbara Kubler, both of German descent. They were able to get two land grants signed by President Franklin Pierce in 1853.

The first grant was on July 16, 1853 and was for 160 acres. The second grant was obtained four days later and was for 80 acres.

Leanhart died in 1864, leaving his wife, Agnes, with the farm and seven children, several of whom had already married.

John and Conrad Kubler, the two oldest sons of Leanhart and Agnes, took over the farm in 1864, but John (Richard Minor's great-great grandfather) died in 1876, leaving his unofficial share of the 240 acre farm to his wife and their two daughters.

When Leanhart's widow, Agnes, passed away in 1882, daughter Mary and her children, along with her brother Conrad, gained control of the farm. Conrad did not pass out of the picture until 1919, leaving his share to his wife, Wilhemina, and their four children — Agnes, Edith, Irvin and Leonard.

Leonard Kubler, who was actually a third cousin of Richard, got control of the farm in 1925 but not for long. In 1930, after Mary Kubler died, Agnes (Leonard's sister), who had married John Eden, was able to buy out her brother.

Incidentally, John Eden was elected to the Iowa Legislature in 1924, and re-elected in 1926.

John and Agnes' son, Richard Eden, and his wife, Melinda, were Richard Minor's grandparents. No information was provided regarding his parents.

The farm now totals 199 acres, with 107 of the acres originally purchased in 1853 still a part of the land on which corn and beans are now being grown.

MAGNOLIA CREST FARM THE LAU FAMILY OF SCOTT COUNTY

Settled 1853

Of the more than 300 responses to the Iowa Sesquicentennial Commission's search for Iowa's oldest farm, there have been few, if any, more complete or more perfectly written and submitted than the report of the Lau Farm of Scott County. Norman Lau, a fourth generation member and farmer in the family, prepared and sent the information.

It is a report which includes pertinent newspaper and magazine clippings; questionnaires answered fully and legibly; beautiful, clear pictures, all properly captioned; and other undeniable proof of the farm's long, interesting history, and that of its occupants.

Nor was all this any great surprise to the author of this book. The Lau farm is located in Lincoln Township in Scott County, within a few miles of the farm where I was raised and worked. Obviously, I have long been mindful of leadership exerted by members of the Lau family, the innovations on that farm, and the family's influence itself.

Moreover, when I was called upon to serve as county leader of some 600 4-H Club boys more than 60 years ago, Norman Lau, then in his early teens, was one of those who took his projects and assignments in total seriousness and always did them "right".

And, as though that is not enough nostalgic inter-

Charles W. Lau, pioneer farm scientist, who introduced alfalfa to Eastern Iowa, and planted hundreds of trees to beautify his farmstead, including Magnolia trees.

est on my past memories of the Lau farm, one of the clippings kept by the family and relayed to me was a long column about "Magnolia Crest", the name of the farm, when I was farm editor of the Davenport Democrat some 60 years ago.

Since that long ago time, generations on the farm have come and gone, but much has remained the same. The farm's history, and that of its occupants, continues to be fascinating.

First to own and settle on the 160 acre farm several miles north of Davenport was a German immigrant family, Peter and Maria Lau, both born in Schleswig-Holstein, Germany, where Peter had managed a large farm estate prior to his departure.

Enroute at sea, two of their four children died. With heavy hearts and with their two surviving youngsters, they boarded a train in New York for Chicago, and then went by prairie schooner to Davenport, then a city of 4500, where many German immigrants had already settled. After reaching what was then being called the "Queen City Of The West", they lost no time looking for a nearby farm.

In short order, they found a 160-acre tract owned by John LaFranz available for $25 an acre. They bought it, and immediately started building a beautiful colonial-style home, which has now served five generations of the Lau family.

Two more children, Charles and Elizabeth, were born on the farm. The tall prairie grass was soon converted to farm land, good crops were grown, hogs, cattle and sheep were raised, and three acres of lawn were set aside where many Davenport and other friends gathered for "gamutlichkeit" (enjoyable and fun) picnics and parties.

In 1881, Charles W. Lau, who had worked on the farm with his father many years, became the farm owner.

Norman Lau standing in front of the oldest Magnolia tree planted by his grandfather in the 1880's. This huge tree has a circumference of more than 15 feet, and continues to bloom annually. It is undoubtedly the oldest Magnolia tree North of its native "Dixie".

His brother, Henry, a Civil War veteran, distinguished artist, and flower lover, was able to get a nearby farm where he kept the grounds like a park.

The same year he acquired his father's farm, Charles married Elizabeth Kreiter, the daughter of German immigrants. As time went on, six children were welcomed, all born on the farm — Alfred, Oscar, Carl, Elmer, Victor, and Cora.

Charles Lau was a most unusual, capable, respected farmer. After finishing their country school classes, he and his brother Henry became two of few farm boys to enroll in, and graduate from, Griswold College in Davenport.

Attendance there prompted Henry to go to Rome to study painting, and must have greatly stimulated Charles' mind also. Throughout the rest of his life, he was regarded as an intellectual leader in many ways.

A strong believer in scientific farming, Charles was one of the earliest advocates of alfalfa and sweet clover, and an early champion for vaccinating hogs against cholera, as well as for the tuberculin test of dairy cattle. Moreover, he always practiced what he preached on his own farm. He spent countless hours speaking in every township, urging farmers to accept Iowa College of Agriculture's recommendations such as crop rotations, seed corn selecting and testing, and much else.

Most noticeable of his efforts, however, were those as a botanist and tree lover. The farmstead where his father had left three acres for lawn beauty became a virtual arboretum under Charles' care and supervision — one that attracted famed botanists like Dr. Pammell of Iowa State College to sing its praises far and wide.

Mr. Lau set out to test virtually every kind of shade, ornamental, or flowering tree known in the Midwest, as well as some of those from southern areas that did not survive. Yet, many of the trees that critics had warned against did grow and thrive.

Ruth and Norman Lau, the fourth generation to live and farm the Magnolia Crest Farm near Davenport, with one of the beautiful Magnolia blossoms grown annually on their Eastern Iowa farm.

One of these was Magnolia trees that not only took root, but are still growing and blooming now, more than 100 years after Charles Lau sought them out and planted them against all the experts' advice. The result was that he named the farm "Magnolia Crest", by which it is still known, and has been visited by thousands over the years.

When this writer wrote about Magnolia Crest Farm in 1937, 108 kinds of trees were to be found as a legacy to Charley Lau, as he was known, and whom, I personally, had known and admired when I was a boy.

At that time, the familiar oak, walnut, elm, locust, box elder, and other commonly known trees were already being supplemented with rare species of beeches, cypress, swamp oak, and others, but it was the Magnolias — cucumber, saucer, yulan, lily, umbrella, and other varieties — that were, and now are, making Magnolia Crest the outstanding, rare, Iowa farm arboretum it still is today.

Of course, the paradise of trees calls for much care and attention, first given by the originator of the project, then by his son, Carl, the next owner, and now by Norman, the fourth of the Laus to own Magnolia Crest Farm.

Carl Lau and his wife did a magnificent job of maintaining what his father and grandfather started, and kept up the pace of modern innovations. He introduced one of the first tractors, a Waterloo Boy, in 1917, maintained the livestock herd, and brought soybeans into the cropping program. He also stressed land conservation and built a pond for stocking fish. He and his wife had two children, with the son, Norman, working with him for many years before acquiring Magnolia Crest for himself.

Norman married Ruth Rosene in 1943. They became the parents of four children — Norman, Jr., Peter, Sue (now Mrs. Kim Evans), and Lisa (now Mrs. Dave Kimball).

Norman, Jr., and his wife and child reside in a new home on the farm.

The colonial home built in 1853 that has served five generations, and may soon be ready for a sixth.

Peter and his wife have two children. There are five other grandchildren as well, so the sixth generation of Lau's is here how, some of them on the pioneer farm.

Looking back on the crops grown and livestock and poultry produced on the diversified farm, it's a rather impressive figure.

The crops include corn, barley, wheat, oats, red and sweet clover, and eastern Iowa's first alfalfa.

The livestock has included oxen, registered Red Polled and Ayrshire cattle, Duroc and Hampshire hogs, Suffolk and Hampshire sheep, and several breeds of work horses.

In the poultry area, it was large flocks of chickens and turkeys; and, as I remember, a 4-H pheasant project. And on top of all that, there are fish in Carl Lau's pond, much to the delight of friends and neighbors who are fishermen.

In 1903, a state-of-the-art barn was built by Charley Lau, with insulated walls, indoor silo, water tank and ventilation systems. A livestock yard was constructed in 1906.

As for machines after that 1917 Waterloo Boy tractor, a Sawyer-Massey thresher was bought in 1918. Then in 1945, Carl got a 4-row corn planter, and in 1971, Norman got an eight-row planter.

In addition to starting the Farm Improvement League in 1912, Charles Lau was also the Master of both his local and Pomona Grange, president of the Farmers Co-op, leader in the Farmers Institute, officer in the German Fire Insurance Mutual, member of the German Pioneers Society, and, with his son, Carl, was a charter member of the Scott County Farm Bureau.

His grandson, Norman, has closely followed in his grandfather's and father's steps. Norman Lau, Sr., has been president of the County Pork Producers, and of the Scott County Farm Bureau; and with his wife, is active in Davenport's First Presbyterian Church, Scott County Crime Commission, High School Athletic Boosters, and the Republican Party. He also has served as director of the Lincoln Leader's 4-H Club, which is dear to my heart because it was my club long, long ago, and is the organization through which I first found Norman Lau.

In military service, in addition to Henry Lau being in the Civil War, Norman, Sr., was in WW II, and both his sons, Norman, Jr., and Peter, served in the Vietnam conflict.

THE MAYBERRY FARM
OF
JACKSON COUNTY
Settled 1853

The Mayberry farm in Jackson County entered the Iowa farming scene on May 3, 1853, when Alexander Mayberry purchased 40 acres from the United States. Cost per acre was $1.75, which was already 50 cents above the cost of homesteading only a few years earlier.

Alexander Mayberry was born in Pennsylvania and had lived in Mercer Township in the Keystone State, where he had been a blacksmith before coming to eastern Iowa. He was the great-great grandfather of William and Wayne Mayberry.

Second to own the farm was William W. Mayberry, Alexander's son. William became the father of Clarence Mayberry, who was the third member of the Mayberry family to own and operate the farm. Clarence's son, Earl Rimmer Mayberry, then became the next family member to own the property.

Earl is the father of William and Wayne Mayberry, the current co-owners of the property that has now grown to encompass 297 acres.

The application to the Iowa Pioneer Farm Family project was submitted by James W. Mayberry, son of William.

THE STOCK FARM
OF
JOHNSON COUNTY
Settled 1853

The Stock Farm of near Lone Tree, Iowa, is easy to summarize on the basis of the Iowa Pioneer Farm Family application submitted to the Iowa Department of Agriculture and Land Stewardship.

Duane Stock, who signed the application, is the grandson of the original buyer of the 160 acre Johnson County farm. He was John Stock who had come to America from England and who bought the land from Jacob Boone. Purchase price was $7.00 per acre.

A new home was built in 1867.

John Stock did not devote all of his time to farming, but there is no explanation of his other work. At the time of John's death, the farm was turned over to his wife, Emma.

Among the children of John and Emma was a son named Fred, Duane's father, who evidently was a full-time farmer. Fred became the second owner. The farm is now the property of Duane Stock.

The farm continues to be comprised of 160 acres and produces corn, soybeans, oats and hay.

No additional information about spouses, children, farm purchase dates or inheritances, livestock or other items was provided.

THE VAN FLEET-RITCHHART FARM OF VAN BUREN COUNTY

Settled 1853

It was in 1853 when Abraham and Mattie Van Fleet were able to buy 160 acres of land in Van Buren County. The land was purchased from George McIntire, who had obtained it from the government.

Abraham and Mattie had six children, and they were the great grandparents of Mrs. Viola Ritchhart of Keosauqua, Iowa, who provided the information relative to this pioneer farm.

One of the children in the Abraham Van Fleet family, Aaron Van Fleet, became owner of the farm in 1865. He and his wife had a family of three, and two of those children—Ralph B. Van Fleet and his sister, Mrs. Nora Guernsey— became the third owners of the property. They made their purchase in 1918. However, the brother and sister ownership only lasted one year. Records show that Ralph and Mamie Van Fleet, the father and mother of Mrs. Ritchhart, gained possession of the farm in 1919.

In 1976, Viola's parents willed the pioneer farm to her. Her father passed away some years ago, but her mother died only recently.

At one time, there was a $6000 mortgage on the farm, but it was all paid off in time by Mrs. Ritchhart's parents.

Half of the original 160 acre pioneer farm has been absorbed by other members of the family, but Viola has retained the remaining 80 acres. She now rents her land to a neighbor, Roger Kirkhart.

In earlier years, crops grown on the farm included corn, oats, wheat, and hay. Horses, cattle, hogs, and sheep were raised by the early owners.

During Ralph and Mamie Van Fleet's tenure on the land, they grew corn, soybeans and wheat, and raised Guernsey cattle, hogs, and sheep. Their first tractor was a Farmall. Later, they used a John Deere tractor.

The land is now devoted largely to corn and soybeans.

During the Civil War, William Van Fleet was a member of the 2nd Iowa Infantry. He was stricken with typhoid fever during the war and died in Mound City, Illinois. Viola's husband, Eugene Ritchhart, served a two-year hitch in the U.S. Navy during World War II.

THE WAGGONER-MAY FARM OF LINN COUNTY

Settled 1853

On July 18, 1853, Barnhart Waggoner, who was born in France, and his wife, May, purchased a 360-acre tract of Linn County land from one Joseph Fisher for $3.25 an acre. Mr. & Mrs. Waggoner were the great-great grand-parents of the present owners of the remaining 80 acres of the original purchase. The present owners are Robert and Julie May of Anamosa, Iowa.

Evidently, Barnhart and his wife had a daughter who married Nicholas May, and they became the second owners of the farm in 1877.

One of their sons, James Franklin, who would have been Robert's grand-father, purchased 160 acres of the original farm, paying $9000 for the parcel of land. That purchase was recorded on April 19, 1913.

The next land transaction took place in February, 1953, when James Elwyn May, Robert's father, acquired the property.

Now, Robert and Julie, the fifth generation in the Waggoner-May family, apparently are in possession, and are grain farmers, but only on 80 acres of the original 360 acres their French forefather secured 143 years ago.

THE PRAIRIE HOME FARM OWNED BY THE BARTLETT FAMILY OF JOHNSON COUNTY

Settled 1854

The Prairie Home Farm in Johnson County was established in 1854 by Lyman Bartlett, and has been in the Bartlett family ever since.

A log cabin was built on the 120 acres Lyman Bartlett had originally purchased for $2.25 an acre. As soon as the sod had been broken, a few acres of corn were planted and some oats were seeded. Some land was left in meadow.

Lyman Bartlett (who was the great grandfather of James Bartlett who now owns the land), and his wife had three children — a rather small family at a time when many pioneer couples raised eight or more children, some as many as sixteen.

One of those three children was Edwin Bartlett, who gained possession of the property in 1902, forty-eight years after the farm was first homesteaded.

Edwin and his wife had a family of six. One of them was Charles Bartlett, who was James' father. Charles bought the farm, which now had become much larger, in 1943 during the height of World War II.

Charles and his wife had three children, one of whom was James, who became the owner of Prairie Home Farm, now 390 acres in size, in 1960.

James is now an absentee landlord. He and his wife have five children, two of which are Mike and Daniel. The two brothers are now operating the farm, and are the fifth generation of Bartletts to do so.

Prairie Home Farm is located near Solon, Iowa, and is now a grain farm devoted almost entirely to the production of corn and soybeans.

In earlier years, oats were also an important part of the rotation, along with corn and meadow. That was long a popular system, usually consisting of two years of corn, followed by oats seeded to clover, and hay land the last of the four years.

In the realm of the military, the Bartletts have quite a record. Lyman, the great grandfather and pioneer owner of Prairie Home, was in the Civil War, serving with the 24th Iowa Infantry. He was captured by the Confederate forces and had to spend a long, difficult year at Libby Prison before being released when the terrible war ended in 1865.

James' father, Charles, was in uniform in World War I, and James' son, Daniel, also of the fifth generation of Bartletts involved in the Prairie Home Farm, was in the Vietnam conflict.

The Bartlett family have all been members of the Roman Catholic faith for many years.

THE BEIERSCHMITT FARM OF BUCHANAN COUNTY

Settled 1854

Five generations of the Beierschmitt family have farmed the same farm in Buchanan County from 1854 through today.

John Anton Beierschmitt was able to buy 40 acres from John and Maria Kermis for $1.25 an acre on January 25, 1854. Mr. Beierschmitt was 29 years old when he obtained the Iowa farm. He was born in Berlichingen, in what was known as the Kingdom of Wittenberg, in Germany on April 15, 1825.

After coming to America, he first settled in Pennsylvania, where he was a carpenter.

One of his sons, John A. Beierschmitt, was the second to own the farm; and one of John's sons, Walter P. Beierschmitt was the third. Walter was the grandfather of the present owner.

Next to acquire the land were Leo E. and Paul A. Beierschmitt, sons of Walter and his wife.

Now owning the farm, which now totals 360 acres, nine times its original purchase size, is Gregory L. Beierschmitt, who raises corn, soybeans, and hay on the land and has a livestock operation as well.

The present home on the farm must have been built well. Constructed in 1870, it is now 126 years old.

No further information of family members, ages, crop yields, or livestock prices was received, or any farm events or achievements was provided.

THE BERRY-LACINA-WHITE FARM OF IOWA COUNTY

Settled 1854

Edward Berry, Sr., the great grandfather of Mary Theresa Lacina and Loretta Ann White, was a native of Ireland, and first came to Chicago to make his living in "The Land of Plenty", as America was known to most immigrants. However, Chicago did not live up to his expectations.

When he learned that there was farm land for sale in Iowa, he and his wife left the "Windy City" in 1854 and crossed the Mississippi, then went another fifty or more miles west, all the way to Iowa County. There, near North English in English township, they found 40 acres for sale by James Faulkner and his wife, Ellen. After looking it over, they bought it and soon started adding land to it.

According to Mrs. Lacina and Mrs. White, their great grandfather, with the help of his wife and some neighbors, first built a log cabin in which the first six children in the family were born. Later, in 1867, they built a story and a half, four room house. The youngest child was born in the new house. Two additions were made to the house over the years. It was later moved across the road.

The house was 112 years old when it burned in October, 1979. By then, five generations had lived in it. Subsequently, a new fully-modernized house was built in 1986.

The barn that is still standing was built in 1903. It was used as a horse barn for many years. In 1956, it was made into a dairy barn. Now it is used as a home for cats, a skinning shed, and a basketball court.

Second to own the farm was a son, Edward Berry, Jr., and James, Ellen, and Michael Berry, great uncles and aunts of the sisters who apparently now own the land. The sisters' father, Lambert Berry, was the third owner.

No information was provided regarding the crops and livestock raised over the years, except that it is known dairy cattle became part of the enterprise.

The farm now totals 160 acres and all but a few acres are in the Conservation Reserve Program.

THE BOWERSOX FARM OF JOHNSON COUNTY

Settled 1854

The brand new owners of a 384 acre farm in Johnson County are David and Kathleen Bowersox of Cedar Rapids. They became the land owners of the farm located near Shueyville in 1995.

In submitting their application for the Iowa Sesquicentennial Pioneer Farm Family Contest, they show themselves to be the fourth generation to own the property. The first to buy was the Reverend James Bowersox, David's great grandfather, who was still living near Stanton, Virginia, in 1854, when the transaction took place.

It was a 180 acre tract purchased from William Shuey, one of the founders of Shueyville, which now has a population of 154.

A photocopy of a March 25, 1854, letter that David has shows that William Shuey wrote to Reverend Bowersox, notifying the Virginia pastor the money for the land had been received by Shuey and the official deed was forthcoming. The seller was a man named Wyatt Wherry, who had not made any improvements on the land.

Evidently, the William Shuey family could spare the 180 acres. Their total holdings at the time is said to have totaled 1724 acres. The family also donated land for a school, a church, and a cemetery. It's no wonder the town was named Shueyville. Original settler in the community was Jack Shuey, who was David Shuey's great-great grandfather.

Soon after the purchase was completed, the Bowersox family moved in a covered wagon from Virginia to their new Iowa land. Two months later, when they reached the Johnson County property, work on building a log cabin began, and breaking of the prairie was started.

After Reverend Bowersox' death in 1880, his widow inherited the farm. Two years later, it became the property of the Reverend James Bowersox Estate.

Next to get control of the farm was James E. Bowersox II, who acquired it in 1899. His son, James W. Bowersox, who was David's father, became the owner some years later.

Diversification was the story on the Bowersox farm all through the years. Corn, soybeans, oats, and hay are the crops now being stressed, while hogs and sheep have been raised over the years.

A home built to replace the log cabin was built in 1865.

THE CHAPIN-ARMSTRONG-BOWERS FARM OF JONES COUNTY

Settled 1854

Jones County is one of the northeast central Iowa counties that can boast of a number of farms that have been held in the same family for more than 140 years.

One of those farms is the one homesteaded by George Chapin, who purchased 40 acres on August 26, 1854. He was the great-great grandfather of Winona Bowers, who sent the Iowa Pioneer Family Farm application to the Iowa Department of Agriculture.

Apparently, George Chapin bought two 40-acre tracts at about the same time. One, which Mrs. Bowers described as the homestead, was obtained from a man named Gideon Peet. The other 40 acres was bought from Joseph Mann.

George Chapin died soon after he bought the land from Gideon Peet. His widow then took it over and kept it until selling it to Stephen Lounsberry in 1855. She then bought it back in 1859, thereby reclaiming the land first bought by her husband several years before. The property has remained in the family ever since.

James Chapin, a great uncle of Mrs. Bowers, was the next to take over the farm. Charles and Eloise Chapin were the fourth owners to come to the farm, and they built a new home in 1882. When Ralph and Winona tore that old home down to build a new house in 1993, they found numerous pieces of sheathing on which several persons had written their names.

One of those was Charles Chapin himself. The other was John Evans, the builder, who was also poetically inclined. One bit of evidence to that effect was a rather crude poem he wrote on the sheathing in which he asserted:

"Life is beautiful
Life is sweet,
and I am the one to get the
mutton and beef."

Original limestone rock walls have been kept in the basement of the new house.

Charles Chapin was Winona Bowers' great grandfather.

Nothing was noted as to Mrs. Bowers' grandfather, but her father, L. Claire Armstrong, was the last person to operate the farm until Ralph and Winona Bowers took over.

Winona Bowers' father, L. Claire Armstrong, is now 97 years old and lives with Winona and her husband in the new house built in 1993. Mr. Armstrong has lived on the farm since February 14, 1920, when he and Lora Newman were married. Winona and her sister, Mrs. James Miller of Martelle, were both born and raised in the house built in 1882 by Charles Chapin and his wife.

THE DEWITT-CAMPBELL-MILLER FARM OF BLACK HAWK COUNTY

Settled 1854

It was 142 years ago when Henry H. DeWitt was able to gain possession of 80 acres in Black Hawk County. The purchase was made on May 20, 1854. Competition for choice land had already become rather obvious by then. It is said that Mr. DeWitt had to pay $35 an acre for the land — a very high price back in 1854. Mr. DeWitt was the great-great grandfather of Ivan Miller, who is the present owner of the farm.

Although the original 80 acres was mainly a crop farm where hay, corn, wheat, and oats were being raised, there were also some wood lots, so trees were cut and sold for cash.

The cabin that became the DeWitt's home was made of a combination of logs, stone, and raw lumber hauled all the way from Dubuque. The cabin was rather crude, and as the family grew, became too small and uncomfortable. Consequently, a second and larger home was built in 1860. It must have been built well, because, today, 136 years later, it is still being used as a second home.

Henry H. DeWitt and his wife were the parents of four children, the oldest of which was a son, Henry Clay DeWitt, who acquired the farm in 1883. He was Ivan's great grandfather. The Henry C. DeWitts had a family of seven, one of whom was a daughter named Linnie Etta, who eventually became the third owner in 1913.

Both father and son volunteered for services in the Civil War.

Linnie Etta had married a man whose last name was Campbell. She was Ivan Miller's grandmother — and was the mother of three. One of the three was a daughter who married a man named Miller. However, the Miller's never bought the land, although they apparently farmed it, presumably on a rental basis.

In any case, their son, Ivan , was greatly interested in the farm, which had now doubled in acreage. Ivan bought it in 1960, after it had been in his grandmother's name for 47 years. The farm is now being operated by a tenant, although Ivan hastens to point out that all four of his children, who are the family's fifth generation, worked on the farm before they left home to pursue other interests.

During Linnie Etta Campbell's ownership, soybeans were added to the cropping program; and dairy cattle, as well as hogs and horses, were raised. However, in 1942, a John Deere "B" tractor started to displace the horses.

Chickens and guinea hens were also raised for many years. However, today there is no livestock on the farm.

Relatively speaking, the $4 a bushel corn during this Sesquicentennial year was cheap compared to the 68 cents a bushel Henry DeWitt received in 1860, when a dollar was worth a lot more than it is now.

Through the years, the family has belonged to the Brethren Church. Many other connections have been evident in more recent years, including a Community Church, the Farm Bureau, the Chamber of Commerce, Rotary and Exchange Clubs, as well as 4-H, FFA and Boy and Girl Scouts for the younger members.

THE EDMUNDSON-HAMPTON-TANCER FARM OF KEOKUK COUNTY

Settled 1854

Edmundson Farmstead, when the Hampton's were the owners.

A Keokuk County farm established in 1854 lists only three different owners and speaks of coal mining, along with livestock, corn and other grains, as income. Moreover, each of the three owners in these 142 years has a different last name.

John Edmundson was the first owner. Records show he bought 165.36 acres near the village of What Cheer for $5.00 an acre early in 1854. John and his wife became the parents of nine children. It was one of those nine, a daughter named Elma, who married a man whose last name was Hampton.

Elma gained access to the property in 1887, and owned the farm exactly seventy years.

Elma Edmundson Hampton was the mother of a daughter named Lillian, who took over the farm in 1951. Her husband is Arthur Tancer. However, the property has been in her hands ever since 1952.

Three children were born to Lillian and Arthur, representing a fourth generation involved in the farm. One of them is a daughter named Rita, who married James Dalziel, and their children are Lillian's grandchildren. Of course, those children are the fifth generation in the family.

Rita's children, like their predecessors, enjoy recalling the many hours they spent at play in the shale piles located on the farm.

Moreover, Mrs. Tancer also speaks of a sixth generation — her great grandchildren — who also enjoy going through the shale piles to search for fossils of plants and other childish treasures.

Mrs. Tancer adds, however, that the once great shale pile where those young "archeologists" of the last three generations of the family had so much fun finding fossils, is being constantly battered by the elements and, in essence, is "melting away".

James K. Dalziel, husband of Rita Tancer, Lillian's daughter, tells about the coal mining history of the Keokuk County pioneer family farm. In an interesting summary written in March of Iowa's Sesquicentennial year, Dalziel says that very early on, during John Edmundson's daughter's ownership of the property, the farm was found to have rich deposits of coal imbedded under its rich, black soil.

"According to the land abstract," writes Dalziel, "the farm had been leased to three coal mining companies." The first was the What Cheer Coal Company in 1888, followed by the Crescent Coal Mining Company in 1894, and finally by the What Cheer Fuel Company in 1904.

In addition to the leasing of the farm's coal mining rights, it was also leased to the Chicago and Northwestern Railroad Company early in this century during Lillian Edmundson Tancer's ownership. Dalziel speculates that the railway leasing was for the sole purpose of transporting the farm's many tons of coal to the line's main tracks a mile east of the farm.

James Dalziel also writes, "During the mine's heyday, there were several mining company buildings located on the farm. Today, that dwindling shale pile (impurities extracted during the mining process) is the only evidence of the once prospering business." This past winter, a local neighbor explained that he and his father used to bring their horses and wagon in and buy loads of the shale to "rock" their farm lanes and roads during the 1930's.

Now that the mining business is long gone, the farm is back in the farming business, growing corn and soybeans.

There is no livestock on the place now, but in earlier years, horses, dairy cattle, hogs, sheep, and chickens were a source of income, along with the crops and the coal. Lambs shown at the Keokuk County Fair were blue ribbon winners.

The first tractor on the farm was a Ford, followed by a Ford-Ferguson.

Quaker church members of the family have also been active in many other community projects, such as the What Cheer Opera House, Dorcas Club, What Cheer Museum, Sew-N-Sew Club, What Cheer Corn Club, and others. Art Tancer also served as an ASCS Committeeman for a number of years.

THE FARLEY-HENKES-KOETHER FARM OF CLAYTON COUNTY

Settled 1854

Another Iowa Pioneer family farm established in 1854 is a Clayton County farm that started out with close to a thousand acres, most of it in woodland. Peter Farley, an adventurous young Irishman, was the original buyer.

Peter had quite a round-about way of getting to Iowa. Born in Ireland in 1824, he came to this side of the Atlantic with his parents when only seven years old. They landed in Quebec in 1831 and lived in Canada until 1843, when they came to the United States.

The family apparently lived in New England for a time, but in 1851, Peter set sail for the Isthmus of Panama. From there, he went to California, where he worked and invested in mining and logging. Striking it big, he earned $8000 in gold dust, and apparently decided it was now time to settle down.

He then bought a good saddle horse and rode all the way to Iowa, where he bought the 1000 Clayton County acres with a good part of his $8000 in gold dust. Soon thereafter, he married Julia Phillips, who was born in New York State and then had come to Delhi, Iowa, after a stopover in Ohio. Six children were born to Peter and Julia.

The many acres were purchased from other early pioneers — John Parker, Alfred Begley, S.G. and Prudence Collins, and others. None were related to Farley or to his wife.

Because there was so much timber on the land, much of it walnut trees, the farm was originally called "Mount Walnut".

A log cabin was built as soon as the land was purchased, but it was replaced by a frame house in 1856.

Wheat was the first crop raised and was soon supplemented with corn and hay land. Oxen furnished the field power for the early years. With more than 500 acres of timber on the land, the oxen were also put to good use hauling logs as well as clearing and plowing farm land.

Livestock involved virtually from the beginning included hogs and Shorthorn cattle. Chickens were also raised.

Second members of the family to own the large farm were Peter and Julia's daughter, Agnes, and her husband, Will Henkes. They bought the land in 1898. They had five children.

Milk cows were added to the beef cattle and hogs when the Henkes took over. They also added alfalfa to the cropping program. Horses served the power in fields and for transportation many years.

A tractor was introduced to the farm in 1940.

Third to own the farm, and who remain as present owners, are Florence, one of the Henkes' daughters, and her husband, Eddie Koether. They bought the farm in 1963. Florence and Eddie have three children. One is a son, Robert, who now farms the land and handles the cattle, which are on a rotational grazing program. The size of the farm has now been reduced to about 400 acres, but there are still over 500 acres of timber.

While he owned the farm in the 1800s, Peter Farley was a director of the Clayton County Agricultural Society, which is now the Clayton County Fair. He also served as Township Trustee, and was president of the school board.

The Koethers are members of the Farm Bureau.

Mrs. Koether has served as County Women's Chairperson, and the family has been active in 4-H work.

THE FLAHERTY FARM OF LINN COUNTY

Settled 1854

When Richard Flaherty became interested in the Iowa Sesquicentennial Pioneer Family Farm contest, he didn't have to go to much trouble to look up the spelling of his ancestors' surnames. All are spelled the same as his, and there is no "in-law's" or "outlaw's" name listed to confuse the issue anywhere.

Richard's great-great grandfather was John Flaherty, who bought 80 acres in Linn County from the U.S. Government in 1854. John Flaherty had come to this country from Ireland where he was born. Before coming to Iowa, however, he had spent some time in LaSalle County, Illinois.

To begin with, he probably had to settle for a log cabin for his family on the newly settled land, but by 1865, he was able to give them the luxury of a new, larger house.

His son, Patrick, was the next to own and operate the farm, followed by Patrick's son, John II, who was Richard's grandfather. Next came James Flaherty, Richard's father, who farmed the land until Richard was able to take over. The 80 acres originally purchased has now doubled to a farm of 160 acres.

Richard has a son, James W. Flaherty, thereby making it the sixth generation on the Flaherty farm.

THE HADLEY-BRINDLE FARM OF HARDIN COUNTY

Settled 1854

An application for the Iowa Pioneer Family Farm project conducted by the Iowa Sesquicentennial committee and the Iowa Department of Agriculture and Land Stewardship was submitted by Paul and Mary Walter of Marshall County. The application notes that Jeremiah S. Hadley, the great grandfather of Mrs. Walter, purchased 80 acres of Hardin County land in 1854. He was a native of North Carolina.

According to the application, the first buyer of the land was John Cook, who got it from the government, but sold it to John Thornton, after which Mr. Hadley purchased it.

No information was given as to the purchase price, but the application shows that two years later, in 1856, Jeremiah sold it to his son, Henry M. Hadley, for $1000.

The farm was located on Honey Creek near Union, Iowa, so the Hadleys were able to set up a sawmill and saw much of the timber on the farm. They sold the finished wood to other pioneers for building homes and barns.

The Hadleys built a frame house of their own in 1868, as well as barns and other buildings.

Mary Walter's grandparents had a daughter, Effie, who married John Brindle. John and Effie have two daughters, Mrs. Darlene Williams and Mrs.

Marilyn Stover-Eiltreim. Their farm has now been incorporated and is devoted to raising corn, soybeans and alfalfa hay.

No other information was provided.

THE HAGER FARM OF ALLAMAKEE COUNTY

Settled 1854

Frederick Hager was one of northeastern Iowa's early settlers. He had come to this country from Germany in 1846. Early that year, he was requested to join the Kaiser's army, but was able to find another man to take his place. Because he was not the oldest son in the family, he saw no way of inheriting land in Germany, so he set his sights on emigrating to America.

After his arrival in this country, he reached Wisconsin, where he worked for several years. His employer gave him a choice either of wages, or of a plot of Illinois land. He chose wages because his goal was to buy some Iowa land. Had he chosen the land, he would have probably become very wealthy because the plot was located in what is now Chicago's loop district. However, Iowa would have been the loser of this outstanding pioneer.

After crossing the Mississippi, Frederick walked from Dubuque to Allamakee County, where he purchased land from the government at $1.00 an acre in 1854. Following the purchase, he returned to Illinois to earn more money which was needed to equip and improve the farm.

In 1858, he married Wilhemina Helming, and they raised a family of eleven. He also sent money to Germany so that two sisters and a brother could also settle in Iowa.

As his own family grew, the original house was replaced by a much larger brick home. Frederick was also instrumental in building a church in Zalmona, a town founded by Frederick and some of his German neighbors.

After Sunday services in Zalmona, the Hagers often treated other church goers to a Sunday dinner. They also enabled girls who came from Germany, and who were engaged to local young men, to have their weddings in the Hager mansion.

Because the stagecoach going from Marquette to Lansing stopped for water at the Hager farm, passengers frequently stayed over in a spare bedroom.

Right after the Spirit Lake Indian massacre, a runner came to the Hager's farm enroute to Waukon where he was to warn people that the Indians were coming. Frederick prepared for a possible Indian attack, but it never came. Soon thereafter, he befriended Indians living in some of his woodlands.

One of Frederick Hager's many accomplishments was aiding neighbors in getting a railroad into Waukon, thereby ending long, tedious cattle and hog drives.

Although highly respected by all his neighbors, Frederick also knew hardship and grief. To succeed meant unending hard work. He lost Wilhemina to tuberculosis when she was only 48. While working on some machinery, he lost an eye. When he died in 1909, his son, Paul, who was a teacher, bought the farm.

Paul married Flora Buedell, also a teacher, and the daughter of the Zalmona minister. They had a family of five. Paul made many building improvements, including a large dairy barn constructed in 1914. Three years later, it caught fire and burned. Fortunately, the livestock was saved and weeks later, all the neighbors came in for a big "barn raising".

Paul's wife, Flora, died from pneumonia in 1936, and their son, Nathan, rented the farm a year or two later. Nathan was the one who had taken a carload of cattle to Chicago the day the stock market crashed in 1929, and came back home with only $26 for the whole carload.

Nathan married Alta Gilbertson in 1942. They welcomed three sons and participated in many community activities. They were members of the Waukon Equity Co-op, the Farm Bureau, and on the Allamakee Community School Board, as well as an elder and deacon of the Zalmona Presbyterian church.

One of Nathan and Alta's sons, James, and his wife, the former Deborah Schultz, rented the farm from Nathan in 1976 and purchased it in 1989.

James and Deborah have two sons, and like James' father, grandfather, and great grandfather, are deeply involved in their community. He is on the Co-op, Farm Bureau, Pork Producers, Dairy and Sheep Producers and Rural Fire Department boards, and is a Township Trustee and ASCS committeeman, and 4-H leader. She is County Youth and 4-H Assistant. Both are active in the Zalmona church.

Many visitors come to family picnics on the 200 acre farm, some of them from as far away as Germany, where Frederick Hager started it all by leaving them 150 years ago.

THE HENDERSON-KERR FARM OF FAYETTE COUNTY

Settled 1854

A Fayette County 213-acre farm near Postville became the property of an adventurous Scotsman in 1854.

Thomas Henderson, who was born in Scotland earlier in the 19th Century, and who had lived in Illinois for a time before coming to Iowa, made the purchase from the U.S. Government. It is likely he did not pay much more, if any, than $1.25 an acre for what was then considered to be a large farm.

The pioneer farmer was the great grandfather of Kenneth J. Kerr, who is now the farm's owner. Kenneth is the father of C. Keith Kerr, who provided the information about the farm and family to the Iowa Department of Agriculture and Land Stewardship.

Second persons to own the land were Mr. & Mrs. George Kerr, Kenneth's grandparents, followed by Mr. & Mrs. Charles Kerr, Kenneth's parents. Kenneth is now the current owner of the 170 acres remaining in the farm.

No record of the dates of ownership were provided, nor was any other information about the farm or family members furnished.

THE KJOMME-LARSON FARM OF WINNESHIEK COUNTY

Settled 1854

A Winneshiek County farm has now been in the same family's hands for 142 years. It is the farm originated in 1854 by Nels Kjomme of Norwegian descent.

A 1996 Iowa Pioneer Family Farm application form submitted by Helen Larson of Wausau, Wisconsin, (daughter of Norris Larson who owns the farm) indicates that Nels Kjomme was the son of Neils Nelson Kjomme and his wife, Margaret, who were both raised in Norway.

Apparently, Nels and Margaret Kjomme were Helen Larson's great-great grandparents.

Date of purchase of the Winneshiek County 60 acres, which became Nels Kjomme's homestead, was August 8, 1854. It was purchased from a United States School Fund Commissioner at a cost of $1.25 an acre.

While waiting to build a cabin, the young Norwegians took shelter under a rock ledge resembling a lean-to. Shortly thereafter, a log house that included mud bricks and a sod floor became the first actual home for the young couple.

Second owner of the land was Ole Kjomme, a brother of Norris Larson's grandfather. Ole built and operated a creamery on the farm, which served the area until 1917 when a Cooperative Creamery took its place.

In 1892, Nels Larson and his wife (one of the Kjomme daughters), who were Helen Larson's grandparents, took over the farm.

Corn, oats, and hay were the major crops and dairy cows the principal livestock, but sheep and hogs were also raised, as were chickens - laughingly described as "fox food".

Nels Larson died at an early age, so his son, Norris, Helen's father, took over the farm and some additional land while still fairly young. However, he did not get to purchase the pioneer farm until 1946.

In 1906, a tornado struck the area. Fortunately, the buildings were spared, but several older members of the family spent several days in the nearby woods trying to retrieve the clothes blown off the clothesline.

Horses provided all the field power until a tractor was bought in 1948 to take over some of the field work. Electricity, however, was the Godsend that made living on the farm much more enjoyable, and the work much easier.

THE KLINGENSMITH-McCOMBS-ANGOVE FARM OF MONROE COUNTY

Settled 1854

Hazel Angove, a Stratford, Iowa, senior citizen, with a long list of volunteering contributions in her community, has been named the outstanding Stratford Community Senior Citizen, but she has also been something of a family genealogist and farm historian.

Her work in keeping tabs on family history goes way back to the Revolutionary War. One of her mother's ancestors — one John Kincaid — served as a Captain in George Washington's army in the battles for American independence.

Then, some 80 years later, another member of the family, William Thompson Kincaid, served more than three years in the Civil War. Nor were these the only expressions of the family's patriotic responses to their nation's call.

When WW I broke out, Rex Klingensmith, Hazel's oldest brother, volunteered in 1916, before the draft began, and served voluntarily in France, where his best friend was killed. Rex came back a war hero. WW II, the National Guard, and Desert Storm are also referred to by the Stratford Golden Ager.

Meanwhile, Mrs. Angove has been more than busy tracing the ownership and activities of the Klingensmith-McCombs-Angove farm near Lovilia, Iowa, where her grandparents, Joseph and Margaret Klingensmith, bought 160 acres of land from the government in 1854. The cost was the usual $1.25 an acre, and the transfer paper was signed by President Pierce.

Joseph and Margaret had eight children, the oldest of which was George, Mrs. Angove's father. George first became a telegraph operator in Chicago, but then came back to Iowa to teach country school and to farm. He married Dora May Kincaid, a descendent of the Revolutionary and Civil War veterans.

When his father died in 1894, George and Dora took over the farm and raised a family of seven. The oldest was Rex, who was one of the first to volunteer in WW I. Each one of the seven children had a specific farm or household chore to do.

Ruby, the second child, married John McCombs, and they farmed the Klingensmith farm several years.

John became a Ponca Indian missionary and a surgeon.

Max rented the home farm after Ruby and John moved elsewhere. The farm had now grown to 240 acres. Max and his wife, Edith, had two children.

Hazel's brother, Ora, the fifth of George and Dora's children, was in the Navy during WW II.

Winifred, who was Hazel's older sister, married Ralph Orr, an Albia business man.

Hazel was the seventh child in the family. It was from Max and his wife that Hazel and her husband, Eugene Angove, were able to buy the farm now in Hazel's hands. Eugene was also in the Navy in 1930-32.

Eugene and Hazel have a family of six, who make up part of the sixth generation on the farm. They are Arthur, Marilyn, Richard, James, Sharon and David. Most went to Westmar College or Iowa State University. Included in their resumes are a surgical doctor; missionary in Peru, Yucatan, and Mexico; high school teacher; civil engineer and inventor; farmer; and soy bean corporation officer. Richard served in the National Guard and a grandson was in Desert Storm.

Prior to Eugene's death, he and Hazel drew up a will where each one of the six children will receive 40 acres out of the 240 acre farm.

Hazel delights in recalling when she could go with her father to the fields where horses were at work and where corn, potatoes, oats, and hay were being grown, and the orchard with all its fruit.

She continues to be active daily in the Congregate Meal Program, the Methodist Church, the Older Iowan's Legislature, and a dozen other community senior citizen projects.

THE LEVENGOOD-LIVINGOOD-SMITH-WILSON FARM OF APPANOOSE COUNTY

Settled 1854

In attempting to summarize the beginnings, and the comings and goings of Iowa's oldest family farms, an amazing variety of activities and undertakings come to light.

One such example is a farm in Appanoose County. It's a 160 acre farm near Centerville now owned by "Bill" and "Jo" Wilson. Among the things mentioned in its resume are its 1854 purchase, a pioneer family musical unit, a huge orchard, a rug loom, a wooden water cooling tank, a left-handed walking plow, gunsmithing, a record 446 bull's eyes in a target shooting match, the K.K.K., membership in a coal mining union, a horse-powered wooden lathe, a 1924 family trip to Yellowstone Park in a Model "T" — and much more.

The farm was introduced to the family by Thomas Levengood, who bought the 160 acres in 1854 for $21.25 an acre. Mr. Levengood was Bill Wilson's great-great grandfather.

In 1855, the next owner, presumably one of Thomas' sons who evidently had changed the spelling of his last name a bit, was Peter Livingood. He was the father of six. One of those six was a daughter, Viola, who married a man named Smith. Viola was Bill Wilson's grandmother.

Mr. & Mrs. Smith had a family of five. One of them was a son named Harold. He was the fourth to own the farm. That was in 1944. However, Harold had no children, but one of his sisters married a man named Wilson, and that is how Bill Wilson entered the picture in 1976 as the fifth owner of the property. Bill was one of the Wilson's several children. He and his wife, Jo, have four children and several grandchildren, making for the sixth and seventh generations involved in the farm.

Although the usual farm crops were grown, and the usual livestock was raised over the years, the farm is probably best known for its huge orchard, said to have been started by Bill's grandfather Smith. Not only did it have many kinds of apples, plums, peaches, pears, and possibly other fruits, but large patches of strawberries and raspberries were also cultivated, as well as long rows of grapes for making wine. A cider press for the fruit was also kept very busy.

The fourth owner, Bill's Uncle Harold, was a noted gunsmith who kept rifles owned by Senator Hickenlooper, Secretary of Agriculture Linn, and others, in perfect order. Moreover, Harold's brother, Don, using a gun Harold worked on, hit a record 446 consecutive bull's eyes with it. Harold himself won the state's highest target trophy with a rifle he worked on after its owner complained, "It won't shoot".

The log cabin, smoke house, chicken house, cattle shed, gun shop, and bee house built on the farm over the years, have now all been torn down and a new home was built in 1986. Still standing, partially out of sentiment, is a milk house, horse barn, and a "two-holer" outhouse.

A few old time machines, including a horse-drawn wooden field rake, and two old plows, one of them a "left hander", still remain in the barn.

The musically inclined family of several generations ago played fiddles, a guitar, and a piano. Today, two of Bill and Jo's granddaughters still play the old Centerville Majestic Theatre's piano, and another plays a violin.

Quite a variety of memberships have been held by family members, including Odd Fellows, Rebekahs, the Christian Church, United Mine Workers Union, the Farm Bureau, and the Ku Klux Klan.

LOCKWOOD-SPURLIN-RASH FARM OF HARDIN COUNTY

Settled 1854

On February 24, 1854, 80 acres of government land in Hardin County were sold to Lyman H. Lockwood, who was the great grandfather of Mrs. Patricia Rash. Mrs. Rash submitted the Pioneer Iowa Family Farm application to the Iowa Department of Agriculture.

Mr. Lockwood was born in Franklin County, Ohio, and lived and farmed there until 1854, when he left the Buckeye State for the "greener pastures" of Iowa. After breaking the sod, he planted corn and grains and established pastures for his cattle. He also had a flock of sheep and some hogs.

Second to own the farm were Pat Rash's grandparents, Samuel and Angie Spurlin. The undivided estate apparently was shared by an uncle and aunt, Dean and Florence Spurlin.

Pat Rash's mother, Theresa, and her sister, Mary, then apparently inherited the property. They evidently sold their portion of the undivided estate to Theresa's daughter, Patricia, who married Joe Rash.

Mrs. Rash explains that her great grandfather served as a postmaster on a stage coach line for a time.

She also tells that crops grown on the farm in more recent years included soybeans and alfalfa, as well as the corn and oats grown previously. Adequate pasture ground for a herd of Angus cattle was always provided. Timber is also found on the farm.

Information about periods of ownership of the land was not furnished, and no explanation was given about children or regarding the undivided estate. Spelling of some names was also blurred on the application, but it is believed they have been reproduced fairly accurately.

THE ROCHFORD FARM OF CHICKASAW COUNTY

Settled 1854

A highly interesting and very detailed report, of which only a fraction can be included in this book, has been received about the Rochford farm in Chickasaw County in northern Iowa, and about its origin and its owners.

The story begins way back in Ireland, in one of the bleakest times the Emerald Isle has ever known. It was back in 1845 at the time of the Irish Potato Famine, when about 750,000 people died of starvation and disease. And, as though that were not enough, the Blackleg Plague among cattle further decimated the countryside at the same time.

Michael Rochford, born in 1829 in County Westmeath in Ireland, was only 16 years old when the double disaster struck. The Irish lad had been born to a poor working class family, and had to leave home at an early age to earn what little he could on a neighboring farm. Nevertheless, his love for the land and stock, and for farming, seemed to know no bounds.

The Potato Famine, along with the livestock plague, was so great, however, that the teenager was totally convinced that Ireland had no future for a person with his inclinations, so his thoughts kept turning to America.

The story is told that one day, when he was asked to take four cows to market, the 16-year old youth sold all four. He then arranged to find someone to take the proceeds of three of them to the cattle owner, and kept the money from the fourth cow for himself. That was money he considered to be in payment of the overdue wages he probably never would have gotten. Accordingly, he started his journey to America then and there.

It was a three-month long ocean voyage by sailing vessel, marked by much seasickness. Finally, in early 1846, he reached New York. There he first found work as a gardener, and then managed to get to Chicago, where he established a drayage business. However, the hope to become a farmer never ceased. While in Chicago, he married Catherine O'Connor, who also had a yearning for country living.

Thus it was that he came to Iowa in 1854 and bought 80 acres of Chickasaw County land from the government for $1.25 an acre. It was the beginning of realizing his dreams, but not right away.

First, he had to go back to Chicago to earn more money through his drayage work. After two or three more years, however, he was able to return to Iowa with his wife and the first three of their six children. The trip was made by covered wagon pulled by two horses, with a cow tied behind, and the children and a dog in the wagon with Mike and Catherine.

Their reception in Iowa was a bit scary, though. Indians, often begging for food, were camped near their farm. In spite of this, the land was broken and crops planted. Hogs were raised and then slaughtered on a cold winter day. The meat was then put on a sleigh and taken to McGregor, where it was traded for a year's supply of food, flour and whiskey.

Much more could be written about the challenges of early pioneer life, but space must be limited to the succeeding generations.

Following Michael Rochford's death, his three sons — Michael, Jr., Thomas, and William — took over the farm. Mike and Tom did not marry, but William did. He and his wife, Mary, had several children. One of them was a son named Francis. The attending doctor when Francis was born was the famous Dr. Pitts, who wrote "Oh, Come to the Church in the Wildwood."

Francis' name was changed to Frank soon after he was born. When Frank was only 15, his father was killed by a team of run-away horses. Frank then spent a number of years living and farming with his Uncle Mike. In 1946, Frank married Olive Servoss. They had four children. One died very young. Another was a son, Charles. The other two were girls. One of the girls was named Frances. The other was Jean, who is now Mrs. Dennis Hoffman and who lives on a farm near Estherville. Mrs. Hoffman provided much of the information about the Rochford family and the farm, and especially of her father.

Frank Rochford is now at the age of 90, but is blessed with an excellent memory. He says the family was never in danger of losing the farm, but it was "damn hard going" in the early 30s. He recalls corn, oats, wheat and soybean production through the years, and helping raise cattle, hogs, chickens, geese, ducks, and turkeys. The cattle included Durhams and Herefords. The hogs were Durocs and Poland Chinas.

Frank had much to do with adding 290 acres to his grandfather's original 80, and remembers helping harness as many as 20 horses during peak harvest seasons.

The first tractor was a McCormick Deering 10-20 bought in 1927. After that, two Farmalls, a John Deere, and three Case tractors were among those used. A wire-trip corn planter was a "big deal" in 1900, as was the first corn picker in 1921, electricity in 1950, and a combine in 1960.

Frank Rochford has been a Farm Bureau member 58 years, as well as a long-time member of the Lion's Club, Knights of Columbus, and the Catholic Church, where the whole family has always been very active.

The church relationship extends far back to when parishes took turns hauling priests from parish to parish to conduct Mass. Frank also helped rebuild the Pinhook Catholic Church near Fredericksburg after the original church, built by his uncles, burned.

Frank has been President of a Fire Safety District, was long a School Board Director, was a County Trustee 35 years, and on the Election Board 30 years.

The Rochford family has paid a high price in the bearing of arms for their country. Two of Frank's cousins were killed in WW II.

A fifth generation of Rochfords is now about to reach maturity, and there are no plans to give up the 370 acre farm, where a great-great-great granddaughter, Nina Rochford Shellhorn, and her husband, Dwayne, are now the renters of the land.

THE CRABAPPLE GROVE FARM OWNED BY THE OLEWEIN-SCHMIDT FAMILY OF FAYETTE COUNTY

Settled 1854

Any Iowan who may have wondered how the city of Oelwein, County Seat of Fayette County, got its name, will find the explanation is easy, though not well-known. The explanation has resurfaced in this search for Iowa's oldest family farms.

The answer takes on some international significance, and is a part of a fascinating story. It's beginning was in Germany nearly a century and a half ago and continues to this day. It's the story of how a Heartland farm community has grown from a small country settlement in the early 1850s to the bustling city of Oelwein, population 7750 or more, today.

A young couple, disillusioned with some of the things happening in their native Germany, and convinced the New World had opportunity to offer, left their home, family, and friends, and sailed for America. Their names were Frederick and Cecelia Schmidt Oelwein.

They came to Fayette County and purchased 105.24 acres of land in Jefferson Township. The land was covered with hundreds of crabapple trees. On leaving Germany, they had sold virtually all their belongings for Reichsmarks, which they had converted to gold, and were able to pay for the land the day they bought it, November 25, 1854.

A large one and a half story cabin was built as soon as possible that winter. Then they cleared a few acres the next spring, and grew potatoes and garden vegetables.

Meanwhile, Frederick's sister, Maria, had married Cecelia's brother, Frederick Schmidt. Maria and Frederick also were not happy with the way things were going in "Deutchland". Their two older daughters were already in Iowa with their uncle and aunt, the Oelweins, and were writing enthusiastic letters about life on the frontier and its "Land of Plenty".

The result was the Schmidts, after waiting for their three younger children to finish their Catechism instruction, also sold their possessions and with their three youngest, were on their way to Iowa, arriving in the fall of 1856.

The next February 14th, they bought the Oelwein homestead and started a Schmidt family farming enterprise which has endured 139 years through five generations and is still going strong.

Meanwhile, Frederick and Cecelia Oelwein purchased another 200 acres in Jefferson Township. Soon thereafter, the Burlington, Cedar Rapids, Northern Railway built its tracks through the Oelwein farm and built a station near the Oelwein family home. A small settlement soon developed, and it was called Oelwein in honor of the family that gave the land. So now you know how Oelwein got its name.

As for the Schmidt family, after buying the original Oelwein homestead called Crabapple Grove Farm in 1856, they grubbed out lots of the native trees, cleared and plowed the land, and centered on growing wheat. Other crops grown were rye, corn, vegetables, and tobacco. Swamp and timothy hay were harvested to feed horses and cattle.

In 1869, Frederick and Maria's son, Gustav and his wife, Adelheid, became the farm's owners. They had two children. In 1873, a new house was built to replace the original large cabin, but Gustav had only a few months to enjoy it when he was caught in a raging blizzard while returning from a mill with a load of ground wheat. The horses bolted and broke away, leaving Gustav to virtually freeze to death. When he died a short time later, he left a young wife and a four-year old son and two-year old daughter.

The son, Otto, grew up to work his mother's farm, clearing the land with a prairie breaker plow, plant crops, and raise a family of six. He and his wife, Ida, took over the farm in 1900. Three years later, they bought 70 adjoining acres.

One of Otto and Ida's sons, Edwin, (who served in WW II), and his wife, Ella, then bought the land in 1949. They are the parents of three, one of whom is a son, Gerald, who is the present partial owner with his wife, Nora. Their purchase was made in 1967. Acreage was increased to total 321 acres. More grain bins were built, and the house remodeled. Gerald served in the Korean War. Nora's great-great grandfather had fought in Gettysburg during the Civil War.

Gerald and Nora have two sons, both with Iowa State University Agricultural degrees. Allen has returned to ISU for a higher degree, and David with his wife, Anne, now have controlling interest in the newly formed Crabapple Grove Farm, Inc.

They have rented additional land to produce more corn and soybeans. They have built a farrow-to-finish hog confinement unit this past year. Dave and Ann have a five year old son, Tyler, who is now the eighth generation to live on the farm, and who already has aspirations to be a farmer when he grows up.

All eight generations in the Oelwein and Schmidt families have been members of the Zion Lutheran Church in Oelwein. More recent generations have been active in the Farm Bureau, ASCS, Oelwein Historical Society, REC, and County Pork Producers.

1993 Schmidt Family Picture. Back row-Son's David, Gerald, And Allan. Front row-David's wife with their son Tyler, Gerald's wife Nora, and Allan's wife Ellen.

THE STARK FARM OF LINN COUNTY

Settled 1854

Andrew Stark
and
Mary Stark

The Stark Farm of Linn County was originated by Mathias Stark in 1854. He was the great grandfather of the present owner, Theodore Stark.

The farm first came into the Stark family when the current owner's great grandfather bought a massive 1200 acres, which covered a good share of the area around Cedar Rapids. Today, only 160 acres of that original purchase are left.

Mathias and his wife had a family of six. A son, Andrew, believed to have been the oldest son, acquired the land, or at least part of it, in 1875. He and his wife raised eleven children, one of whom was Charles, who gained control in the year 1900. Charles and his wife also had a family of eleven.

One of those eleven was Herbert Stark, who owned the land for a time. However, Herbert had no children, which is how it happens that Theodore was able to buy the now much smaller farm than when the great grandfather bought the 1200 acres. Theodore and his wife have a family of five.

Wheat, corn, rye, and oats were the first crops to be grown on the farm, but soybeans have been added in a big way since the first third of the 1900s.

Horses for field work, cattle for feeding, milk cows, hogs, and chickens were raised over the years. The horses were of the Belgian breed and were the popular work stock. Shorthorns were the cattle favorites, and Poland Chinas the preferred hog breed.

An International tractor was purchased in 1935.

Stark Farmstead

Three members of the family have served in a United States uniform, one of which lost his life.

All members of the Stark family belong to the Catholic Church.

THE BROOKFIELD FARM CORPORATION OWNED BY STEVEN TUBBS OF CLINTON COUNTY

Settled 1854

One of the many Clinton County farms listed among the older of Iowa's farms in which the control has remained under the same name over 140 years is the Tubbs farm. It was started on October 26, 1854 by George Tubbs, great-great-great grandfather of Steven Tubbs, the present owner. Since its 1854 purchase, eight generations of the eastern Iowa family have lived on the pioneer farm.

The original parcel was only 40 acres in size when purchased by George Tubbs from Amos Babcock for $25.00 per acre. However, the farm, now known as Brookfield Farm Corporation, has been increased in size to where it now comprises 600 acres.

Second owner of the Tubbs land was Marvin Tubbs, Steven's great-great grandfather who gained control in 1878. Marvin outlived his only child, Edward, so that generation, which would have been a great grandfather, was lost.

The next generation, that of grandfather, who owned and operated the farm was in the person of Clifton Tubbs. He took over in 1932. Clifton's son Edward L. Tubbs, , then became the farm's owner in 1950. The next ownership went to Steven E. Tubbs, son of Edward L. Tubbs. He became the farm's owner in 1995.

Steven's ownership, however, has not ended the generational procession of the Tubbs family. Ownership by Tubbs family heads George, Marvin, Edward (who died quite young), Clifton, Edward L., and Steven makes it six generations, but there are two more "in the wings." Joel W. is the son of Steven, and Joel has a small son, William A., who was born in 1995, thus making a total of eight generations of Tubbs who have lived on the 142 year old farm.

The present home on the farm was built 106 years ago and has been remodeled several times since then.

Through the first half century, corn, oats, and hay were produced, almost always with good yields. Beef cattle and hogs were raised. The only significant change from the beginning in the cropping program has been the addition of soybeans beginning in the first third of this century.

In 1978, the farm was incorporated under the name, Brookfield Farm Corporation. This was done for the sole purpose of facilitating generational changes. Presently, Steve, who already has a son and grandson to consider, owns 100% of the farm's stock.

THE WOLD FARM OF CLAYTON COUNTY

Settled 1854

The Wold farm in Clayton County is near St. Olaf and is one in which anyone with Norwegian ancestry can relate. It was founded in 1854 by Endre Wold who, along with his wife and two little sons and a daughter, had come to the United States and purchased 204 acres near a new community with a good Norwegian name. Their sons were named Thor and Ole — about as Norwegian as it was possible to be.

There is no question that Endre and his wife faced quite a challenge when they started their farming venture in what was indeed a "New World" to them. With considerable timber on the land, a log cabin was erected in a short time. Hard work became a daily reality as the land was cleared, the soil tilled, and the crops planted, and cows, chickens, and pigs, along with oxen, raised.

Nor is there any question about Thor's and Ole's willingness to work. Don Wold, present owner of the farm, cites proof of that. Don is the great grandson of Endre and his wife, and the grandson of Mr. and Mrs. Thor Wold.

Don tells how hard Endre's sons worked, and how Thor became the owner of the homestead farm, and Ole was able to buy an adjacent farm. Then, when the steam engine era came in the late 1800s, Thor bought one of the lumbering, whistle-blowing giants and a threshing machine to go with it. After threshing the wheat and other grains on their own farms, and probably some of the neighbors', the brothers loaded the equipment on some flat cars in St. Olaf and took it to North Dakota, where they threshed wheat all fall.

Cost of the long haul by rail to the Dakotas, where many growers with Norwegian or Russian backgrounds lived, was only $25 for the simple reason that the railroads wanted the wheat threshed so they could haul the grain back to millers in the east.

Don's father, Harrison Wold, was one of nine children in the Thor Wold family and the third generation member to own the farm. Harrison bought it in 1929, about the time of the stock market crash and the historic Depression of the 1930s. It was nip and tuck to maintain the farm, what with 10 cents a bushel corn and two anguishing years of drought. Sometimes livestock shipped to Chicago did not sell for enough to pay the freight.

"In fact," opines Don, "the farm would have been lost except for the fact nobody wanted it."

Don and Berniece Wold

Shorthorn milk cows, Hampshire hogs, Leghorn chickens, wheat, barley, corn, soybeans, prairie grass, pasture, and alfalfa hay have all been raised on the farm at one time or another. The first tractor was a 1921 Samson, followed by several Farmalls. In 1950, contouring was started on the land.

Harrison, who fought in the trenches in France in WW I, and his wife had a family of five and held on to the farm until Don and his wife, Berniece, acquired it in 1961.

When they first got the farm in 1961, Don and Berniece were still in the dairy business. In addition to the twice-a-day, 365-days of the year task of milking cows, they also were raising hogs and chickens. However, the old dairy barn was about done for, so it was torn down when the milking ended, and some hog barns built in its place.

Farrowing was done four times a year, and up to 600 butchers were raised annually. When it came time for marketing, Berniece, and their daughter, Dawn, who was Clayton County Pork Queen, helped with the sorting.

The farm is now 170 acres in size and is now in the fifth year of the Conservation Reserve Program.

Looking back on a few more Wold Farm highlights, Don recalls that the great grandfather, Endre, had a lot to do with the establishing of Luther College in Decorah. His father has been a life-long active Farm Bureau member. His brother, Harrison, Jr., flew P-38 Fighter planes in WW II, while his sister, Ruth, was a member of the WAAC during that war. Don, himself, has served on the ASCS County Committee, as well as on the FHA Board and the Pork Producers.

For virtually all immigrant Norwegians, religion was given priority. Their Lutheran faith was always uppermost in their minds, so it is no surprise that the Norway Lutheran Church in their community is where the Wold's remain active.

AMANA FARMS, INC.
OF
IOWA COUNTY
Settled 1855

Iowa's largest farm is also among the oldest farms in the state. It now totals some 26,000 acres in Iowa County, and is made up of many units, the first of which was sought out and bought in 1855 and consisted of 800 acres. It marked the first step in a gigantic move to Iowa of a large religious communal organization, known as "The Community of True Inspiration". An entire book would be needed to tell the whole story of the move and what has transpired since then, but space will not permit anything more than excerpts.

As Arthur Selzer, a member of the Board of Directors of what is now the Amana Society, points out:

"It all began when Indians were still roaming the countryside, prairie grass was lush and prairie flowers were abloom, deer and other game plentiful, and a small scattering of pioneer settlers were using oxen on heavy breaker plows to unlock the riches of the soil."

Selzer and Michael Shoup, the Society's secretary, have been kind enough to supply the author of this book with a myriad of details. Unfortunately, space will allow only some highlights to be included.

The Amana Saga actually began in Germany when a rather large number of devout Christians became disillusioned with their mother country and came to America in 1840 to settle on some 5000 acres in the Buffalo, New York, area. They called their new community, "Ebenezer", based on the biblical scripture that it was a place of "Hitherto the Lord has helped us."

Bringing in a load of hay in Amana.

However, after only a few years, the nearby city began to encroach on their simple, communal life style. It was decided to send out search parties into the Midwest to find a suitable new environment.

The first group of searchers went to Kansas, but were disappointed in what they saw. They then turned back through Iowa, and when they reached Iowa County in 1854, they found what they had been seeking. Here was an area rich in timber, surrounded by thousands of acres of largely unsettled fertile land, with streams of clear, blue water running all through the area. Moreover, they also discovered there was still considerable land available from the government at $1.25 an acre, and many of the settlers already there were willing to sell improved, partially cleared land at up to $20 an acre, which represented a handsome profit to the settlers.

A summary of their findings was relayed back to "Ebenezer". The communal leaders were quick to approve the purchase of the first 800 acres. Craftsmen were immediately dispatched to the Iowa area, and the building of the first of seven villages began.

Additional land purchases were made in 1855 and in succeeding years until up to 26,000 acres had been accumulated at the peak of the Society's holdings some years later. In the meantime, the New York land was sold parcel by parcel.

The move to Iowa by the "Ebenezer" people was slow in the beginning. Only 74 persons, mostly craftsmen and farmers, were counted at the end of 1855, but then the exodus to Iowa began in earnest. Within a year, the

Going to church in Amana in the 1860's.

number of new residents had doubled, and within two years, it quadrupled, many of them wives and children of the first men to arrive.

Meanwhile, the need for farmers increased dramatically, as did the call for more carpenters, masons, sawmill operators, millers, shepherds, and countless others. A church was one of the first public places erected, followed by schools. Teachers, as well as doctors, gardeners, and others followed.

By then, the religious communal society had named its leaders, with Christian Metz continuing at the head. A name for the colony was also chosen.

The name chosen for the new colony was "Amana", which in biblical terms means "Remain Faithful". There was little question about the newcomers to Iowa remaining faithful to their religious heritage. They held fast to their traditions and their beliefs.

It was a colony of hard-working people. Four villages had already been started by the end of 1857. They were Amana, High Amana, West Amana, and South Amana. Next to be started was East Amana and Middle Amana. Then Homestead, a nearby pioneer stagecoach stop, was purchased to round out the seven villages.

As more land was purchased, more colonists poured from New York. Many new homes were erected, although none were ever painted. Shops were established. Merchants started up businesses. A woolen mill was built and continues to operate to this day. A furniture factory and woodworking shops sprang up. Harness makers soon became busy. An example of ingenuity on the part of Amana leaders was the creation of a six-mile long canal to provide water and water power for the woolen mill, saw mill, calico factory, furniture factory, and other industries.

By 1860, it was known that a railroad line would be coming west from Iowa City and go through Homestead, which had long been an important stagecoach stop. Once it looked like a certainty of getting the railroad to come through, many Iowa County residents joined in the frenzy about getting the "Iron Horse" to come through the area, contributing many thousands of dollars, including much Amana Colonies' money. In fact, Homestead bought 200 additional acres just to be sure their village would become a station stop, as it eventually did.

At that time, much hand work was still the vogue. Thirty or more plodding oxen were needed on farms, although horses would soon be taking over. At one time, as many as 300 horses were harnessed and used in the fields regularly. New steel plows replaced heavy breaking plows, and were a boon in breaking sod and preparing fields. Harrows replaced wooden drags. Eventually, mowers and reapers made scythes obsolete, and binders replaced hand cradles.

New, modern tools also came to the machine shops in the villages. In the 1860s, a New Haven machine lathe that cost $450 was purchased and revolutionized the machine shops. Power tools, engines, and belts soon followed.

Back on the farms, a new Aultman-Taylor steam engine and a threshing machine certainly beat flailing and hand separating methods, as did the clover hullers.

The first tractor was introduced amid much skepticism in 1913, but after farmers proved that it worked, Amana farming became more and more modern.

Wheat, corn, oats, rye, barley, hay, buckwheat, potatoes, and almost every other field crop was grown on the huge acreages. Carefully nurtured home gardens, and neat highly productive orchards added to the colonies' ever-growing food needs. Early on, vineyards supplied the grapes for the wineries.

In 1932, the communal system of farming in the Amanas was abandoned and replaced by a corporation known as Amana Farms, Incorporated. A farm manager was employed; and in 1933, hybrid seed corn production began. It was only five acres that first year, and it called for hand planting, hand pollinating, and hand harvesting.

By tying in, and contracting with, the Pioneer Hi-Bred Corn Company, that was the very beginning of what has proven to be an unusually successful and profitable enterprise on Amana's farms. By 1935, more than 1000 bushels of seed were delivered to the Pioneer plant in Durant, Iowa; and in more recent years, Amana has continued to have good relations with Pioneer and also Holden's Foundation Seeds, Inc.

Dairying and butter and cheese making was done for many years, both before and after incorporation. One of the cows, named Golden Homestead and recorded as #2933229, produced a record 17,139 pounds of milk and 665.3 pounds of butterfat in a single year.

Purebred Hereford beef cattle were also raised on the farm, and as many as 2500 beef cattle are still on the farm. For many years, thousands of sheep were also raised annually to supply wool for Amana's famous woolen mills.

In the beginning, when communal kitchens were in every village, large flocks of chickens provided eggs and "country fryers" for hungry workers.

Innumerable, accurate financial records have been kept all through the years on all aspects of the Amana enterprise, from the beginning to this day. In the farm section, one example is the inventory shown in 1933 listing 534 dairy cows, 401 dairy heifers, 805 sows, 1035 beef cattle, and many sheep and horses.

That same year, 80,000 bushels of corn were harvested at a value of 30 cents a bushel, along with 28,000 bushels of oats at 25 cents a bushel, as well as 1400 tons of hay at $2.50 a ton. What's more, ten barrels of sauerkraut were also sold for $10 a barrel.

Amana's tasty food, the Society's highly acclaimed hospitality, excellent tourist accommodations, and its countless attractions, as well as its fascinating history, bring an ever-increasing number of visitors annually. Every third year, the National Farm Progress Show is held in Iowa on a huge Amana exhibit field. In 1988, the World Ag Expo was staged on that same field.

Although always recognized as a pacifist society, a number of its men felt the call of the northern states strongly enough to take part in the Civil War, and later in the Spanish American conflict. And by the time of WW II, at least 150 Amana Society men and women answered the call to arms.

Many traditions still prevail and the Christian ethic remains strong throughout the one-time communal colony. There is little of the plainness and simple life of the mid-1850s, or any reminders of pioneer hardship left except in the Amana Museum. Where Indians once roamed, there are now seven flourishing villages, busy merchants, modern motels and restaurants, gas stations, and all the other conveniences of modern life, and a host of shops offering interesting goods are now to be found. And, whereas 74 persons were in a single village in 1855, there is now a population of some 1780 in the seven scattered villages amid 26,000 acres of fertile farm land.

The Good Book is still on every home's book shelves, and is still the community's guiding concept. Everything else in the Amana Society is as modern as a 1997 model auto — quite a contrast from the plodding oxen of 141 years ago.

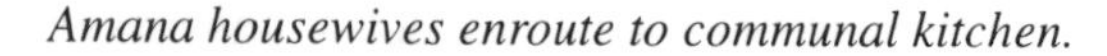

Amana housewives enroute to communal kitchen.

THE EVERGREEN FARM OWNED BY THE APPELMAN FAMILY OF FAYETTE COUNTY

Settled 1855

Douglas and Margie Appelman on their 25th Wedding Anniversary.

Information provided your author about Iowa's oldest farms and the families who own them, or live on them, varies from entire books and lengthy well-written family and farm histories to one page, badly scribbled, penciled forms. Some of the information is not very interesting or exciting, but much of it is fascinating and quite historic. The latter is certainly true of the material submitted by the Appelman family of the Evergreen Farm of Fayette County.

In a one page summary of the Appelman family, Douglas and Margie Appelman, the current owners of the 141 year old Iowa pioneer farm, are many interesting revelations of family and farm history, more than space allocation will permit. Some of them are:

Direct descendancy from John Alden, who came over on the Mayflower in 1620, and his wife, Priscilla —

A great grandfather, Gustavus Appelman, who was a sea captain many years, and who regularly sailed around the world —

A great aunt who married William Larabee, who became Iowa's Governor in 1886 —

Other family members who are owners of an early 1800s whaling vessel trunk —

The family farm was established in 1855 by their great grandparents. They were induced to come to Iowa by the daughter of the first couple to be married after the first colonists arrived at Plymouth.

It was Gustavus Appelman, the sea captain, who brought his wife, Prudence, and their six children to Iowa in 1854 from Ledyard, Connecticut, the port from which he had sailed for many years. The purpose of the journey to Iowa was to get the children away from the sea. Prudence' brother, Judge Elias Williams had settled near Garnavillo several years earlier, and is credited with inducing the Appelmans to come to Iowa. They purchased a 280 acre farm near Clermont from the government in 1855.

Bricks from the then small village of Clermont, known as "Brick City" for years, were used to build the Appelman family's first home, which was finished in 1856. Interestingly, part of the 140 year old structure is still intact and has been incorporated into the remodeled, modernized home now serving the family five and six generations later.

The first crops grown included wheat, barley, corn, and clover hay. Growing them was quite a challenge to the retired sea captain.

Dairy cows and hogs, as well as horses, were raised at the beginning.

In 1887, Elias and Mabel Appelman took over the farm. Elias was one of the six children brought to Iowa from Connecticut. He and Mabel had a family of five. Elias apparently passed away in 1929, at which time his wife became owner. Evidently, she lived into her 80s, because it was not until 1951 that a daughter, Winifred, acquired the property. Moreover, it was not until 1979 that Douglas Appelman, the great grandson of the sea captain, and his wife, Margie, gained possession.

Doug and Margie raised three daughters — Sarah, Amy, and Laura. They were the sixth generation to live on the pioneer homestead.

In the intervening years from 1855 to 1996, the farm has been increased in size from 280 to 435 acres.

During Elias and Mabel's ownership, the farm was given the name, The Evergreen Farm, an appropriate name that continues to apply.

Shorthorn cattle were bred and raised many years, along with hogs and poultry.

Their first tractor was a John Deere.

Doug and Margie recently retired from active farming, and now rent the land to Mark Nelson.

During the 1950s, Douglas served in the U.S. Air Force. Through the years, the Appelmans have belonged to the Episcopal and Lutheran churches, and have been active Farm Bureau members. They have also been involved with the Fayette County Extension Service and as 4-H leaders. Doug has also been a Township Trustee.

The Douglas and Margie Appelman Home, 1995.

THE BENSON FARM OF DALLAS COUNTY

Settled 1855

When the Benson family's application in the Iowa Pioneer Family Farm project first found its way to your author's desk, a famous Agriculturist and churchman bearing that name immediately came to mind. It was the name of Ezra Taft Benson, U.S. Secretary of Agriculture under the Eisenhower administration and later head of the Mormon Church in Salt Lake City.

Could there be any relationship? Not very likely. After all, though there are not as many Bensons as there are Smiths, it is, nevertheless, a fairly common surname.

Imagine my surprise a few moments later when I got down to noting the fourth generation of the Benson family to write about. There she was — Inez Benson Russell — a seventh cousin of the famed Ezra Taft Benson.

And not only was she a distant cousin, but when I talked to her son, Wilbur, he informed me that when the Benson clan had a family reunion in Salt Lake City in 1973, his mother, Inez, received a formal invitation to attend.

Of course, she accepted, but that wasn't the end of happy surprises. On her arrival at the world famous Mormon Temple — site of the reunion banquet — the Dallas County farm wife was ushered right up to the speaker's table where she spent an unforgettable evening hobnobbing with the Secretary and other dignitaries.

As for the Dallas County Benson's farming background, it was in 1855 when Inez Benson Russell's great grandfather, Lewis B. Benson, and his wife, Melinda, were able to homestead 80 acres near Earlham. There they raised a family of ten, one of whom was a son, Thomas. He was the next to own the land. Tom and his wife, Emma, had five children, and one of their sons, Edgar, and his wife, Daisy, were the third couple to live on the farm.

Edgar and Daisy had two daughters. One is Ethel Benson Oakes, and the other was Mrs. Inez Benson Russell, who was one of those who graced the Benson family reunion banquet table in the Mormon Temple back in 1973.

The 80 acres bought 141 years ago by Lewis and Melinda Benson, who used oxen to break the prairie, has produced well over these many years, and is now being rented out to Richard Kenworthy.

Wilbur, Inez's son, is a Korean War veteran and has served as a Township Trustee. In addition to the Dallas County homestead that his great-great grandfather established in 1855, the family had several other pioneer land patents.

THE HILLTOP FARM
Owned by the DOUGHERTY FAMILY
OF TAYLOR COUNTY
Settled 1855

On June 15, 1855, Abner Dougherty bought 160 acres of Taylor County land secured by way of a Land Patent from the U.S. Government. The farm is known as Hilltop Farm, and is now owned by Harry E. Dougherty, a great cousin of the original owner.

Wheat, corn, and oats were the first crops raised in the mid-1850s. Cattle and hogs were the first herds of livestock on the farm. Chickens were also raised.

Second to own and operate the farm was another distant cousin, Lucinda, and her husband, Melvin Dougherty. They took over after Abner Dougherty passed away.

Harry Dougherty, the present owner, recalls when corn sold as low as 10 cents a bushel in the early 1930s, and that chinch bugs ruined crops in those difficult years. While Harry was operating the farm, his son, Allen, helped with the farming. Harry raised hogs as well as both Hereford and Shorthorn cattle and took pride in his Belgian horses until he got his first tractor, a John Deere in the mid-40s. He also has used Case, Farmall and Sampson tractors.

The farm remains at 160 acres and is now rented to a father and son, Max and Jim Park. Soil conservation practices, including terracing, contouring, tiling, and establishing grassed waterways have been emphasized on the land through the years.

The Doughertys are members of the Methodist Church and Harry is also in the Rotary Club, Masonic Lodge, Shrine, Farm Bureau, and Leon Chamber of Commerce. He has also served on the Leon City Council .

Harry had a brother who was a Seabee in World War II.

THE DYSART-NICHOLS-HANSEN FARM OF TAMA COUNTY

Settled 1855

For anyone interested in the question of how the town of Dysart in Tama County got its name, the answer is simple.

Back in October, 1855, Joseph Dysart, a native of Pennsylvania, came to Iowa, bought 600 acres of land, and when a little village started to spring up in that area, it logically was named after the donor of the land. The land was some that Joseph Dysart had purchased from the U.S. Government.

Joseph Dysart was the great grandfather of the present owners of some 200 remaining acres of the original purchase. They are Patsy Hansen and Gloria Nichols, who listed their address as Kittitas, Washington, on the Pioneer Family Farm project form they sent to the Iowa Department of Agriculture in early 1996.

In submitting the application, the two great granddaughters tell that Joseph Dysart not only was a successful pioneer farmer, but that he was also highly regarded as a leader, as is evidenced by the fact he was elected Lieutenant Governor of Iowa.

When the little village that bears his name was formed, it had only a few residents. Today, Dysart is a thriving Tama County town with a population of more than 1250 persons.

THE ELLIS FARM OF DALLAS COUNTY

Settled 1855

Back in 1855, the Iowa frontier had moved well into central Iowa and was already encroaching into western counties.

One of those pioneers able to buy land from the U. S. Land Office in Dallas County was William B. Ellis who acquired 120 acres for $1.25 an acre in 1855.

Mr. Ellis had come to Iowa from Greene County, Tennessee. He and his wife, Susannah, had a family of ten children, one of whom was named William Arthur. He was the second to own the farm.

Apparently the Ellis family has genes for longevity. In any case, whereas the farm originated in 1855, Harold Ellis, William B. Ellis' grandson, did not obtain ownership until 1973, 118 years after it was first homesteaded.

Harold was one of three children born to William Arthur Ellis and his wife, Edna, who, as stated above, were the second generation to take charge.

Harold and his wife, Margaret, also had a family of three — Judith Ellis Cummings, Charles (who married Wilma), and Janet Ellis Madern. The three of them presented Margaret with eight grandchildren, and now she is proud to also speak of six great grandchildren who make up the fifth generation in the Ellis family. Some of them still live on the original farm.

The home built in 1871 is still in use, but has been remodeled numerous times.

The Ellis farm has now been enlarged to 200 acres, and is in the charge of a renter, Kurt Keeran. Today, corn and soybeans are the major crops.

THE FABER FARM OF DUBUQUE COUNTY

Settled in 1855

The name Faber rings a bell for many Iowans for a number of special reasons.

One of those reasons centers in the world of baseball. Another is in the realm of politics. A third reason, though somewhat less acknowledged, is in Iowa Pioneer farming circles.

It all started back in 1855 when Johann Faber, an Easterner who had heard about the great and endless opportunities "Out West", came to Dubuque County, Iowa, and bought 80 acres. During the next 25 years, through good farming and shrewd investing, he increased his holdings to 473 acres by 1880. Quite a testimonial for a hard working pioneer farmer and father of five. He was the great grandfather of the present owner, Harold Faber and his wife, Gladys.

The next Faber to make quite a name for himself was Mathias, one of the five children born to Johann and his wife. Best known as Matt, he acquired the farm, now quite large for that era, in 1883.

Matt Faber not only was a top farmer, but he also became deeply involved in politics as an early champion of the Farmer-Labor Party. As a matter of fact, at one time he was the party's candidate for Governor of Iowa.

Recognized both for his remarkable memory and as a strong advocate for fairer taxes for farmers, he was a popular convention speaker. He was

1995 picture of the Harold Faber family taken in the Faber remodeled home first built in 1863.

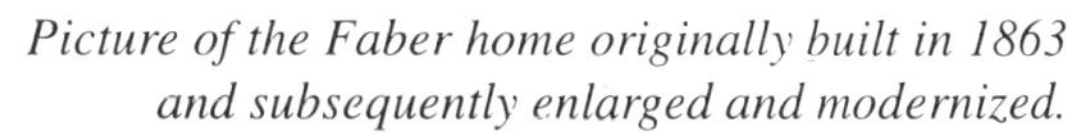

Picture of the Faber home originally built in 1863 and subsequently enlarged and modernized.

often invited by Dante Pearce of the Iowa Homestead, Henry Wallace of Wallaces Farmer, and other Iowa leaders, to address major state meetings. He was also a strong local leader, serving as the first president of the Cascade Farmers Mutual Insurance Association, once one of Iowa's strongest Mutuals.

Most famous of the Fabers, however, was Johnann's grandson, Urban "Red" Faber, one of baseball's greatest major league pitchers. "Red" won 253 games for the Chicago White Sox, including three World Series games for his team against the New York Giants in the 1917 Series, just before he went into WW I. After the war, the one time Cascade farm boy won 25 games for the Sox in 1921. He was regarded as the greatest of all "spitball" pitchers. Faber was a household name from 1914 until his retirement in 1933. He was inducted into Baseball's Hall of Fame in 1964.

As for the Faber farm, 210 acres have been owned by Harold and his wife, Gladys, since 1946, while Harold's nephews, Robert and John, own close to 200 acres of the rest. Harold and Gladys now rent their portion to their son, Al and his wife, Maureen.

Harold is a three year WW II Air Corps veteran, and one of their sons, Jim, was in the war in Vietnam.

Through the years, the farm has been highly diversified. Beginning with wheat, crops have included oats, corn, and soybeans. The livestock has included purebred Hereford beef cattle, hogs, sheep, and dairy cows, as well as poultry.

Sometimes there were as many as twenty Percheron horses furnishing the field power for the farm until a Fordson tractor was bought in the late 1920s. Since then, Farmalls were used several years, and now its John Deere 620s and 4020s.

In 1939, the R.E.C. brought in welcome electricity to the Faber farm.

THE FURLONG FARM OF MUSCATINE COUNTY

Settled in 1855

Another "Son of Erin" name, John Furlong, was added to the Irish born pioneer Iowa farmers' settlements when he bought 40 acres of Muscatine County land in 1855. The tract was purchased from John and Catherine Pursealle for $7.50 an acre.

Not surprisingly, the area where the 40 acres was located was primarily an Irish Catholic settlement.

Joe Furlong, the son of John and his wife, was the second member of the family to own the land. Joe was followed by his son, Leo J. Furlong, and then Michael Furlong, best known as "Mike", son of Leo.

Present owner of the farm, now totaling 120 acres, is Chad Furlong, Mike's son. A first cousin, Tom Furlong, now rents and farms the 120 acres.

In the fall of 1995, a barn originally built in 1903 was restored in a unique manner. A "Barn Raising" party, similar to those held in pioneer times, saw 45 neighbors and other friends come to the Furlong place and make short work of what became known as "Save A Barn Saturday".

Chad Furlong represents the fifth generation to own the Muscatine County farm, now 141 years in the same family.

THE GUFFIN-HALL-MILLER FARM OF JOHNSON COUNTY

Settled 1855

If there had been an Internal Revenue Service back in 1854 when Josiah Guffin brought his wife and six children to Iowa from Sharon, New York, he would have received quite an allowance for his expenses. Guffin and his family made the long trip to establish a pioneer farm in Iowa. They settled on a large tract in Johnson County, part of which is now farmed by Josiah's great grandson, Glenn Miller.

A journal meticulously kept by the pioneer settler, and carefully preserved by Delbert Miller, brother of Glenn, reveals all of the many expenses incurred during that long ago journey. Here are some of them.

Railway fare from New York to Rock Island, Illinois, which was then the most westerly stop on the line, $162.80. Hotel accommodations for one night for all eight in Buffalo, New York, $6. In Chicago, it was $8. Steamboat fare up the Mississippi to Muscatine, $16. In Muscatine, the hotel cost $12, and the stage coach from Muscatine to Iowa City, $17.

Soon after purchasing the farm, expenses also piled up. "Lilly", a white cow, cost $30, while a red cow was only $25. A team of horses cost $215; a yoke of oxen, $110; a cow bell, $1.25; while a butter bowl was 50 cents and a pound of candles, 15 cents. A box of matches cost a dime.

Guffin must have been pretty well "healed" to absorb all those expenses. However, they were really only incidental because the record shows he paid $27.50 an acre for land and bought 360 acres of it.

One of the Josiah Guffin family's six children was Mary Guffin, who was quite a scholarly lass. An 1856 certificate shows that she was granted a scholarship in the Normal Department of Iowa State College at Ames and reportedly received the highest grades the teaching area offered. After graduation, she taught school until after the Civil War, when she married George Hall, who had served heroically in the War Between the States.

George Hall must have been a remarkable person. Orphaned at age 11, he was compelled to support himself as a young teenager, working on farms for $3.50 a month. Later, he became an apprentice to a brick mason, then followed that trade for a time. Of English descent, his ancestors had come to America in Colonial times. A staunch Republican, he proudly cast his first ballot for Abraham Lincoln, then enlisted in the War Between the States in 1862.

As for Civil War exploits, George Hall was soon promoted to Captain of his unit and somehow survived many of the worst battles of the war, including the Battle of Gettysburg and Sherman's March To The Sea.

After the bloody war ended, he came to Iowa, working again as a brick mason and clerking in stores. Then he met and married Mary Guffin.

In 1869, George and Mary became co-owners of the Guffin farm. The young couple lived in a brick home that George had helped build from the time of their marriage until it burned in 1886. They immediately rebuilt with the help of many good neighbors. This is the home where their grandson, Glenn Miller, and his wife, Marjorie, who now own the farm, have lived for many years. Marjorie's brother was a WW II pilot in Europe.

Purebred cattle and hogs, along with corn, oats, and hay were raised on the farm through much of the Halls' ownership.

The Halls had four children, two sons and two daughters. About the time the daughters were reaching maturity, a young man named Earl Miller came to the area from Pennsylvania. Miller soon started to work for his uncle, Ezra Yoder, who ran the Sharon Center General Store and Post Office. Young Miller's job was to run the "huckster" wagon, loaded with about everything from groceries to boots, through the countryside offering wares to the farm housewives.

The wagon went a different route every day, and although there is no official document on it, the assumption is the Hall farm was on one of those routes. If so, the young man would have soon noticed the attractive Ruth Hall.

In any case, Earl married Ruth, and he soon started farming with his father-in-law. Two sons, Glenn and Delbert, were born to Earl and Ruth. Earl and Ruth gained possession of the farm in 1915.

Two of the years in the '30s weren't all that good. In 1933, they sold corn for only 10 cents a bushel. In 1934, they had a drought.

Glen married Marjorie Schwenley, the daughter of a Sharon Township farmer. Glenn and Marjorie took possession of part of the pioneer farm in 1941. They welcomed a family of four.

Beginning way back in the 1850s, the Guffin, Hall and Miller families have been civic-minded all through the years. As soon as he arrived in Johnson County, Josiah Guffin , the original owner of the farm, took a deep interest in his community. Among other things, he headed a committee that formed Sharon Township, named in honor of his Sharon, New York, birthplace.

Captain Hall was regarded as one of the prominent agriculturists of his time, and was a breeder of Shorthorn cattle and Poland China hogs.

The Earl Millers were also active in their community and church, as are the Glenn Millers, whose four daughters have all been prominent in 4-H work. None of them married farmers, but all love to come back to the home farm and bring their children, who now represent the sixth generation of the family.

The Glenn Millers remain active in their church and are members of the Farm Bureau.

THE HEMANN FARM OF MITCHELL COUNTY

Settled 1855

The Hemann farm of Mitchell County, now owned by Mr. & Mrs. Matt Hemann, came into being in 1855 when Nicholas Hemann bought 344 acres near what is now the town of Stacyville.

Nicholas was born in Prussia and came to America in 1846. Three years later, he married Mary Fruend, also a native of Prussia. They lived in Illinois six years before coming to Iowa in horse-drawn wagons.

The farm was bought from the Government Land Office, then located in Dubuque. Price was $1.25 an acre. Because Nicholas and Mary were the first settlers in the area, they had first choice of land and chose the large tract on the banks of the Little Cedar River because of the constant source of water for the family and for the livestock they planned to raise in the future.

A log cabin was built as soon as they moved onto the farm. Several years later, when lumber became available, the log cabin was replaced by a large house.

When Nicholas and Mary first settled, friendly Indian hunting parties often came along the river. When the Indians first saw the white settler's cabin, they stopped for a closer look. Mrs. Hemann quickly whipped up a large batch of pancakes, which the Indians liked so much that every time they came by, they would stop to get their fill of pancakes.

The larger house replacing the log cabin became a Godsend, because, in time, their family numbered eight daughters and a son, Mathias. Then in 1893, Nicholas and Mary sold the farm to their son.

Nicholas was considered a progressive pioneer farmer because he started right out with horses instead of using oxen to break the prairie. He then grew flax, timothy, barley, oats, and other small grains, as well as some corn, those first years.

Mathias married Gertrude Hackenmier several years before making the farm purchase. They became the parents of six daughters and four sons.

When Mathias took over, he also had modern ideas. A gasoline engine was bought in 1905, a silo was built in 1913, and the first tractor in the area, a one-cylinder Hart-Parr, was purchased in 1915. Then when Mathias bought a six-bottom plow, hitched it to the tractor, and started turning the soil six furrows at a time, many neighbors were seen shaking their heads. A mule team hauled kerosene, then at only 6 cents a gallon, to the Hemann farm.

Mathias had a penchant for all things modern. In 1916, he started to drive his new Hupmobile over the dusty country roads, and in 1918, he installed an electric plant in the farm home. He was also quite a community leader as well, serving as president of Stacyville Co-op Elevator, Stacyville Co-op Creamery, and Stacyville Savings Bank, all at the same time.

The livestock program during Mathias' ownership included Holstein dairy cattle and Hereford beef cattle, as well as hogs. Chickens and geese were also raised.

Third owner was one of Mathias' and Gertrude's sons. He was Bernard Hemann, who married Olive Halbach in 1927. They became the parents of five sons and three daughters, all of whom attended college. Half of them chose to serve the Catholic faith. Three sons became priests and one of the daughters became a nun. Bernard and his wife were active 4-H leaders and in the Co-op, County Fair, and Knights of Columbus.

Another son, Matt, became the fourth Hemann to buy the farm. Matt married Karmen Penny in 1962 and they started farming that same year. Their two children, Kurt and Lynda, are both graduates of the University of Iowa and both are married. Their children are now the sixth generation of Hemanns to have a connection with the 141-year old farm.

The farm now totals 500 acres, but in addition to that, some 900 more acres are rented. Some 140 head of cattle are fed out annually, and 1200 hogs are custom fed for a neighbor. Both their son and their son-in-law help out on the farm on weekends. Corn and soybeans now make up the cropping program.

Matt has been a licensed airplane pilot for 30 years, and has always maintained a runway on the farm. His two brothers-in-law and the brothers who are priests also use the landing strip.

The Hemann family has made a four-hour home video involving 272 segments of farm life to show city-born family members and friends what life is like on the farm. Entitled "20th Century Farming", it has been shown from coast to coast and also in Germany and Turkey overseas.

Family members all have been, and are, active in the Catholic faith, and some have served in World Wars I and II, and in Korea.

THE HILL FARM OF JASPER COUNTY

Settled 1855

In submitting an application in connection with the 1996 Iowa Sesquicentennial Commission's search for Iowa's oldest farms, Eugene Hill of Jasper County called attention to his grandfather, Hugh Hill.

Hugh Hill was another one of those early Iowa farm pioneers who was born in Ireland, where he had experienced the poverty brought on by the Irish Potato Famine and the Blackleg plague among the cattle. It was because of those twin disasters, and reports of opportunity in America, that he set forth for the U.S. in the early 1850s. After a number of stops at different points in this country on his way to Iowa, Hugh finally reached our relatively young state in early 1855.

It was May 1, 1855, when he purchased 120 acres of good Jasper County land from the U.S. Land Office in Fort Des Moines. Hugh and his wife evidently moved right onto the property and started right in to prepare for crops. However, less than a year after the purchase, Hugh Hill died, leaving the land to his widow, Jane.

Some time before 1886, Jane Hill must have sold 40 of the 120 acres to her son, Robert, because on March 5, 1886, George Hill, another of Jane's sons, bought that same 40 acres from his brother. The Warranty Deed transferring the property was dated on March 5th of that year.

George R. Hill was the father of Eugene Hill, the present owner. George acquired the inherited shares of other members of the family in 1897. The record shows it was the other 80 acres of the original purchase and was by Quit Claim Deed by the other sons and daughters of Hugh and Jane Hill, both then deceased.

At the time of his father's death in 1918, Eugene Hill inherited 40 acres of the original parcel, and then in 1946, bought the other 80 acres to account for the 120 acres originally acquired by his grandfather in 1855.

However, George Hill had also bought an additional 80 acres before his death, 60 acres of which went to Eugene by inheritance, and 20 that he had purchased, thereby making for today's 200 acre farm. This 200 acre farm has been in the Conservation Reserve Program since 1959.

THE HOLLIDAY FARM OF WAYNE COUNTY

Settled 1855

The Holliday Farm had its beginning in 1855 when Ransom Holliday purchased 160 acres of Wayne County land from the government for $2.00 an acre. The farm has been in the Holliday family's hands ever since.

The first crops raised after the prairie sod was broken were wheat and corn. Timothy hay soon followed, and then alfalfa.

As for livestock, cattle and hogs were brought in early on, and chickens were always raised for home consumption of meat and eggs.

Apparently, oxen were already starting to lose out by 1855. In any case, mules and horses were the power units on the Holliday Farm until into the 1940s when a Ford tractor was introduced.

Second family to own the farm was James Floyd Holliday and his wife.

Third owner was Gibson Holliday, widely-recognized Des Moines attorney, who was chosen to serve as a District Judge in 1967 and served on the bench for 17 years.

After Gib Holliday's death in 1991, his widow, Ruth, became the farm's fourth owner. The farm is now rented out, with Doug Kent the operator. Kent continues to raise cattle and hogs on the Wayne County farm, along with corn and soybeans and hay to help feed the cattle.

THE IVERSON-NELSON FARM OF CLAYTON COUNTY

Settled 1855

If every farm family would do what the Iverson and Nelson family members have done, it would answer a great many questions that come up from time to time in every household. Members of the family wrote a book entitled, "The Homestead and Family of Andrew Iverson". And, as Nancy Nelson says, "I'm glad we wrote the book when we did, because some of the ancestors who provided much of the essential information about the family history have now passed on."

The softback printed book opens with a prayer of gratitude, and then chronicles six generations of family history beginning in Norway where Andrew was born.

The son of the Halle family of aristocrats, Andrew fell in love with and married Ingeborg Rudy, the pretty daughter of a commoner who worked in the fields of Andrew's parents. So angered by their son's marriage were his parents that they totally disinherited him from the Halle family riches and asked him and his bride to leave the large estate at once.

The young, penniless couple did so, and Andrew found work with a family named Klobakken.

Distressed by what his parents had done to him and his wife, Andrew dropped the name Halle and changed it to Klobakken. Then, after welcoming two babies and doing five years service with the Klobakkens, Andrew and Ingeborg had saved enough to buy a sizable sailboat.

The boat was then loaded with possessions, food, and a barrel of fresh water, and, with their two children in arms, the intrepid couple set sail for America, the land of their dreams.

How they survived the thirteen weeks on the rough Atlantic Ocean and managed to reach New York is a mystery as well as a miracle.

The dangerous ocean voyage and the rail trip to McGregor, Iowa, where Andrew bought a team of horses and lumber wagon that took them to their future farm and home in Clayton County, is only the beginning of a fascinating story — a story of courage, determination, and perseverance that would be almost impossible to duplicate today.

The months after their arrival were busy times. First, Andrew changed his name from Klobakken to Iverson. Then he and his neighbors started finding land and then splitting logs and building a cabin near a fresh water spring near the Clayton-Fayette County line east of Clermont. Then came the work of clearing land, breaking sod, and putting in a few crops. The farm was 160 acres bought at a cost of $1.00 per acre from 1812 war veterans.

Space does not permit elaboration on all that has happened since then. Mrs. Nelson points out Andrew and Ingeborg's oldest daughter, Anna, married A.D. Nelson and took over the Iverson's 160 acres. Anna and A.D. had seven children, and their son, William, was the great grandfather of John Nelson, the son of Robert and Nancy, who is now the present farm operator. William and Alma had six children, as did their son, Elmer and his wife, Alice, who had bought the farm in 1940.

Robert and Nancy, in turn, acquired the land in 1967, with their family of two. Their son, John, did not get to take over until 1995, and is now half owner with his mother.

There is already a seventh generation in the family, a three year old nephew of John.

Registered and grade Holsteins on the farm won the Clayton County top production award four years in succession. Hogs, chickens, and horses were also raised, along with corn, oats, alfalfa hay, and soybeans.

Four members of the family have been in military uniform, one in the army and three in the navy.

Church activity has been paramount in the family from the time Andrew helped build a log structure in which church services were held in Norwegian back in the 1850s until now. In 1876, A.D. Nelson, Andrew and Ingeborg's son-in-law, and their daughter, Anna, helped build the East Clermont Lutheran Church.

Robert, Nancy, John and Mary Nelson

The Andrew Iverson family book, written in 1975, is crowded with the activities, anecdotes, achievements, and pictures of the Norwegian immigrant's family. It reveals that 37 members of the family, in six generations, have lived proudly and happily on the farm during the more than 140 years since Andrew first started splitting logs for a home in Iowa, the land where their dreams came true.

THE MASHEK FARM OF WINNESHIEK COUNTY

Settled 1855

Up in Winneshiek County in northeastern Iowa, the seventh generation of the Mashek family is now living on the farm purchased by a great-great grandfather, Matias Mashek, in 1855 after he emigrated to this country from Karlof, near Pisek, Bohemia, with his family. Now, for over 141 years, it has been owned and operated by Matias or one of his descendants.

Wenzel Mashek, son of Matias and his wife, inherited the land; and Wenzel, in turn, turned the property over to his son, James, a third generation member of the family.

James Mashek was born October, 1869, in a log cabin on the Mashek farm. He followed in the footsteps of his father and grandfather, tilling the soil for his living and constantly striving to improve the property. In addition to enlarging the property, James brought about many improvements to the buildings. He erected a machine shed, hog house, chicken coop, double corn crib, and built an addition to the barn.

The terms of the life lease entered into by Wenzel Mashek and his wife, Katrina, with their son and daughter-in-law were rather amusing. James and his wife, Rose, were to deliver to the older couple, on or before March 1 of each year, six loads of wood, 40 bushels of wheat, and 40 bushels of corn. All of the above corn and wheat needed to be delivered on, or before, the first of January of each year. Two tons of hay, 15 bushels of oats, 400 pounds of pork, one load of straw and $50 in cash was also part of the deal. James was also required to furnish enough posts to fence the premises of his father's property, and to do any necessary hauling.

The Mashek homestead was originally 120 acres, but James Mashek increased the acreage considerably. In 1915, he purchased the 200-acre farm adjoining his property on the west. Three years later, he further enlarged his holdings by purchasing 35 acres, and then added another 30 acres in 1935.

James and Rose's nephew, Walter, and his family then lived on the original homestead for a number of years after James retired.

It then became the home of William Mashek for a time. William married Regina Shileny and they were the parents of five children. In 1962, John, William's son, bought the property. John started out with 34 Brown Swiss cows, beef cattle, hogs, and crops. His buildings consisted of a barn, machine shed, chicken coop, granary, and corn crib. John also owns all of the original homestead land, which he purchased from Walter's estate in 1974.

In 1991, John purchased 53 additional acres and now owns a total of 469 acres.

The house that was on the original homestead land dates back at least to 1898, as it was here that James brought his bride. The house has been taken down. James and his wife retired to Calmar in 1934 and celebrated their Golden Wedding in September, 1948.

It is interesting to remember that Walter and William Mashek were twins and lived in their respective homes on the land originally purchased by their great grandfather.

John and Dorothy Mashek, who are the fifth generation, are the parents of Deb, Sue, Mary, Dennis, Dean, and Doug.

In 1981, Dennis, who is a member of the sixth generation, started farming with his parents, John and Dorothy. In September, 1984, Dennis married Barb Vrba of Fort Atkinson. Dennis and Barb have three children — Joshua, Kyla, and Tanner, the seventh generation to live on the farm.

The Mashek family has had its share of troubles and triumphs, all the way from an age of no running water, no auto, no electricity, droughts, and floods, and disastrous prices, to good returns, nice automobiles, modern tractors, satellite dishes, and computers.

Back in 1918, a tornado wiped out the original home and farmstead. Seventy years later, another tornado struck, again causing frightening losses and damages. That same year, 1988, drought also hit, causing feed shortages among 80 purebred Brown Swiss cattle. Then a few years later, up to 60 inches of rain caused devastating crop and soil losses.

Yet, despite all this, John and Dennis Mashek and their families, not only survived, but their purebred Brown Swiss cattle enabled them to prosper as they sold bulls and heifers throughout much of the U.S., as well as in some foreign countries. And where a tornado's wake was once a sorry sight, now remodeled or new buildings stand.

In January, 1989, John and his wife, Dorothy, and Dennis and his wife, Barbara, joined into a 50-50 partnership, which ended with John and Dorothy's retirement four years later.

The farm is still the property of John and Dorothy, but Dennis and Barb have purchased all the livestock, feed and machinery, and are renting the land, and realistically hope the Mashek family, which has succeeded and happily survived seven generations, will carry on into future generations to come.

THE McGINNIS FARM OF UNION COUNTY

Settled 1855

A Union County couple, Dale and Linda McGinnis, now operate a 120-acre farm that has been owned by members of the McGinnis family for 141 years. It first came into the family's hands back on May 22, 1955, when George Washington McGinnis received an Abstract of Title on 80 acres not far from what was then the small village of Creston. It was purchased directly from the U.S. Government. However, the land could not be recorded as purchased in the Record of Land Patent's office in Washington, D.C. until June 16,1856.

George Washington McGinnis, the great grandfather of Dale, was born in Pennsylvania in 1832. His parents must have been quite a patriotic family to give a son a name like that. He was 22 years old when he first set foot in Iowa in 1854 and quickly became enamored with Iowa land and its future possibilities.

In fact, after spotting the Union County tract, George wanted to buy it immediately, but first he returned to Pennsylvania to marry his sweetheart, Mary Jane Trimble. He then lost no time in talking her into coming to Iowa to establish their home on the land he had chosen, for which an Abstract of Title was obtained right after the young couple's arrival.

The present McGinnis farm operators. Dale and Linda McGinnis, center. Son, Marvin, top. Daughter Shirley Rectenbaugh, bottom.

No time was lost either in building a stone house and starting to break the prairie soil and plant crops. The marriage clearly must have been very successful. Twelve children were welcomed in the ensuing years. The farming must also have been highly successful by the McGinnis family because at one time, the original 80 acres had grown to over 1000.

For many years, horses were used on plows, discs, harrows, mowers, reapers, binders, wire-trip planters and other implements. Then, in the late 1940s, a Ford-Ferguson tractor was bought and was followed by a Ford, an International, and now a John Deere tractor.

One of the sons in the large family

was Minor McGinnis. He and his wife became the second owners of the land. They had a family of four, one of whom was a son, Fred McGinnis, who took over the property in 1950. Fred became the father of seven. One was a daughter given the unusual name of Indus Hope. She was married to a man named Slater. They had no children, so when she passed away the farm, now only 120 acres left of the one-time large holding, was placed in a life estate for Fred McGinnis' descendants.

Present ownership is shared by Dale, the current operator of the farm, and his sisters, Shirley Fleharty, Rosa Lea Weisshaar and Helen McKinney. There are a number of sixth and seventh generation members now in the family, and the hope is some of them will eventually own part of the pioneer farm.

One of Dale and Linda's children, a son named Marvin, helps with the present farming operation which includes a Simmental and Dutch Belted beef cow and calf herd, and the growing of corn, soybeans, oats, and hay.

The McGinnis's are Methodists and are active in Masonic programs.

THE McMILLAN FARM OF TAMA COUNTY

Settled 1855

A 40 acre Tama County tract of land owned by the John McKune family was sold to Gilbert McMillan in 1855. The price paid was $6.00 an acre.

Because McMillan is a familiar Scottish name, it should be no surprise to learn that the pioneer Tama County farm owner was born in Scotland. As a matter of fact, Gilbert McMillan and his wife, Sarah, whose last name had been Wilson, both came to Iowa in the early 1850s, accompanied by other members of the Wilson family.

The farm had a lot of oak and hickory timber on it when the McMillans bought it, and was called the "Four Mile Grove" because the "Four Mile Creek" ran through it. The original home burned, but was soon replaced with boards, some of them sawed from the timber on the 40 acres. Appropriately, a herd of Scotch Shorthorn cattle was the first kind of livestock raised on the McMillan farm.

Peter McMillan, one of Gilbert and Sarah's sons, was the second to own and operate the land. One of Peter's sons was the next owner. His name was Albert, and he and his wife had three daughters — Nelle Erickson, Doris Madera, and Kay Hoppe. All this while the farm kept increasing in size to where it totaled 346 acres by Sesquicentennial time.

Albert and his wife also had two grandsons, John and Gilbert Kibby, who make up the fifth generation on the farm.

THE NEIDERHISER-STASTNY FARM OF LINN COUNTY

Settled 1855

The Neiderhiser farm in Linn County was established in 1855. The original buyer was John Neiderhiser, a Pennsylvanian who wanted an Iowa homestead badly enough that he left his wife and children in Pennsylvania and made the long trek to Iowa alone.

The 80 acres cost $3.00 an acre. As soon as the purchase was completed, the task of building a home and barn was started, along with the clearing of land and planting of crops. It was a long time before the building was finished and crop production was fully on its way.

Because it was a hilly area, it was possible to build both the house and barn partway into a hillside like those the Iowa pioneer had known in Pennsylvania, thus providing greater warmth in the winter and more coolness in the summer.

After five years of getting everything ready, John went back east to get his wife and their six sons and two daughters. So diligently did the family work, they were able to buy additional nearby 40 acre tracts from time to time, and later John Neiderhiser was able to provide each son a small farm for himself when he married.

Bundles of grain being thrown into a 1923 model threshing machine at work on the Neiderhiser-Stastny Farm in the 1920's.

One of the sons, Isaiah, chose to stay on the homestead farm, paying his parents $1500 for the property in 1875. Isaiah and his wife, Jane, had three daughters and two sons.

During Isaiah's tenure, cows were milked, and instead of selling cream, butter was churned and sold in 100 pound lots weekly at up to 16 cents a pound. The proceeds paid for groceries and other household needs.

After Isaiah's death, his wife turned the farm over to their daughter, Laura, who had married Joseph Stastny in 1923. Beef cattle, hogs, and chickens were raised and cows were milked. Joseph and Laura had two children — Lloyd and Ozella, to whom they gave the 80 acres in 1948.

Lloyd and his wife, Evelyn, had two daughters, Janine and Annette. Lloyd then bought his sister Ozella's 40 acres. Lloyd passed away in 1993, only a year after he and Evelyn had retired in Ely, Iowa.

The farm is now 140 acres in size and is being farmed by a son-in-law. The barns built in the 1800s are still in place. It is interesting to note that five of the six sugar maple trees John Neiderhiser planted over 100 years ago are still producing maple syrup.

THE REINERT FARM OF DUBUQUE COUNTY

Settled 1855

Glenda and Ray Reinert, present owners of the 141-year-old farm.

Immigrants were coming to America at the rate of more than 30,000 a year when Nicholaus Reinert was one of the many German youths who no longer believed their native homeland was really "Deutchland Uber Alles"

Members of the Reinert Family and their new car.

(Germany Over All). So it was that in 1852 he fled to America with its promise of opportunity and the chance of owning land.

After disembarking at the New York harbor, he went to Chicago, then a city of only 30,000, to find work. With two years' of earnings, he bought a yoke of oxen and a covered wagon and headed west. He crossed the Mississippi at Dubuque in 1855 to settle on a 53 acre tract near the village of Sherrill. The farm was chosen because it offered wood, water, and rocks.

There, the German immigrant turned pioneer Iowa farmer, worked hard, married, and he and his wife raised eleven children. The home the children grew up in was built of stone, so the "rocks" Nicholaus was looking for came in handy right from the beginning, even though not exactly conducive to farming.

In 1891, one of the sons, Nicholaus, Jr., bought his father's farm, which had already increased to 108 acres. Nicholaus, Jr., and his wife also had a large family, numbering ten children, one of whom was a son named Joseph.

However large the earlier Reinert families had been, Joseph and his wife outdid them all with 14 children. The Joseph Reinert family bought the pioneer farm in 1925. Dairying with a top herd of milking Shorthorn and Holstein cows was the main en-

Nicholaus Reinert, Jr. at 84 in his cornfield.

terprise for years, but some beef steers and hogs were also fed and lots of chickens were raised. Purebred Poland China hogs were also bred and sold.

The first tractor was a Massey-Harris four-wheel drive type, followed by another Massey-Harris, an International, and a John Deere.

Joseph, the father of the large family, owned the farm until 1964, when Raphael, one of his several sons, bought the home place. Raphael and his wife have a family of four, and until very recently have continued dairying, feeding steers, and raising a small beef herd. The farm is now nearly 200 acres in size and the crops grown have been corn, oats, and hay.

One of Raphael's sons, Chris, and his brothers, Peter and Frank, help out on the farm in the busiest seasons.

Latest to buy the 140 year old farm are the brand new owners, Roy and Glenda Reinert, members of the fifth generation of Reinerts in Iowa.

All of the Reinerts have long been very active in the Saints Peter and Paul Catholic Church, and also in 4-H, Secretary of the Dubuque County Farm Bureau, Swiss Valley Farms, and ASCS committees, and in the Rosary Society.

THE FUESSLEY FARM OF LINN COUNTY

Settled 1855

It was in 1855 when Jacob Schafle bought 80 acres of Linn County land located near Troy Mills, some 20 miles north of Cedar Rapids. At Jacob's death in 1871, his wife, Elizabeth, became the farm's owner. However, she did not own it very many years. A man named Adam Boebel also had part ownership for a time.

In 1875, August Fuessley, a German immigrant bought the land from Elizabeth Schafle, and while it is assumed he broke some of the sod and raised some crops, it was not until 1892 that anything was done in the way of buildings.

That year, August Fuessley's brother, John Henry, who also had emigrated from Germany, bought the 80 acres. John and his wife, the former Katharine Krapf, who had also been born in Germany and who John married after they had met in Illinois, brought their family to the Linn County land.

There they erected a two-story home, a barn, and some other outbuildings. In addition, shade trees were planted, as well as a large orchard and a vineyard. A large colony of bees was also established and 80 more nearby acres were purchased.

John and Katharine's three children included sons Albert and Henry, and a daughter, Clara. Albert, the oldest son, married Anna Werner, and they lived in Troy Mills, where he was a blacksmith for a number of years. Then Albert and Anna took over the farming in 1919. A second, and smaller, house was built for John and Katharine.

While he did the farming on the 80 acres, Albert also continued his blacksmithing. John Henry passed away in 1940, but his wife, Kate, lived on until she was 95 in 1968. Meanwhile, Albert rented the farm for many years, and finally bought it in 1955. Hogs, cattle and sheep were raised. Corn, soybeans, oats, and hay was grown.

Albert and Anna had four thildren — Paul, Albert, Jr., Irene, and Marguerite. When Albert, Sr., passed away, Anna continued to live on the farm, but her son, Albert, Jr., took over the farming operations. In 1957, he and his wife, Lura Marie, bought the farm. Their family of four — Gale, Gary, Karen, and Rita — became the fifth generation of the Fuessley family to live on the farm.

Through the years, the original shade trees planted by the great grandfather have died and been replaced. The orchard has been removed and several new buildings built. However, the old house is still there with a great granddaughter, Karen Fuessley Seltrecht, and her family making it their home. Joe Dorothy now rents the land.

THE SCOTT-WAGNER-BAUMLER FARM OF FAYETTE COUNTY

Settled 1855

James and Marsha Baumler of West Union now own the 141 year old farm that was bought by William H. Scott, Sr., a great-great grandfather, in 1855.

According to the form prepared for the Iowa Department of Agriculture and Land Stewardship in conjunction with the Iowa Sesquicentennial Commission's search for Iowa's oldest farms and submitted by James and Marsha Baumler, their oldest known ancestor was born and raised in Ohio. He was also named William Scott.

The form filled out by Mr. & Mrs. Baumler shows that William Scott stayed with his mother, apparently after his father died, until other children in the family grew up and could take over. He then moved to Ohio, got married, and became the father of William H. Scott, Sr.

Next to be mentioned is William H. Scott, Jr., a maternal great grandfather, who evidently was the second to own the farm. Apparently, he had a daughter who married C.E. Wagner and they are listed as the third owners.

Next owner of the property was Clair Wagner, an uncle of the present owner, James Baumler and his wife, Marsha.

No other facts about the farm or the families were shown on the Sesquicentennial form provided for this book, except that the farm now consists of 120 acres on which beef cattle are now fed and corn and other crops are raised.

THE SEELY FARM OF KOSSUTH COUNTY

Settled 1855

There are many ways in which decisions were made to locate a pioneer family farm, but there are very few as unusual as the way Andrew Seely found the land the Seely family has farmed for 141 years.

It was 1855 and Andrew Seely was 26 years old when he wrote out a list of provisions he would need to make a northern Iowa trip with William Harvey Ingham. One of those items was a compass, and it was that instrument that directed him to the area which would become the Seely family's home in all the years ahead.

The compass led Andrew to land near the east fork of the Upper Des Moines River. There he noted some rough ground along the river that had two natural flowing springs. To him, this was assurance that there would be drinking water for the family and water for livestock both summer and winter. Moreover, there was considerable timber nearby, as well as land suitable for pasture. So it was that right then and there Andrew Seely decided to buy the land to which the compass had led him.

All through the years since 1855 when Andrew Seely bought the 80 acres from the government, the land has been owned by a member of the Seely family. First it was Andrew and his wife and their five children. Next, it was one of their sons, James. James and his wife had three children, one of whom was Claude Seely.

Claude and his wife had a family of two, one of whom was a son named Kent. Kent and his wife also had two children and one of them, Alan Seely, Andrew's great-great grandson, is the current co-owner and operator of the pioneer homestead. Alan is in partnership with his father and his grandmother, Beulah Seely. Alan and his wife also have two youngsters, making for the sixth generation of Seelys on the farm.

The first home on the farm in the mid-1850s was of logs and frame. A sheep shed also built early on is still in use.

The first crops were corn, oats, and hay.

Kent Seely, Andrew's great grandson and well-known farmer and cattleman, says much has changed during his lifetime alone. He recalls cattle selling for less than a cent a pound, hogs for $2 cwt. and corn for 8 cents a bushel. That's quite a contrast to 1996 values.

He recalls the devastating 1930 droughts, and also the happiness felt when their two-horse professional hitch won enough money at the Iowa State Fair to build a brand new corn crib.

The first generation of Seelys used Western Mustangs for field power, but later turned to Clydesdale horses, as well as to Shorthorn cattle, Hampshire hogs, and Southdown and Polled Dorset sheep. More recently, a national champion Salers bull has been introduced in the Seely cattle herd.

In 1936, the first John Deere tractor was purchased and John Deeres have prevailed ever since, some with air conditioning and stereos.

Pride in the history surrounding the farm which now totals 400 acres is evident when Kent Seely points out where his great grandfather shot the last buffalo in the area, and then turns around to show where the last Indian battle took place. And he always smiles proudly when he speaks of the compass that directed his beloved ancestor to the farm where members of four generations of the family now live.

THE SHERMAN-SHAFER FARM OF ALLAMAKEE COUNTY

Settled 1855

The great grandfather of John Shafer, who now owns and operates a 317-acre farm in Allamakee County, Iowa, was Herman Sherman. The farm includes an 80-acre tract in Jefferson Township that Mr. Sherman was able to buy by way of a Land Patent from the government in 1855.

Second to own the land was Herman Sherman's son, Herman, Junior. Herman, Jr., and his wife had a daughter named Ella, who married John Shafer's father. At first, she shared ownership of the Sherman homestead with a relative named Charles Koehring. However, in 1942, she and her husband gained full ownership. They also managed to add considerable acreage to the original eighty.

Then, in 1960, their son, John, along with his sister, Lorna, became the present co-owners. The farm is now rented to Glenn Grimstad, and it is devoted to dairying. Major crops are corn, oats, and hay. In earlier years, hogs were also raised.

John says that as a child he remembers that there were horses doing all the field work, but that a John Deere tractor was purchased in 1940. He also recalls the wire-trip corn planter's arrival.

John Shafer's father was in France in World War I, where he was wounded and received a Purple Heart Award. John, himself, was on active duty in the Korean War, serving 45 months all told. He is a member of the American Legion, VFW, Farm Bureau, and the Christian Church.

THE WALTER-McMECHAN-LISKA FARM OF GRUNDY COUNTY

Settled 1855

In the early 1850s, like many others born in Germany, George and Elizabeth Walter saw little future for themselves or their children in the land of the Kaiser. Others from their community who had left for America earlier were sending back glowing reports of opportunities in the New World. Especially was that true of those who had emigrated to Iowa.

George and Elizabeth decided they, too, wanted to start anew in the "Promised Land". So it was that they and their six children came to Grundy County on July 3, 1855, and bought 160 acres of prairie sod shortly thereafter. Cost was $6.42 an acre. That was just two years after the first white settler had come to the county.

Construction of a log cabin from some of the timber on the farm was the first order of business and was accomplished with the help of their new neighbors.

Breaking the prairie sod with oxen pulling a single share plow was no easy task. Roots of some plants were said to go down nine feet. However, the soil was also deep, and very rich.

Nor was the first winter easy. Bitter cold and severe blizzards raised a few doubts about the wisdom of the move. Wild buffalo and herds of elk also had a hard time surviving.

When spring and summer came, the first crops were planted and then harvested. However, it was rather slim pickings the first few years, so George worked as a wagon maker to make ends meet. In time, the farm production increased and the children grew up.

One of the sons, Warren Smith Walter, was the next family member to acquire the farm, and one of his sons, Warren Eldon Walter, became the third owner. Warren Eldon Walter and his brother, Paul, were one of the few pairs of brothers to serve in the Iowa Legislature at the same time.

Warren Eldon and his wife raised two daughters — Ardis Joanne Walter McMechan and Donna Elizabeth Walter Liska. Both are the great granddaughters of George and Elizabeth, the original owners. Both are now co-owners of the farm with their husbands. The acreage has increased considerably and now totals 280 acres.

In the Pioneer Family Farm application considered by the Iowa Department of Agriculture and Land Stewardship, there is no mention of dates of ownership, or the crop and livestock programs conducted by the different generations on the farm, nor about the families themselves.

THE WALTON FARM OF HARDIN COUNTY

Settled 1855

On May 16, 1855, Benjamin and Catherine Walton were able to buy 40 acres of Hardin County land from Sylvenos Kinnan for $200.

Benjamin was born in New York State, and he and Catherine had lived in Andalusia, Illinois, for a time before moving west to settle in Iowa. Land clearing began very shortly after they moved into their new home, which was built out of stone.

In addition to a lot of hard work at clearing the land, Benjamin also helped build roads and he was also a bee keeper.

Second owners were a son, George, and a daughter, Amanda. The third owner listed on the Pioneer Family Farm registration form is Gus Walton. Marie Walton, widow of Gus, is the fourth and present owner shown on the application blank.

The farm is now listed as 78-1/2 acres in size. Corn, soybeans, and hay is now being produced on the 141-year old farm.

THE WHISTLER-LAMANSKY FARM OF JEFFERSON COUNTY

Settled 1855

Eight or more generations have been involved in a Jefferson County farm located near Brighton, Iowa. It is a 120 acre farm originally purchased in 1855 by Abraham Whistler, who was the great-great grandfather of Joseph C. Lamansky, the present owner of the property.

Abraham Whistler was a native of Pennsylvania and was located in Ohio for several years before coming to Iowa. He was a Homeopathic physician by profession, but had a strong desire to own Iowa land. During his youth he earned money by driving mules that pulled boats through the Erie Canal.

Abraham was married three times. The first time it was at Mansfield, Ohio, where Anna Heim became his bride. They had nine children. She died after the birth of their ninth child while the family was still in Ohio.

The second wife was the widow of his brother Jacob. She was named Sarah and was the mother of three daughters from her previous marriage. She and Abraham then had three more children of their own. Those three, plus Sarah's three from her earlier marriage to Jacob, along with Abraham's nine, made for quite a household and for a lot of "my children", "your children", and "our children" dissension. The result was that the marriage broke up.

By now, Abraham had also established his Homeopathic practice in Brighton, Iowa, and was the owner of a Jefferson County farm. He then married another widow. She was his third wife, and her name was Catherine. They became the parents of five more children, totaling 17 in all, fathered by Abraham, not counting the three step-children .

In 1866, Abraham sold his land to a son, George Whistler, who sold it in 1869 to Peter Lamansky, great grandfather of the present owner. Peter Lamansky sold it to his son, John, in 1892. John held ownership of the farm for 42 years before selling it to his son, Roy, who farmed the property 28 years. Roy then sold it to a nephew, Harry Roy Lamansky, father of Joseph, the present owner, who acquired it in 1978.

Joseph's great-great grandmother, Harriet Whistler Buck, married a Sac and Fox Tribe Indian Chief whose given English name was John Buck. They had seven children, one of whom was named Mary, who married John Lamansky, Joseph's great grandfather. Thus, the present Lamansky farm owner can proudly claim Indian blood in his veins, as well as in those of his father, and grandfather, as will also be true of any future generations.

The Lamansky farm remains at 120 acres. Corn, soybeans, and hay are the crops now grown on the land. Hogs are the only livestock being raised.

The farm has had good years and bad. 1994 was an especially productive year. However, 1996 began with a question mark when crops that should have been planted in early May could not be put in until mid-June or later because of a month or more of rain delays.

THE FALCON FARM OF LINN COUNTY

Settled 1856

The Falcon Farm 1870's Model Farmstead.

Linn County has a surprisingly large number of farms with families that have owned the same land for from four to seven generations, and continue to own it to this day.

One such farm is owned by the Falcon family that has operated a large acreage near Springville all of the past 140 years. It was in 1856 when Anton Falcon bought 320 acres in Main Township. However, Anton only owned it for two years when he sold it to his brother, William Falcon, in 1858. Both brothers had come to America from Bavaria, Germany, in the early 1850s.

The early improvements on the farm were rather remarkable and were considered some of the finest in the area. By the 1870s they included a new spacious house and a barn 86 feet long and 40 feet wide with 20 foot high center posts and a cellar stable under the whole of it. It was one of the largest farm buildings in east central Iowa.

William Falcon married Gerdrut Leininger, also a German immigrant, in 1856. They had nine children, six boys and three girls. One of the sons was named Anton, and he became the second owner of the farm, purchasing it in 1899.

Anton married Francis Alice Carpenter, and they had a family of two — Gladys and Norman.

Norman married Esther Hurwitz in 1927, and they bought the farm in 1943. They also had two children, both sons, Gene Anton and Walter Phillip. Gene married Betty Ketelsen in 1950 and bought the Falcon farm in 1966. Gene and Betty's three children are Larry, Julie and Kathleen.

Betty, who provided the information for this book, and her husband, Gene proudly point to their five grandsons. She also tells that in 1928, Norman, her father-in-law, added still more space to the huge old 1876 barn in the form of a large cattle shed. Earlier, a garage was built in 1913 to house one of the first Buick automobiles in the county. In 1923, a beautiful new brick home was constructed.

In 1937, Norman also bought a new McCormick-Deering threshing machine and threshed grain for a full run of neighbors.

Dairy and beef cattle, along with hogs and chickens, were raised year after year.

The farm now numbers 288 acres and is rented to Ron Meythaler, who raises corn, soybeans, and hay.

The family belongs to a country Methodist Church and has been active on Co-op elevator, school, County Fair, Fire Department, and other boards, as well as in 4-H, the Lions Club, the Masons and Eastern Star. Several have also served as Township Trustees.

THE HOGAN FARM OF WEBSTER COUNTY

Settled 1856

The Webster County farm of Harold and Anna Hogan was first established in 1856 when Harold's grandfather, John Hogan, bought it on June 16 of that year. The purchase totaled 160 acres at $1.25 an acre. The seller was Michael Halpin.

John Hogan was born and raised in Ireland and made it a point to get to America as soon as he reached maturity. Once having made the Atlantic crossing, he headed directly to Iowa where land was still within his financial reach.

Right after he bought the land, he apparently spent the rest of his life living and working on the farm. He and his wife had a family including a son, also named John, but with an initial "F." representing a middle name.

John F. became the second owner. He and his wife also had a family, one of which was a son, Harold J. Hogan, who is the current owner.

No further information on the farm or the Hogan family was provided the Sesquicentennial Commission other than that some of the original 160 acres were sold and the farm now totals 79 acres.

THE JEWELL-TEETERS-HOUCK-CHRISTENSON FARM OF WEBSTER COUNTY

Settled 1856

Eight generations can already be counted as having been, or will be, involved in a Webster County farm that had its beginning in 1856 when a Licking County, Ohio, man decided Iowa offered more opportunity than the Buckeye State.

He was Samuel J. Jewell, and he obtained 400 acres near what is now Vincent, Iowa, by way of a U.S. Land Patent on October 30, 1857. This was after he had first filed a claim on April 28, 1856. Mr. Jewell was the great-great-great grandfather of Genevieve Houck Christenson, who is the present owner of 160 acres which include a part of what Samuel Jewell first claimed 140 years ago.

Samuel Jewell and his wife, the former Sarah Jones, did not own the pioneer farm very long. One of their children was a daughter, Mary, who married Frederick Teeters. Frederick and Mary were the ones who originally bought Samuel Jewell's 400 acres for $3000, which figured to exactly $7.50 per acre. Inasmuch as they apparently were the first settlers in the area, Frederick Teeter, who was Mrs. Christenson's great-great grandfather, named the township Newark Township in honor of Newark Township, Ohio, where he had grown up.

Shortly after making his Iowa land purchase, Frederick Teeters built a log cabin on the property. It must have been built well because it was not taken down until 1946.

Frederick and Mary had a family, including a daughter, Sara Jane, who was named after her Grandmother Jewell. Sara married Emery Houck, Mrs. Christenson's great grandfather. Sarah and Emery's family included a son named Calvin, who was the next to own and farm the land. Calvin and his wife became the present farm owner's grandparents. Among their children was a son, Cleo Houck, who married Alice. Cleo and Alice were the parents of Genevieve Houck, who now owns 160 acres of the 400 acres her great-great-great grandfather purchased 140 years ago. Genevieve's late husband's name was Ernest Christenson.

The land is now in a Trust for the Christenson's son, Michael. The Trust is so written that in the event of Michael's death, his two sons, Mark and Matthew, will be the eighth generation in the family to own this farm.

Meanwhile, corn and soybeans are being grown. The house built in 1939, the third home constructed on the farm, is still being used.

Of special interest to the family is the fact that Samuel Jewell and his wife, Sarah, and their daughter, Mary Teeters, are buried on the land first obtained in 1856, while Frederick Teeters, Emery and Sarah Jane Houck, Calvin and his wife, Cleo and Anna Houck, and Genevieve Christenson's late husband, Ernest, have all been laid to rest in the nearby Newark Township Cemetery.

THE JOHNSTON FARM OF DELAWARE COUNTY

Settled 1856

Apparently the letter "t" makes quite a difference when added to the name Johnson. In any case, when the added letter is included, the person with that name no longer needs to have been born in Sweden or have Swedish ancestors.

A case in point is Richard R. Johnston, who was born in Ireland. However, like so many other Irish youths, he headed for America the first chance he had. New York was his first stop, but not for long.

Getting some Midwest land was his goal, and on November 25, 1856, that dream came true. That day, Richard was able to buy 40 acres in Delaware County.

Johnston went right to work growing pioneer crops. He and his wife had a family including a son, James Alexander Johnston, who was the next to own and farm the land, and to add many acres to it.

Today the farm now comprises a total of 360 acres and is devoted to corn, soybeans, and hay. It is presently owned by a Trust known as Harland R. Johnston Trust. Harland is James Alexander's son. His wife's name is Thelma.

No further information was provided the Sesquicentennial committee either about the farm or the Johnston family.

THE MINOR-ANDERSON FARM OF LINN COUNTY

Settled 1856

Among Iowa's older farms is one in Linn County that is most unusual in one respect. It is the farm owned by Myra Minor Anderson, whose great-great grandfather bought the land in 1856.

The unusual aspect of this farm is that all the buildings built back in 1856 —with but two noticeable exceptions — are still standing and in use. They include the house, two barns, a machine shed, and another shed. It is somewhat surprising to mention an 1856 machine shed when there were so few machines on farms, but it was probably used for some other purpose before being converted to house the mechanical reapers, mowers, and other haying and harvesting equipment that became available in the later 1880s. The "noticeable exceptions", of course, are the "two holer" outhouse and the wood house.

Mrs. Anderson's great-great grandfather was Josiah Minor, who was born in Pennsylvania. He bought a few more than 140 acres on April 24, 1856, paying close to $1800, approximately $12 an acre, for the open land. Construction of the home, barns and other buildings began right away.

Actually, one of Josiah's sons, John Minor, had come to Iowa about ten years earlier, probably the year Iowa became a state. He established a 100 acre homestead for $1.25 an acre in the same area where his father bought. Undoubtedly, his reports back to Pennsylvania about Iowa productivity and opportunity had a bearing on Josiah bringing his wife and other family members to the Hawkeye State.

Another son, Sam, inherited the farm in 1914, and one of Sam's sons, Paul, who became Mrs. Anderson's grandfather, was willed the farm in 1957. Mrs. Anderson's father, Gene Minor, inherited the land in 1973, and it was willed to Myra Anderson in 1990. However, through the years, parts of the original 140 acres were sold off, or willed, to other family members.

The result of such sales and gifts is that there are now only 43 acres left of the 140 for which Josiah Minor originally paid $12 an acre. Mrs. Anderson is a member of the fifth generation to be involved in the property and her son is likely to become a sixth generation member owner.

THE NOLAN-HANLON-JENKINS FARM OF GUTHRIE COUNTY

Settled 1856

There were very few pioneer family farms settled as early as 1856 in Iowa as far west as Guthrie County, but that's when Daniel Nolan and wife, Ann, established an 80 acre farm near Guthrie Center. Daniel Nolan was the great grandfather of Bette Hanlon Jenkins, who now owns the farm with her husband, Dean.

Daniel Nolan raised horses and cattle and grew corn, wheat, and oats. This was in the period when plowing was still all done with a horse-drawn walking plow, but discs, rotary broadcast seeders, and an endless chain cutter type mowing machine had just come into general use.

Six children were born to Daniel and Ann.

In 1897, Dan Nolan hauled wheat all the way to Sioux City in wagons and would come back with lumber with which to build the frame house that is still in use. He maintained ownership of the farm until his death in 1912, when of one his daughters, Cora, who had married one of the Hanlons, bought the property.

Cora and her husband had two children, one of whom was a son, James, who became the farm's owner in 1924.

James and his wife, Olga, also had a family of two children — Jane and Bette. Tragically, their father was killed in a tractor accident in 1927 by the first tractor the family had owned.

It was at that point that James widow, Olga, had to take over. She owned the farm for 20 years, when Bette and her husband, Dean, gained possession in 1947.

In addition to corn and soybeans and other crops, they raised hogs, cattle, and chickens. Bette says the eggs produced were sold as hatching eggs.

Dean served in the U.S. Navy Air Corps in WW II. He became an organizer for the National Farmers Organization (NFO) soon after returning from war duty.

Bette's great grandfather was the largest donor to the St. Cecelia Catholic Church in Guthrie Center when it was built in 1907. All members of the family have worshipped there ever since.

The farm is now totally in the CRP Program.

THE RORABAUGH FARM OF JASPER COUNTY

Settled 1856

The Rorabaugh name is one of the more unusual names on any of the land patents, abstracts, deeds, or any other papers or documents associated with one of the smaller farms in Jasper County.

It was in 1856 when the first name to be put on any document connected with the farm was the name of Israel McQuillan Rorabaugh. He was the great-great grandfather of John O. Rorabaugh, who now is the owner of the 60 acre tract.

Succeeding Israel McQuillan Rorabaugh as farm owner was one of his grandsons, John McQuillan Rorabaugh, whose son, Fred Orland Rorabaugh, was the third to own the land and the father of the present owner, John Orland Rorabaugh and his wife.

There was nothing further provided on the pioneer family forms application in the Iowa Sesquicentennial Commission's search for the state's oldest farms, except the fact that corn and soybeans are now being grown on the Rorabaugh acreage.

THE SMITH-SEWARD-LeCLAIR-BRAIN FARM OF HAMILTON COUNTY

Settled 1856

One of the longest lists of predecessors of an Iowa owned pioneer farm is the one for the 480 acre farm currently owned by S. Everett Smith and his wife, Delores, who live in Blairsburg, Iowa. It is a farm in Hamilton County that was obtained by Harriet Levantia Campbell Smith, S. Everett's great grandmother, on February 8, 1956. It was an 80 acre tract deeded to Mrs. Smith as a homestead military grant because of her father's participation in the War of 1812.

The second owner was Douglass Smith, Everett's great uncle, whose wife was named Maratha. Next name on the list is that of a great aunt, Sarah Seward, the wife of Arthur L. Seward.

The Smith name came back in the picture when Dwight Smith, Everett's grandfather, bought the property. It next went to Frederick Smith, apparently a brother of Dwight, who apparently had a son, Seward Smith, Everett's father. However, Seward Smith evidently let the farm go to A. Dwight Smith, one of Everett's uncles.

Then a strange turn of events must have taken place. The next name on the long list was Everett's grandmother, Lulie Smith LeClair, followed by her husband, William LeClair, Everett's step-grandfather, after which Everett's own father's name, Seward Smith, shows up again, and then the name of his mother, Ida Smith. Two brothers, Dwight J. Smith and Edward G. Smith, apparently were the next owners, and then finally the name of S. Everett Smith is listed as the present owner.

No dates of ownership are shown, and the names of Everett's brother, Delbert Smith, and sisters, Lucille Smith Brain and I. Lorraine Smith, also appear, but there is no explanation why they are on the list with its total of 17 names.

At one time, when S. Everett Smith's grandmother, Lulie Smith LeClair, owned the land, she was told she could get $3 an acre "for those swamps". She refused to sell, and it most certainly is a fortunate thing for the Smith family that she did decline. Those "swamps" have all been meticulously drained since then, and are now highly productive corn and soybean growing acres each worth up to $2000 an acre or more.

The 480 acres are now in what is called the S. Everett and Delores Smith Revocable Trust.

THE WILSON-RICKOFF FARM OF CLINTON COUNTY

Settled 1856

Matthew Wilson came to Iowa from Ireland by way of Pennsylvania and must have liked what he saw in Clinton County back in 1856. He looked the county over and bought 80 acres on which to settle.

Born in Ireland, he came to the United States as a young man, just as thousands of others who had lived through the trying Potato Famine years and could see no future for themselves on the Emerald Isle. After coming to this country, he spent some time in Pennsylvania before coming to Clinton County with his family by horse and wagon.

Matthew and his wife had only three children. A log cabin had been built immediately after the land was bought, but it was replaced by a larger stone house in 1865. Two barns were also built, also largely of stone. Both of those buildings are still standing on the farmstead.

One of the three children was a son named John L. Wilson. In 1894, John became the second owner of the farm by virtue of a deed from his parents. He and his wife had five children. Considerable land was added to the property during John's tenure.

It was during the very late 1800s that the farm was named the Walnut Stock Farm and grew to 480 acres. Evidently, large numbers of cattle and hogs were fed and probably some sheep were also raised. Mechanization replaced much of the hand labor and the horses so common in earlier times during the more than 50 years of John's ownership, but he also raised and sold draft horses until the tractor age set in.

Mr. Wilson served in the Iowa Legislature for 24 years on the Democratic ticket, first as a Representative and then as a State Senator. He was also an active 32nd degree Mason.

In 1949, the farm was deeded to Charles M. Wilson, one of John's sons. Charles and his wife had only one child, a daughter Ione, who is married to a man named Rickoff. Through the years, most of the once large farm has been sold, but the 120 remaining acres were deeded to Mrs. Rickoff in 1979 and are now rented to a neighbor.

Mrs. Rickoff is a 50-year member of Eastern Star and the mother of two.

THE ZIMPFER-FAY FARM OF BUCHANAN COUNTY

Settled 1856

It was in early 1856 when Mr. and Mrs. Adam Zimpfer of Baden Baden, Germany, known as "Herr und Frau" Zimpfer over there, were getting a lot of mail from America. Each letter had interesting reports about opportunities and advantages available in what was then still regarded as the "New World".

The more Adam and Caroline read, the more they were tempted to make the move themselves, and finally they decided to bade good-bye to Germany. With their one-year old son, Adam II, they boarded a sailing vessel bound for America.

The difficult voyage took several weeks before they landed in New Orleans, then went by steamboat up the Mississippi all the way to Dubuque, Iowa. There they disembarked and the husband worked in a saloon long

Adam and Caroline Zimpfer, German immigrants and first owners of Pioneer Farm.

Raymond and Annabel Zimpfer, second owners of Pioneer Buchanan County Farm.

John and Vivian Zimpfer Faye present owners of Pioneer Farm.

enough to buy a team and wagon and then they headed west.

Adam and Caroline kept on traveling until they reached the small town of Quasqueton in Buchanan County. Then, after looking around for several months, they found 400 acres of government land not so far from Quasqueton. They then bought the tract for $1.25 an acre.

Adam and Caroline immediately had a home built with hewed wooden oak beams. Thus, they could survive the harsh winter. The next spring, the first land was broken and the first corn and oat crops were put in.

Seven more children were welcomed, so the cabin was soon getting rather crowded. It was replaced by a large house in 1872. In the interim, most of the land was cleared. Considerable hay land was added, as well as pasture land, because dairy cattle and hogs had become a successful livestock program, and horses had to be raised for field work.

The farm remained in Adam Zimpfer's name until 1920 when one of his grandsons, Raymond Zimpfer, the father of the present owner, took over.

At one time in the trying Depression years, there was danger of losing the farm because of a $300 unpaid debt, and there was much consternation. Fortunately, however, a friendly banker found an account the great grandfather had left Raymond and had been forgotten. With the interest that had accumulated, the account was large enough to pay off the mortgage.

One of Raymond Zimpfer's daughters, Vivian, is the person who submitted the Pioneer Family Farm information. She is one of the four children born on the farm to Raymond and his wife, Annabel.

Vivian married John Fay just before he was sent in military service to Japan and Korea. One of her brothers was also in WW II. Right after her young husband was sent overseas, she resumed her work as a teacher. On his return from the war, John also became a teacher. They are the parents of two sons. Now both retired, they are active in historical societies and other groups, teachers' associations, Farm Bureau and other organizations and in the Presbyterian Church.

Vivian and each of her siblings inherited 40 acres of the pioneer farm. Vivian and John and her brother, Ernest, rent their land to Wayne Webster for grain farming.

THE DINAN-LEONARD FARM OF CLAYTON COUNTY

Settled 1857

An 80 acre Clayton County farm purchased back in 1857 by Patrick Dinan has become the 280 acre farm of William J. Leonard, a great-great grandson of the pioneer land owner.

Dinan came to Iowa some time in the mid-1850s. In any case, he looked around for a while and then settled on the 80 acres he was able to buy from Michael and Margaret Hand on April 16, 1857. He paid $6.25 an acre, which was higher than most farms were selling for, but that may be because a cabin had been built on the farm in 1854.

Patrick and his wife had a family including a daughter, Mary Ellen, who married Richard Leonard. They were the next to own the farm.

Richard and Mary Ellen's children included a son, John, whose future wife's name was Catherine. John and Catherine became the parents of Stephen, who is William's father. Stephen and his wife, Kathryn, owned the farm before William took over.

No information was provided as to what years each of these five generations owned the land and for how long, nor when and how the acreage was increased to 280 acres.

The farm is now enrolled in the Conservation Reserve Program.

THE LOFTSGARD-ROOD FARM OF CLAYTON COUNTY

Settled 1857

Readers of Norwegian descent or any that were born in Norway, will find this Pioneer Family Farm's summary interesting, and probably a little confusing, or amusing. The information was provided by Craig and Jane Ann Loftsgard Lechtenberg Rood.

In submitting the application for the Sesquicentennial committe's search for Iowa's oldest farms, Jane Rood admits that some of the Norwegian names in her families' backgrounds have various spellings. For instance, Oley Tostenson Loftsgard, the great-great grandfather who emigrated from Norway and bought 40 acres of Clayton County land for $5 an acre on August 10, 1858 could have spelled "Tostenson" three or more different ways — Tostensen, Torstenson, and Torstensen. "Loftsgard" could be written with two "a" instead of just one. In fact, he could also have shortened Oley to Ole.

The great grandfather, who had actually preceeded his father to America by a year, and purchased the first land in 1857, could have used four different ways to spell his first name, "Torston", and several different ways to spell "Oleson", his second name.

Torston's son simplified things somewhat. While his first name was Theodore and second name was Torsten, he simply used the initials, "T.T.", followed by the surname, Loftsgard. As for Craig's last name, Rood could easily be Rude, Ruud, or Roode.

So much for spelling Norwegian names.

Before coming to Iowa, both the great-great grandfather and the great grandfather lived in Wisconsin a couple of years.

Land was added generation after generation to its present 225 acres. The farm is now in the Conservation Reserve Program, but Jane's husband,

Craig, is now raising hogs and calves on the farmstead.

Much effort has been put forth by Jane's ancestors in the realm of soil and water conservation. In fact, Jane's father won the District and Regional Conservation Sweepstakes awards on the farm they are now on, and where the terraces her father built are still a source of great admiration. A Century Farm sign identifies the farm that was first established 139 years ago.

Jane and her husband and four small children moved to the farm from the city less than two years ago, and they are mighty glad they did. Jane says, "Our children are so excited when we see all the wildlife that live out here. Animals that we have seen are deer, pheasants, grouse, squirrels, turkey, mink, opossum, woodchuck, raccoon, coyote, hawks, and bald eagles."

She continues her testimonial for country living by emphasizing the winter sleighing, spring beauty and mushroom hunting, finding Indian arrowheads in the summer, and harvest fun in the fall. Then she adds, "I'm blessed to be able to bring up my children on our 139 year old family farm."

THE PENNE-STEIMEL FARM OF BLACK HAWK COUNTY

Settled 1857

Earl William Steimel of Waterloo is a member of the fifth generation owners of a pioneer Iowa family farm originally purchased by his great-great grandfather, John G. Penne, back in 1857. Penne and his wife, Anna, and their six children had come to Black Hawk County the long and hard way across the Atlantic all the way from Trier, Germany.

The journey had been made twelve years earlier and had resulted in the Penne family working hard in many ways to save enough to buy 80 acres of good land from Sellick Lobdell for $5 an acre.

Other pioneers had already established themselves when the Penne family started farming. One of those couples was one of their own daughters, Catherine, who had married Calvin Eighmey and had come from Dubuque by way of an oxen drawn covered wagon to settle in Black Hawk County two years earlier.

After breaking up their prairie soil, the young couple grew some of the first wheat produced in the county, but had to take it to Cedar Rapids to have it milled.

Undoubtedly, Catherine was influential in getting her parents and siblings to settle near their own pioneer homesteads.

Occasionally, a group of Indians would come in hopes of getting food from the early pioneers. The food was always freely given. The same is true of hospitality given to weary early travelers.

The first order of business for the new family of German immigrants was to build a cabin from some of the rough lumber from nearby timberland on the farm.

Back in that era, life on a pioneer farm was anything but easy, and the weather anything but pleasant. In fact, 1858, the first year after the farm was established, proved to be one of the worst winters of Iowa's entire 150 years of statehood. For the pioneers then, the only heat was that from the wood-burning kitchen stoves.

The cold was so severe that people had to cover their heads with part of their heavy blankets to keep from freezing their noses and ears. And it was not unusual for snow to drift through the cracks of the cabin walls and pile up over the bed covers.

Somehow, the hardy settlers survived and were able to grow crops. Some even prospered. In the case of John Penne, he was able to buy an adjoining 80 acres within ten years after arriving in what, by then, was known as Eagle Township.

The first marriage in the new settlement was that of Anna Penne, one of John and Anna Penne's daughters, to Wilhelm Henry Steimel, Earl's great grandfather, in 1859. The groom had also emigrated from Germany, and had had a long difficult 65 day ocean voyage from Antwerp, Holland, to New Orleans. Then it was twelve more days by barge up the Mississippi, and several more before he became a farm hand on an Illinois farm. After two years in Illinois, he headed west to Black Hawk County where he met and married Anna. The couple became the parents of 13 children, one of whom became Earl's grandfather, William Edward Steimel.

In the meantime, Anna and her sister and brothers became interested in the Penne pioneer farm and ultimately Anna and Wilhelm were able to buy the 160 acres for themselves. Incidentally, Wilhelm became Eagle Township's first tax collector and went on to become county assessor, as well as township clerk, school secretary, and school treasurer. He and Anna were also founders of the first Catholic Church in their area. Mass was held in their home every third Sunday.

William E. Steimel married Mary Beck in 1892, right after he had bought the farm from his father. The couple raised eight children, including two sets of twin sons. One of those sons was Frank William Steimel who married Sylvia Reber and became the father of six. One of those six was Earl, the present owner of the Steimel holdings. Earl was one of four sons and had a set of twin sisters.

Incidentally, Frank points out that his parents, William and Mary Steimel, celebrated their golden wedding in 1943, with dozens of their family members present. And Earl, their grandson, points out that at one time his grandparents had six children, all under six years of age. In order to keep the house warm for those little ones and their mother, Earl's grandfather sat up all night, fully dressed, so he could put wood in the stove hourly.

Frank and Sylvia spent their entire married life on the farm, which they had purchased in 1945.

Their son, Earl, is a part of the family's fifth generation on the farm and became its owner in 1974. In 1954, he had married Miriam Driscoll and they became the parents of six, one of whom is Jerald, who is the sixth generation farmer on the remaining 125 acres of the 139 year old farm.

Military contributions made by the family have been many. Frank and one of his brothers were in WW I. One of Earl's brothers was in WW II. Earl was in the Korean War and one of their granddaughters, Carol, in now a Marine. Jerald is in the National Guard.

As for their religious bent, the Steimels have been devout Catholics throughout all these years, as far back as Germany. Today, the family is active in St. Mary's Catholic Church in the Eagle Center community.

Frank Steimel adjusting steering guide on 1920 tractor.

STOLTENBERG-BROCKMANN FARM OF SCOTT COUNTY

Settled 1857

A Scott County 100-acre plot has remained in the same family's hands for 139 years. However, it is one of the few Iowa Pioneer Family Farms where no member of the family actually farmed the land until recently.

Elmer J. Brockmann of Walcott, the present owner, writes to tell that he has in his possession the Land Grant for the property actually written on sheepskin and issued originally in 1847, just a year after Iowa became a state. Detlef Kloppenberg was the original owner.

The 100 acre parcel is located near Walcott, Iowa, and came into the Brockmann family's hands when Heindric Stoltenberg, Brockmann's great-great grandfather purchased it in 1857. The price was $45 an acre. Heindric's name was later changed to Henry.

With the names Kloppenberg, Stoltenberg, and Brockmann the only ones appearing on the official documents all these years, as well as the locality of the farm in the Walcott area, it's a safe bet that a lot of German was spoken on the farm, at least until World War I.

Stoltenberg and his wife had a family of only three, one of whom was a daughter named Louise, who married a Brockmann and became the third owner of the farm, and the second person in Brockmann's family to do so.

Louise became the mother of four children and was Elmer Brockmann's grandmother.

One of those four children was Melinda, Elmer's aunt, who never married, but became the third generation owner of the farm in the family. It was next passed on to Elmer Brockmann. It was not actually farmed by anyone in the family until 1984 when two of Elmer's sons, John and Jim, who represent the fifth generation, started farming the ground and still do.

There is no record of the type of farming done by tenants of the farm all those earlier years before the 1980s, but it is presumed it was devoted both to corn and other crop production and to livestock. John and Jim currently are doing only grain farming.

The farm now totals 140 acres, 40 more than when it was originally purchased from the government.

Although his family has actually only farmed their rich farm ground in recent years, Brockmann emphasizes it has always been a highly productive tract of land for over 149 years, and he has in his possession a land grant originally issued to Detlef Kloppenberg in 1847, the year the prairie sod was first broken.

THE OGLE FARM OF FAYETTE COUNTY

Settled in 1858

The Ogle farm in Fayette County was established on December 2nd of 1858, when Joseph Ogle of Carroll County, Ohio, bought the first 80 acres of the 202 acres now being farmed by his great grandson, Joseph Jerome Ogle, and his wife, Sharil.

A page out of a Fayette County history book points out that Joseph Ogle helped his father clear land in Ohio. He married Sarah Barnhouse there in 1844. They had nine children. After a number of years of farming in Ohio, they decided to procure land in Iowa. Presumably, they made the 34-day trip to Fayette County in horse drawn wagons. At the end of the long journey, they found a 160-acre tract with a log cabin on it and some partial clearing.

With the help of the older sons, Joseph set to work with a will; and in time, had a productive farm, a comfortable home, and herds of livestock. He was regarded to be a successful farmer. He was also active in the Methodist Church and Republican politics.

In 1889, one of the sons, Fremont Ogle, took charge. Six years later, Fremont married Mary Wilson. Of their three children, a son, John Thomas, worked closely with his father and eventually took over the farm.

Fremont Ogle was considered an outstanding stockman. He was a successful breeder of Poland China and Duroc Jersey hogs and Shorthorn cattle.

His son, John Thomas, who worked many years with his father, became the third owner of the farm. John has been followed by his son, Joseph, who is the current owner, along with his wife, of the 202 acre Fayette County pioneer farm.

THE SWOPE-KNIPFER FARM OF IOWA COUNTY

Settled in 1858

William Swope was born in West Virginia in 1818, and lived in Indiana for a time before coming to Iowa County, Iowa, to buy land in 1858. On August 11 of that year, he acquired 40 acres in Fillmore Township from one John Turner.

William and his wife raised a family of ten children and were the great-great grandparents of Ross Knipfer, the present owner of a 160-acre farm. This farm includes the 40 acres originally purchased by his great-great grandfather.

The first crops grown were corn, oats, and hay, and pasture was provided for the sheep and cattle raised during the early years.

During the Civil War, one of the sons of the family, Benjamin A., served as an Infantryman in Company B of the 8th Iowa Volunteers. He served until the end of the war between the states and was mustered out down in Selma, Alabama.

On his return from the war, Benjamin continued to farm with his father and eventually bought the farm. He and his wife, Laura McKinstry, had a family of four. Laura had been a school teacher before her marriage, so she made sure the children were well-educated.

The present home was built with native lumber and wrought iron nails during the late 1800s.

Benjamin passed away in 1926 and the farm was then placed in an estate for his widow's use. A grandson, Ernest Knipfer, rented the farm from her for many years before her death in 1954 at the age of 102. Ernest then purchased the farm from the estate later that year.

In the meantime, there were good years and bad. The drought years in the '30s were the worst. One year, Ernest was able to raise corn on only one field, and a Missouri firm was quick to buy that corn for seed purposes.

Soybeans were added to the crops being produced during Ernest's ownership, as well as a good herd of Holstein cattle. Hogs were also raised, and a good laying flock produced extra income.

The first tractor was a seldom heard of GO tractor purchased in 1933. A Fordson and a John Deere have followed the GO tractor on the 138 year old farm.

Ernest and his wife had five children and were the parents of Ross Knipfer, who now owns the farm which he purchased in 1977. Ross and his wife have a family of four. One of them is a son, David, who now does much of the active farming, which includes growing corn, soybeans and hay, and raising hogs and sheep. The farm now totals 160 acres.

THE DRAPER FARM OF TAMA COUNTY

Settled in 1859

The Draper farm in Tama County, now owned and operated by Richard E. Draper and his wife, Connie, was established by Richard's great grandfather back on September 24, 1859.

The great grandfather's name was Norman Draper, and he had come from Lysander, Illinois, to buy 80 acres of good Tama County soil. Cost was just $3.75 an acre.

Tama County, now the homeland of the Mesquakie Indian tribe, had a smattering of Indian residents back then, but they caused the new settlers like Norman Draper and his family relatively little trouble.

One of Norman Draper's sons, Elmer, was the next to own the land; and one of Elmer's sons, Fred, who is Richard's father, was the third generation to own the property before turning the land over to Richard and Connie.

The original house built in the early years of the property has been remodeled several times and is still in use.

The farm now totals 160 acres with corn and soybeans now the principal crops.

No additional details were furnished about period of ownership, family members and events, or farm management practices.

THE MUSCHAWECK FARM OF BENTON COUNTY

Settled in 1859

Wolfgang Muschaweck was born in the Kingdom of Bavaria in Germany in 1826. He was one of thousands of young Germans totally disillusioned with the Kaiser and all the little kingdoms where only those with royal blood shared in the nation's prosperity.

Determined to get away from it all, he set out for America in hopes of finding a better life in his profession as a woodworker. However, after reaching this country, he realized that in America, it was possible to acquire land even though you were not a part of the nobility.

In the late 1850s, he set his sights on Iowa and on April 28, 1859, he managed to get possession of 40 acres of Benton County land.

There are no details about his trials and triumphs, but his great grandson, Albert Roy Muschaweck, who now owns 158 acres of that rich Benton County soil, indicates that after Wolfgang's death, his widow, Walburga, continued to operate the farm until their son, Augustin Muschaweck, was ready to take over.

At Augustin's death, his wife, Ina, who was Albert's grandmother, carried on until their son, Roy Muschaweck, became the third generation owner. Roy is Albert's father and has passed ownership on to Albert, who now concentrates on growing corn and hay and raising beef cattle on the farm his great grandfather Muschaweck bought back in 1859.

THE SCHRUNIC-STRADER-HAGER FARM OF CLAYTON COUNTY

Settled in 1859

Another Clayton County farm established by an immigrant from Germany is the one now owned by Clark and Michal Strader, and Walter and Ardythe Hager. They report that their great grandfather, Charles Schrunic, who had left Germany to come to America and then to Clayton County, had bought a farm in that county on December 17, 1859.

The description of the location of the tract was given as "Southwest Quarter of Southeast Quarter and Northwest Corner of Southeast Quarter. All Section 13, Tws 91 North Range, 3 West of 5 pm."

That may not be a very easy way for a lay person to find the farm, but that's where it's supposed to be located.

A son of Charles and his wife, John Schrunic, was the next to own the land. Evidently one of the children of John and his wife must have been a daughter who married Clark Strader, Sr.

Today, the 240 acre farm, which includes the great grandfather's original 80 acres, apparently is owned jointly by Clark Strader, Jr., and Ardythe Hager, children of Clark Strader, Sr., and great grandchildren of the German immigrant who came to seek and find a better life in America — and specifically in Iowa.

THE HELMING-KRUGER FARM OF ALLAMAKEE COUNTY

Settled 1860

A German immigrant, August Helming, must have been pretty "well fixed" when he came to Iowa from the "Old Country" in 1860. Official records show he bought 240 acres of Allamakee County land for $6.25 an acre — a total of $1600. The farm was bought from Andrew Rodgers and his wife, Louise.

August Helming and his wife had a family of twelve, one of whom was a son named Albert, who bought or inherited the farm in 1921. Albert and his wife built a new home on the property. They had only one child, a daughter named Joan. Joan married Benjamin Kruger, and they are now the owners of the Helming Farm, having purchased it in 1965. Benjamin and Joan have three children.

Corn, oats, hay and pasture land were some of the first crops grown by August and also by Albert. August, who was Joan's grandfather, also had a small dairy herd and raised horses and twelve beef cows.

During the early '30s, drought struck hard all over Iowa, including the Helming farm.

As the farm progressed, purebred livestock was introduced. Featured were registered Brown Swiss cattle. Another dairy breed in the dairy operation was Holstein.

Angus beef cattle also were raised, as well as hogs, chickens, and ducks.

Soybeans were added to the cropping program when Albert was doing the farming.

The first tractor was bought in 1941. It was an International "H" model. Later, the International "M", 1086, and 450 Farmall tractors were also used.

Mrs. Kruger's grandfather and his brother, Conrad, along with several other German immigrants, organized and built the Zaloma Presbyterian Church in Allamakee County back in the late 1850s, even before land was bought in 1860. To this day, members of the Helming, Kruger and other families in the area still worship in the church, now nearly 140 years old.

THE REITH FARM OF BREMER COUNTY

Settled 1860

The Reith farm in Bremer County was established by Joseph Reith of Pennsylvania on December 14, 1860. It was a 120 acre parcel bought from Joseph Ennis and Henry Plant for $2.66 an acre. Mr. Reith was a blacksmith in Pennsylvania before he became a pioneer Iowa farmer.

Joseph Reith was the grandfather of Leo Reith, who is the third generation member of the family to own the farm. Joseph and his wife had seven children.

They grew up in a home that when it was built, lumber was hauled by horse and wagon from Independence, some 30 miles away. A barn was built at the same time. It had hewed tree beams to hold up the hay loft, and it is still in use today.

As was true of most of the 1860 era pioneer farms, the first crops grown were oats, corn, and hay. The first livestock raised was a herd of beef cattle.

Joseph's brother, Jacob, started to go on west to Kansas one year, but in trying to cross the Wapsipinicon River west of the farm, he was drowned. His body was recovered and was first buried on Joseph's land and later moved to a cemetery in Fairbank.

Second to own the land was another of Joseph's brothers, Frank, a great uncle of the present owner. Frank and his wife had only one child. Then in 1943, Leo's father, Lewis Reith, bought the farm and added acreage to it. He also became greatly interested in Farmers Hybrid hogs and a herd of Hereford beef cattle, and added soybeans to the crop rotation. Chickens were also raised.

Leo Reith, the present owner of what is now a 230 acre farm, took possession in 1967. He and his wife, Kathryn, have three children, who represent the fifth generation on the farm.

During WW II, Leo served 2-1/2 years on the highest scoring submarine, the U.S.S. Tautog. The sub sank 26 Japanese vessels. Interestingly, Leo's son, Jeff, also entered the submarine service on the nuclear-powered Francis Scott Key.

On his return from WW II service, Leo joined his father on the farm before taking control himself to raise beef cattle, corn, soybeans, and hay.

Leo is now retired and the farm is rented to a neighbor, Kevin Voy.

A member of the Farm Bureau, Leo also belongs to the Knights of Columbus, the American Legion, and Submarine Veterans of World War II Association.

THE SCHMIT FARM OF KOSSUTH COUNTY

Settled 1860

Mike Schmit
Kossuth County Pioneer

One of the few pioneer farms that still has the original log cabin, built some 136 years ago, intact, is the Schmit farm established November 17, 1860, in Kossuth County by Mike Schmit. It was an 80 acre tract located in Plum Township and purchased from the U.S. Government. Mike was the grandfather of the present owner of the farm, Michael Peter Schmit.

Mike Schmit was born in Luxembourg and came to this country as a young man. His wife's name was Barbara, and they had three children, one of them a son named Peter, who was born in the cabin, as were his two siblings, Mary and Louis.

The land was all in prairie when it was purchased, but after being broken, grew good crops of corn, oats, and hay. The livestock was mainly milking Shorthorn and Guernsey dairy cattle for many years. Hogs and chickens were also raised.

It was not until 1927 that Peter Schmit and his wife, Sarah, gained possession of the farm. Peter and Sarah had a family of six children, of which Michael Peter, the present farm owner, was the oldest. His sisters included Cecelia, Donna, and Sarah, and his two half sisters were Dorothy and Mary.

After Peter passed away in 1949, his widow, Sarah, owned the land until her death in 1951, after which it went into an estate. Then in 1956, Michael Peter was able to buy his siblings' shares, and now he and his wife are the sole owners.

Since Michael Peter's ownership, the farm has largely become a seed-producing enterprise for Pioneer seed corn and Pioneer soybean seed. Some oats and hay are also raised and so are some feeder pigs. There is still a small area of prairie kept on the farm, which once was completely covered with prairie grasses.

Of course, there have been countless changes on the farm in those more than 135 years, from all hand work in the beginning to full mechanization now. And the farm is now much larger than when it was first homesteaded.

Michael says, "One of the big changes in my lifetime came with the purchase of a 234 picker that had a husking bed that could be easily removed and a sheller unit attached. Since I raise seed corn, it is first picked and then I can use the other unit for shelled corn. The picker is mounted on the 560 tractor. I also have a John Deere combine 6600 with oat, corn, and bean heads."

As for the log cabin still on the farm, it was left untouched until 1977 when it was taken down log by log. The marked logs were then placed back in the same order except for those that needed to be replaced. The result was the finished task made it a genuine pioneer log cabin just as it was in the beginning. The present family's daughter and her friends enjoyed it for slumber parties and called it "Little House On The Prairie".

One of the Schmit ancestors was in the Civil War. The cost of World War II came home with devastating reality when Michael Peter's brother was killed at Pearl Harbor while aboard the West Virginia.

The Schmit family is active in Catholic Churches in Bode and Algona.

The original log cabin built about 1860 on the Schmit farm in Kossuth County.

THE SHIELDS FARM OF HOWARD COUNTY

Settled 1860

Four generations of Shields family members have been involved in Howard County farm land since the late 1850s.

Christopher Shields, a native of Ireland, came to America some time in the mid-1850s and to Iowa soon after his arrival in the United States. Information for this book indicates that he filed a claim on a 160 acre tract in Howard County on April 19, 1857. However, there is no record of the cost of the land, or of receiving a Land Patent, or any other official document then.

There is, however, ample evidence that Christopher's brother, John, left Ireland in the 1850s to join his brother's farming enterprise. Moreover, there is evidence he was able to buy a sizable share of Christopher's holdings some time after coming to Iowa, but that he was unable to get a Land Patent, signed by President Buchanan, until late in 1860. This may also have been true of the land on which Christopher had filed claim.

Christopher Shields was the great uncle and John Shields was the great grandfather of Eugene Shields, who now owns 40 acres of the original land.

Records show that John Shields received official title to 120 acres near Lime Springs in 1860 and went ahead with his farming venture from the start. John and his wife, Catherine, had two children — a son, James, and a daughter, Annie.

Wheat, corn, oats, and hay were raised in the early years after the land was cleared. Cattle, hogs, sheep, ducks, chickens, and geese were also raised during the first two generations of ownership.

John passed away in 1885, leaving the land he owned to his son, James, and daughter, Annie, and his widow, Catherine. When Catherine died in 1912, the farm was passed on to her children. Annie remained a spinster, so she gave her brother a quitclaim deed in 1925, making him sole owner.

James and his wife, Mary, had a family of ten. All went well with the family and the farming of the 120 acres until the Depression years of the 1920s and 1930s. That is when all but 40 acres were lost to the hard times with their low farm prices, droughts, chinch bugs, heat, and other troubles.

Although it was a difficult blow, it did not end farming for James Shields, Sr. Instead, he rented additional land and went heavier into dairying with a good herd of Holstein cows. Hogs were also fed. He was able to buy an International "H" tractor in 1945 and followed that with a John Deere "B".

James, Sr. continued farming until he and Mary sold what was left of the original farm to one of their sons, James, Jr.

James, Jr. and his wife, Vivian, made the purchase in 1951, and they carried on where James, Sr. and Mary had left off. James and Vivian became the parents of Eugene, the current owner, and of three other children. Corn, oats, hay, and soybeans were raised for a time, but for the past ten years or more, the farm has been in the Conservation Reserve Program.

Eugene was an active Future Farmer of America member while in high school. He had a hitch in military service in Vietnam in 1963 through 1964, and then was called back in 1968, when he was wounded in action over there.

Eugene and his wife, Alice, have three children and now live in Columbia, Maryland. Both Eugene and Alice are employed in Washington, DC.

When Eugene retires, he and Alice plan to come back to the farm in Howard County.

Meanwhile, Eugene's parents, James, Jr. and Vivian, still live on the farm and plan to continue to do so until Eugene and Alice return.

THE DALY-HOEFT FARM OF FLOYD COUNTY

Settled 1861

Another of the "Sons of Erin" to come to America in the 1850s was Dennis Daly. He was born in Ireland and left that country in his teens, determined to one day own land in the United States.

His first employment in this country was in Pennsylvania, where he received his naturalization papers in 1855. In the meantime, he had met a comely Irish lass, Mary Ann McCauley. Soon after he got his papers, they were married. Three children were born to them during the next five years. Dennis and Mary Ann then decided to go out "west" to Floyd County, Iowa, where they bought 40 acres.

Apparently the first order of business was to move into a log house, and the second must have been to increase the size of their family. As a result, five more children arrived, making for a somewhat crowded dwelling.

Although it was hard going those first years, they prospered and were able to buy 20 more acres in 1874 and 36 more in 1876. A new home was built in 1880.

After Dennis and Mary Ann's death, one of their sons, Charles, bought the 96 acres from his sisters and brothers for $50 an acre in 1907. He married Nellie Lonergan and they became the parents of three.

One of Charles and Nellie's children was a daughter named Margaret, who married a man named Hoeft. In 1963, Margaret became the third and present owner of the farm which had grown to 111 acres in the meantime. One of Mrs. Hoeft's three children, now Mrs. Rita Berns, has helped with the farm over the years, but most of the property is now in the CRP program, although dairy cows, hogs, and cow-calf herds were raised on it for many years. Corn, oats, barley, hay and soybeans were also grown. The dairy cows were Holsteins and the beef cattle were Angus. Chickens, ducks, and geese were also raised.

Horses were used many years until a tractor was bought in 1940. The family has had a Farmall, a John Deere, an Oliver, and a Ford tractor since then.

Mrs. Hoeft has many memories of her family and farm, some pleasant, some not. She especially recalls the death of her baby brother caused by the 1918 flu epidemic, followed by the loss of her mother six months later on the day that would have been her parent's 11th wedding anniversary.

She also remembers the large threshing rings for which the wives had to prepare meals for up to 25 hungry men.

Mrs. Hoeft and her husband started farming right after WW II. Her youngest daughter with her husband and three children now have moved into the farm home, making the fifth generation to live there.

THE NEYLAN FARM
OF
CLAYTON COUNTY
Settled 1861

Michael Neylan was born in Ireland, but came to the United States as soon as he could. Like virtually all immigrants who came to this country from Europe, he was convinced that this was "The Land of Plenty". While it may not have been quite as perfect as some had made it sound, the young Irishman never had cause to regret his decision to come all the way to Iowa.

The year Michael bought 40 acres of Clayton County farm land was 1861, just as the Civil War was getting underway. Family records suggest he and his wife plunged right in and took to Iowa farming fairly fast. However, the records were not all saved. It is known that the Neylans had three grown children at the time of Michael's passing, but it is assumed there may have been others who predeceased him.

One of Michael's children was named John, who bought the farm in

1894. John and his wife had a family of seven. One of those seven was a son named James, who became the farm's third owner in 1906. James and his wife had eight children. Their farming activities included production of dairy cattle and beef cattle, along with chickens and hogs. Eggs, corn, oats and hay production were also included.

However, hard times befell James during the Depression years of the 1920s, when he was farming. The farm had increased in size, and he was coping with the economics of low farm prices and a big mortgage. There was danger he might lose it all when two maiden sisters, Jennie and Margaret, came to the rescue by taking over the mortgage in 1931.

There was nothing easy about holding on during the next several years of drought and depression, but they managed. John W. and Kevin Neylan then entered the picture. John became a Life Tenant and Kevin is his nephew. Kevin is now the owner according to his sister, Kathleen, who provided much of the preceding information.

The farm now consists of 160 acres.

Three brothers — Clarence, Raymond and William Neylan — all served in WW II. The family has long been active in the Catholic Church.

THE TAAKE-LEETE FARM OF CLAYTON COUNTY

Settled 1861

Wilhelm Taake came to America from Germany in the early 1860s, and wound up in Clayton County amid many other German settlers, where he became the owner of a 176 acre farm on December 12, 1861. He was the great grandfather of Mary Taake Leete, who, with her husband, Karl, still own 170 acres of the original pioneer farm.

While he was in Germany, Herr Taake, as he was then known, was a respected and successful miller of grains. On his arrival in Iowa, he fully intended to pursue that trade here. Accordingly, when he was looking for a farm, he bought the 176 acres along a stream where he intended to establish a mill and continue his trade. However, before the mill could be completed, the water level in the creek fell so low that he had to abandon his plans.

The result was that instead of carrying on as a miller, he became a successful farmer. That stream he had planned to use for grinding grain has been known as Dry Mill Creek ever since.

After Wilhelm's death, one of his sons, August Taake, became owner of the farm. Among the children August and his wife raised was a son named Ervin Taake. Ervin and his wife also had a family, one of which was a daughter, Mary. Mary married Karl Leete and is now the owner of the property along with her husband.

Mary points out a granary was built on the farm in 1862, and that it was so well constructed, it is still in use today. The original home was built of logs and stone, but was replaced in 1914.

The farm is now highly diversified. Beef cattle and hogs are fed and crops like corn, oats, and hay are grown.

THE GANNON FARMS, INC. OF JASPER COUNTY

Settled 1863

Imagine an Iowa farm family, descendants of Irish immigrants in the 1860s, who had worked long and hard to accumulate 800 acres of good Iowa land in the early 1900s, only to lose it all in the depth of the Depression in 1930.

What a cruel blow that must have been — enough of a turn of events to cause most people to give up.

Now, imagine that same family staying on that same land, first as caretakers, then as paid employees, and then as beneficiaries of a refinancing plan, thanks to the founder of the Maytag Company.

Finally, imagine that family deciding to buy the 800 acres back, and getting it done within ten years' time and then starting right out to buy more land.

It's enough to boggle one's mind, but much as it may sound like a fairy tale, it's the Gospel Truth. All this did happen and was accomplished by a widely known, respected central Iowa farm family — the Gannon family of Jasper County.

However, it's only part of an interesting story.

The story begins with William Gannon of County Kilkenny, Ireland, who, like thousands of other young Irishmen who had lived through the Potato Famine, saw no future over there, and came to America in 1860.

In Chicago, he found both work and a pretty Irish lass named Mary. They were married, and within a year or two decided to come to Iowa. They first stopped in Polk County for a short time, then went to Jasper County and in 1863 bought approximately 180 acres at $12 an acre.

After establishing themselves in Iowa, the William Gannons sponsored another Irish family, the Phalens, to come and settle in Iowa.

Their first home was mostly of hewn logs set on a rock foundation. William prepared a seed bed and planted crops the first year. Associated with cattle farming while in Ireland, he soon was feeding two year old steers and marketing them here. Eight children were born to William and Mary.

In 1885, the railroad workers, while pushing their way westward to Des Moines and eventually to Omaha, Nebraska, laid tracks within a few rods of the Gannon farmstead, necessitating the building of a new house on higher ground some distance away in 1887. The barn and other buildings had to be moved as well. The 1887 home has been remodeled and modernized several times since then, and is still the farm home.

Four of William and Mary's children were sons — John, Michael, Hugh and W.J. Sometime, probably in the 1890s, the brothers formed a partnership, bought out their parents and other siblings, and started the Gannon Brothers Farm. John, the oldest, married Mary Maher. They had two children, but Mary died only a week after giving birth to their second child, a son named William Patrick.

John, like his father, was also a cattleman. He and his brothers added to the land holdings.

In 1910, John's son, William Patrick, married Ada Flynn, and soon thereafter, they took over what had been the Gannon Brothers Farm. William and Ada worked hard from the beginning and had some good years with crops and livestock. They had a family of three — John J., who is the current farm owner; Helen, a nurse; and Elizabeth, a deeply religious young lady who became Sister Elizabeth, a Catholic Nun.

The whole Gannon family from its beginning in Ireland has always been devoted to the Catholic Faith, and William Patrick was a leader in the National Catholic Rural Life movement led by the noted Monsignor Liguitti. Their place of worship here in Iowa all these years has been the Valeria Sacred Heart Catholic Church.

Many horses were needed on the ever-growing farm through the years until an Oil Pull tractor was bought in 1919. Since then, International, John Deere and Minneapolis-Moline tractors have also been used, along with about every other modern piece of farm equipment.

Things went well for the Gannons. They prospered with their cattle enterprises and bought more land until the total reached 800 acres. John, the son, was an enthusiastic 4-H member, showing Duroc hogs at the County Fair and prize purebred Angus heifers at the State Fair. Those prize heifers became the foundation stock for a purebred Angus herd that is one of his prides today, some 70 years later.

Then came the terrible crash of 1929, followed by devastatingly low farm prices, plummeting land values, the Depression, droughts, insect infestations, and other problems in the early 1930s — and the Gannons lost the 800 acres.

It was a bleak time, but William and Mary were able to keep their home and serve as caretakers of the farm and as hired employees. Then Fred Maytag, founder of the Maytag Company and a long-time friend of William's father, offered to help with refinancing. As indicated earlier, the Gannons seized the opportunity and within ten years were able to win their farm back.

William Patrick, best known as "Bill", was a devoted soil and water conservationist. Three stock ponds were built on the farm under his direction.

The son, John J., who had started the Angus herd some years earlier, worked with his father through the lean years. He also married pretty Helen Mead and they started their family, which would eventually number seven boys and seven girls, 14 children in all.

They are Sheila, Dan, Jim, Michael, Robert, Marianne, Richard, Joseph, Jean, Maureen, Chris, Elizabeth, Annie, and Eileen. Nine live in Iowa, but the other five are widely scattered from New York to Minnesota, San Francisco, San Diego, and Hawaii. In addition to homemaking and farming, they represent eleven different professions. When their parents celebrated their Golden Wedding, they were given a book in which each child told the story of his or her life. Three of the sons were in the Vietnam War at the same time.

In 1938, John entered into a partnership with his father, and he and Helen started on the road to buying the large farm from his parents and the shares of his sisters. In the meantime, the farm has been incorporated as Gannon Farms, Inc., with each of the 14 children included among the stockholders, along with their parents.

One of those children, their 13th, a daughter, Annie, married an energetic young man, Dan Wassom, and they now farm with John and Helen and live in a home nearby. They have a boy and a girl, two of the John Gannons' 23 grandchildren.

More land has been acquired to where the farm now totals 1076 acres. Corn, oats, soybeans and alfalfa hay are now the major crops. The purebred Angus herd started with those two prize 4-H heifers, now number 170 cows and their calves. Duroc hogs are also fed out. Foundation hybrid seed corn for the Black's Seed Company of Ames has been grown for several years.

THE HARL FARM OF APPANOOSE COUNTY

Settled 1863

The Harl family of Appanoose County is now best known because of a fourth generation member, Dr. Neil Harl, distinguished professor of Agricultural Economics at Iowa State University, but the Harls are also known for their long-time interest in southern Iowa farms.

The fact is: Dr. Harl's great grandfather, John T. Harl, bought 80 acres in Appanoose County for $4.90 an acre back in 1863. Later on, he bought additional land adjacent to the original eighty. That additional land proved to be a king-size headache for the family for a long time, but today it is safely back in the Harl family again.

The original 80 acres, like most other southern Iowa farms of the 1860 era, produced corn, hay, and pasture. Cattle and hogs were also raised. The first crops on the Harl farm were grown at the height of the Civil War, a period when a great uncle, Washington Bales, fought and died of wounds during the struggle between the states.

Second to own the Harl land was Elza Ernest Harl, one of John Harl's sons, and Dr. Harl's grandfather. He was one of the twelve children raised by the great grandparents. E.E. (Dick) Harl gained possession of the property in

Aerial View of the Harl farm.

the year 1900. He and his wife had a family of six. Apparently, he was very successful the first dozen years of his farming. In any case, in 1913, he purchased an additional 160 acres, but that proved to be a monumental mistake. Land prices plummeted soon after the close of WW I. The family came very close to losing all. In fact, had it not been for the six children pooling the dimes and dollars they had earned teaching and working, the mortgage payments could not have been met.

One of those children was H.P. Harl, Dr. Harl's father. He had learned such bitter lessons through the land crash, Joint Stock Land Bank mortgages, and bank failures in the Depression years, that he made, and kept, a resolve that he would never borrow a cent. That it was a good decision for him is seen in his ability to make a cash purchase of the home farm in 1950 and additional land thereafter. At his death in 1977, he owned 200 acres totally debt free.

As for that additional land the great grandfather had purchased in 1890 and mortgaged to Mutual Benefit Life Insurance, it was lost because John Harl had guaranteed a note for another family member. That 80 acres became the property of a well-to-do neighbor September 29, 1892. Interestingly, exactly 100 years after it was lost by John Harl, Dr. Neil Harl and his wife were able to reclaim it for their branch of the Harl family.

The 80 acre tract bought back in 1992 is a part of the 640 acres Harl and his wife, Darlene, now own. Part of the home farm land was purchased from a brother, Richard, and a sister, Marjorie Sutter. Another sister, Merna Donald, still owns a small part of the home farm.

Dr. Harl says that 1994 was the best year the farm has ever had in its133 years of existence, and the worst year was 1995 when not one hill of corn could be planted because of continuous rainfall.

Marjorie Sutter's husband, a U.S. Air Force Captain was killed in a jet plane crash in Japan. Neil was a Captain in the Army. His brother, Richard, also served in the military.

Over the years, livestock on the farm included Hereford cattle and Spotted Poland China, Landrace, and Chester White hogs. Chickens, geese, turkeys, and guinea hens were also raised. Two tenants now operate the large farm — Matthew DeVore on a livestock lease and Roy Cook, a cousin, is on a corn-soybean crop share.

1994 picture of Neil Harl with tenant, Roy Cook. This was the best corn crop ever on the farm

OLD HOMESTEAD FARM
Involving the
HUGHES, NEWTON, KELLER, RUCKER AND MAIN FAMILIES OF MARION COUNTY
Settled in 1863

An entire book could be written about the origin, production, trials, tribulations, and triumphs of The Old Homestead Farm. Space will only allow a few highlights.

In the early 1850s, William and Bethany Newton, with their three sons and a daughter, left Indiana by covered wagon and stopped their travels in Marion County, Iowa. Before leaving Indiana, Bethany was given $500 by her parents with the stipulation they come to Iowa to farm.

It was not until July, 1863, that they bought 40 acres, presumably with part of the $500, and apparently from the Hughes estate.

Mary Ellen, the only Newton daughter, married Charles David Keller in 1871, and they took care of Mary's aging parents on the farm, as well as farmed the land, which they bought in 1884. The Kellers had one child, a son named Constant, who married Minnie Hol in 1891. Just as was true of Mary Ellen and Charles taking care of Mary Ellen's father and mother, the Newtons, in their "sunset years", Constant and Minnie took care of Mary Ellen and Charles when they reached those years.

Upon Mary Ellen's death in 1911, Constant and Minnie inherited the farm. In the meantime, the farm had increased in size. Constant supplemented the farm's income with a rural mail carrier job. He also built a new barn where he stabled three horses for the mail route and three for field work.

Evidently it was quite a barn because in addition to stalls for the horses, there were stanchions for milk cows, a cement feeding floor for pigs, storage room for buggies and the mail carrier wagon, granaries, as well as the large haymow.

Six children were welcomed. In the 1920s, several early model cars, one for carrying mail, were purchased. A new home was built in 1933 during the depth of the Depression, and some mortgages were incurred.

After carrying the mail for 30 years, Constant retired shortly before his death. To pay for her husband's medical and funeral bills, Minnie had to mortgage the new home for $2100. It was hard going, but she rented the land on a 50-50 crop share basis, raised chickens, milked cows, and raised hogs to make ends meet. However hard she had to work to pay on the mortgage, she never stopped keeping the house, barns and lots neat and trim. A quitclaim deed signed by her six children gave her title to the farm.

For years, every Sunday, the six children and their families gathered at the home, which meant great fun for all the young cousins.

After Mary's death, none of her six children wanted to give up their shares of the farm, so Old Homestead Farm was owned by six families. However, Minnie's home, although only 25 years old, was not occupied — except by squirrels and raccoons, and occasional trespassers. Finally, it was struck by lightning and burned to the ground.

After years of waiting, in 1951 when she was 80 years old, Elizabeth, one of Minnie's children, who had married a man named Rucker, was able to realize her dream of buying the farm with its $26,000 mortgage. Although she was glad to finally get the land, her age precluded her farming it and caring for the barns as was necessary. The windmill was stolen, and the once proud barn burned down.

Since then, one of Elizabeth's four children, Leland Rucker Main has assumed the mortgage and now owns the farm and has it rented to Dan Kuening.

The family has done its part in answering their country's call in time of war. Mary Keller's husband served in the Civil War. Minnie Keller had four grandsons in WW II, and three of Elizabeth Rucker's sons were in the U.S. Navy.

The family's affiliations were many. Included were Methodist Church, Masonic Lodge, V.F.W., Patrons of Husbandry of the Grange, and Jasper County Historical Society.

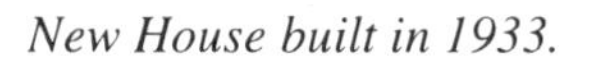

New House built in 1933.

THE LAW FARM OF CERRO GORDO COUNTY

Settled 1863

Thomas Law, Jr. founder of the farm in 1863.

The Law Farm in Cerro Gordo County came into being in 1863 when Thomas Law, Jr., bought 80 acres of land at $1.76 an acre. Thomas and his wife had a family of eleven children. Thomas was the grandfather of James Robert Law, the present owner.

Mr. & Mrs. James Law have kept pretty close tabs on the farm's history, and the families who have lived on the farm since its inception. Ruth, who is James' wife, is especially interested in history and genealogy and has found much to record.

Ruth points out that the original buyer was born in Scotland and came to the United States by way of ocean vessel to New York, and then to Iowa by way of Michigan and Wisconsin.

Once he acquired the Iowa farm, he had some "hard sledding" for a time. It took him several years to pay for the farm, as well as provide the urgent needs for his rapidly growing family. The purchase was made during the Civil War and times were tough. As a matter of fact, Thomas' brother, John, fought in the war between the states, and later, one of his sons, John B. Law, was in the Spanish American War.

During those first years, a log cabin and a barn had to be built. The barn, with foot thick timbers, is still standing.

Corn, oats, and hay were the crops grown after the land was cleared. Milking Shorthorn cattle and hogs were raised as the first livestock projects. Barred Rock chickens were also raised.

Early on, there was considerable butter making done north of Mason City at a place appropriately called Creamin, Iowa. Because everybody made use of the creamery, a post office was established in the building. However, demands to handle cream and butter were so great, the post office had to be given up. It was moved to the Law farm, where the mail was first dumped into a washtub and then sorted into "pigeon holes".

One of the Thomas Law, Jr.'s sons, James Garfield Law, became the second owner of the farm in 1914, right after his father died. James Garfield and his wife had two children. One of them was James Robert Law, who is the present owner of the 133 year old family farm.

James Garfield had a brother, George, who had a farm next to his. They farmed the two farms together and called them the "Law Family Farm". However, in the Depression years of the 1930s, they came close to losing it.

While the brothers were in charge, the livestock program expanded to include purebred Holstein cows, as well as Duroc, Hampshire, and Chester White hogs.

The brothers also bought their first tractor in the 1920s, a Rumily Oil Pull, followed by a Farmall, and six John Deere models — JD-13, 60, 630, 3020, 4030, and 4040.

Third to acquire the farm, now totaling 160 acres, was James Robert Law, best known as Bob, who was James Garfield's son. James Robert had served in the U.S. Navy in World War II at Guadacanal and Guam.

Of course, when Bob took over in 1951, it was modern mechanical farming all the way.

In 1988, the farm observed its 125th birthday amid much rejoicing and celebration.

Members of the family have attended the Wheelerwood Baptist Church out in the country for three generations. James Garfield and his brother, George, were strong Farmers Union supporters.

Bob and Ruth's son, Randy, and his wife, Leslie, now rent the farm from Bob and Ruth. Randy and Leslie have three children, who are the fifth generation in the Law family living on the pioneer farm.

Three generations of the Law family.

THE WANGSNESS-HALVERSON FARM
OF
WINNESHIEK COUNTY
Settled 1863

The Wangsness farm in Winneshiek County was established by Ellend Wangsness in 1863. He was the great grandfather of the present owner, Howard Wangsness. After his death in 1871, Howard's great grandmother, Brita Wangsness became the owner until 1879, when Howard's great uncle, Lewis Wangsness, became the buyer.

After Lewis' death in 1932, his widow, Kaia Wangsness, had the farm in her possession until 1938 when Ingrid Wangsness and her husband, George Halverson, second cousin of the present owner, had the farm until 1956, when Howard took over.

The information provided for this book is minimal.

The cropping program in early years centered on corn, oats, and hay. The livestock included dairy cows, hogs and chickens.

Today, there is no livestock being raised, and soybeans have been added to crop production, as is true of almost all Iowa farms.

When he bought the land in 1863, Ellend Wangsness procured 160 acres for $68.75 an acre. Currently, the farm is reported at 80 acres.

Howard and Verna Wangsness bought the property in 1959. The land is now rented to Joe and Paul Elsbernd.

Howard and Verna are members of the Lutheran Church where Howard is an officer. They are also members of the Farm Bureau.

THE DECKER-BISBEE FARM
OF
MITCHELL COUNTY
Settled 1864

It was in March, 1864, when Martin and Susan Decker bought 126.47 acres of Mitchell County land from John Gerth for $250. That figures right at $1.98 per acre. The Deckers were the great-great grandparents of the present owners, Mr. & Mrs. Jerald Bisbee. The farm is still a 126.47 acres.

Martin and Susan Decker had a family which included a son, Fred, the Jerald Bisbee's great grandfather. Fred and his wife, Emma, also had children, including a daughter, Edna, who married Bradford Bisbee.

Fred and Emma were the second owners of the farm, and their daughter, Edna, and her husband were the next owners. Edna and Bradford also had a family. One of those children was a son, Neil, who eventually became the fourth in the family to own the land.

Neil and his wife, Lucille, are the parents of Jerald Bisbee, whose wife's name is Patricia. Jerald and Patricia are now the owners of the Mitchell County farm established during the Civil War, and which has endured through at least seven wars since then.

No other information about the farm and families has been forthcoming, other than that the farm now centers on growing corn and soybeans and raising hogs.

THE FRITZ FARM OF BREMER COUNTY

Settled 1864

In Bremer County, Martin Fritz has a 160 acre farm that his great grandfather bought in the mid-1860s while the Civil War was raging. At that time, he paid $1000 for the 160 acres, just a bit over $6 an acre. The purchase was made from Gustavus Pockels on April 19, 1864.

Martin's great grandfather was John Fritz, who was born in Germany, but like so many other young Germans, wanted no part of the military program then already in force over there. And so it was that young John Fritz cast his eyes in the direction of America and left the "Old Country" for the New World and for Iowa.

In doing so, he followed in the footsteps of some 40,000 other of his countrymen who had already come to Iowa, most of them to settle on farms in the eastern third of the state.

The house the young German built after reaching Bremer County is still in use today.

John married and had a family, including a son, Leonard, who became the second owner of the farm. Leonard and his wife also had children, one of whom was a son, John Fritz, who became Martin's father, and who was the next to own the land.

For years, the farm was highly diversified with cattle and hogs fed, chickens raised, and corn, wheat, barley, oats, hay and possibly other crops grown.

Today the 160 acres under Martin's ownership is devoted to a corn and soybean rotation.

No additional information about the farm and its production, or about the Fritz family was provided for this book.

THE HENRY GRUNEWALD TRUST FARM OF BENTON COUNTY

Settled 1864

Ernest Grunewald was born and raised in Germany, but, like thousands upon thousands of other German youth, he wanted to get away from the Kaiser's Prussian Army officers and their "Deutschland Uber Alles" (Germany Over All Else) philosophy. So, when Ernest kept hearing about the opportunities and freedoms in America, he undoubtedly started making plans to come over here.

In time, he made the crossing, evidently disembarking in the New York harbor. In any case, for a time he found work in New Jersey, and it was not until 1864 that he reached his goal in Benton County, Iowa.

He must have converted German marks into dollars on arriving in this country, and then earned more in New Jersey, so that when he came to Iowa, he had enough money to make a sufficient down payment on 240 acres of Benton County's rich soil at $15 an acre. He pitched right in with tilling and planting, and found the harvest good. He and his wife raised a family. One of them was a son named William, who became the second owner of the farm.

William and his wife also had a family. One of their children was a son named Henry, who eventually became the third to own the farm. Henry and his wife also had a family, including a son, also named Henry. Henry, Jr. and his wife had a daughter named Elizabeth, who married a man named Kimm. According to the form filled out for, and sent to, the Iowa Department of Agriculture by Elizabeth Grunewald Kimm, the farm is now 160 acres in size, and produces corn and soybeans, along with alfalfa hay. Sheep are raised.

The returned questionnaire lists the Henry Grunewald Trust as the current owner of the 160 acres.

THE McCOLLISTER-SHOWERS-COOPER-BLUMGREN-BACKUS FARM OF JOHNSON COUNTY

Settled 1864

When a retired Rear Admiral in the U.S. Navy supplies an outline with a four-page, single-spaced, typed letter about his recollections of being raised on, and participating in, a pioneer farm established by his great grandfather, it gets attention. Especially is this true when he enumerates the seven breeds of cattle and hogs, five types of poultry, seven kinds of crops raised on the farm, plus the Shire horses and the Fordson and Case tractors he helped use when he was a young man on that farm. Moreover, there are many other details he painstakingly provided.

Nor is that all the information furnished about the 50 acre farm bought by James McCollister in Johnson County in 1864. The Admiral's two sisters and a brother also went to great lengths to tell about the history and the happenings on the McCollister farm.

To include all of the information provided would call for dozens of pages. Space limitation will enable only brief summarizations, along with a sincere "Thank You", to Admiral Donald "Mac" Showers of Arlington, Virginia, his sisters, Mrs. Portia Cooper of Iowa City, Mrs. Susan Blumgren of Scottsdale, Arizona, and a brother, "Jim" Showers, of Cedar Rapids.

The information includes the purchase of the 750 acres of land by James McCollister of Ohio in 1864. It also tells about the 14 room mansion — the back half of which was built during the Civil War and the front half some 15 years after James McCollister bought the large farm.

Much of interest about the huge mansion is told. The outside walls were of triple brick construction with air space between the tiers of bricks for insulation. Two wood-burning furnaces were in the full basement, one of which called for wood three feet in length. Hard work was essential in the building process, and Mrs. McCollister was very pregnant at the time. One evening, after carrying bricks all day, she gave birth to their only daughter, Minnie, who became the grandmother of four of the present farm owners.

Of course, those four are the Admiral and his brother and two sisters, the children of Charles N. and Hedwig Showers, who followed their great grandfather on the farm.

Neither Admiral Showers or his brother, Jim, or their sisters have any actual record of their great grandfather or grandfather's cropping programs, but it is assumed wheat, rye, corn and hay were the main crops. However, when it comes to their father's program, they know exactly what crops were grown because they worked with them. All four mention corn, wheat, oats, soybeans, and many truck garden crops such as tomatoes, sweet corn, strawberries, cucumbers, peppers, and similar vegetables sold in city stores.

In his report, Jim also tells of his father's enthusiasm for hybrid corn after he first planted DeKalb hybrid seed and got 100 bushels per acre.

When it comes to livestock, Jim and "Mac" mention purebred Shorthorn bulls, as well as raising about 100 head or so of Shorthorn cattle annually, along with some 20 sheep and purebred Tamworth hogs in large numbers. Mac also recalls a few Hereford beef cows.

Both brothers also remember a mixture of some 20 to 30 dairy cows. Some were Guernsey. Others were Jerseys, Holsteins, or milking Shorthorns. The milk was run through a cream separator with the sweet cream sold for butter production.

As for the poultry on the farm, that became the mother's and sisters' business involving chickens, ducks, geese, turkeys, and even guinea hens that roosted in trees.

However informative the Showers brothers were, their sisters were equally so, and although confirming most of what their brothers recalled, they added some more fascinating information.

The younger sister, Mrs. Susan Blumgren, who now lives in Arizona, offers a few additions to her brothers' comments. She tells that one Shorthorn bull, "Lettston Laddie", was snow white, and so were some of his calves, and they'd be hard to see and find during a snowstorm. She also tells that her father bought a Hereford bull.

Mrs. Blumgren recalls when all four of the Showers' children were out in the fields helping shock oats, wheat and rye, Portia, the older sister, frequently got away from the pesky wheat and rye beards because she would be asked to ride on the binder. She also remembers the strawberry picking and other work connected with the selling of garden crops to folks in Iowa City.

Mrs. Blumgren says there was a lot of timber land on their farm used for grazing cattle, and where various groups, both those invited and those uninvited, would come to picnic, and some would get rides, sometimes with sleigh bells on the horses.

Mrs. Portia Cooper, the older sister, had much to add about the mansion. She tells how one of the six rooms downstairs was a large living room with a bay window and a floor of alternating boards of walnut and ash, including special designs in the mitered corners. There was a bathroom in the house as early as 1920 with running water from a cistern up on a hill. Of course, it also had a large kitchen, a big cupboard, and battery-powered electricity.

Mrs. Cooper also tells of the orchard of apple, cherry, pear, and peach trees her great grandfather planted. Evidently, James McCollister was a man ahead of his time. Not only was he thinking about the fruit he could grow and sell, but, because his land was close to the village of Iowa City — and he was convinced Iowa City would become the State Capitol — the city would expand. However, he did not want it to cover his land, and by planting an orchard through which he was sure city streets would never go, the farm would be spared.

Actually, the farm included the site of the town of Napoleon which was the site of Johnson County's first courthouse, and was the James McCollisters' temporary home when their daughter, Minnie, was born. They also had a son, Jeff McCollister, who lived all his life on another of his father's farms, 294 acres in size.

James McCollister suffered the loss of a leg when he was 81 years old, but with the help of a "Kiddie Kar" his grandson, Charles, made for him, he managed to get around some. He passed away on Christmas Day, 1928. His wife, Mary, followed him in death a few years later.

In his will, James McCollister provided that the farms, much of which had been sold off, remain in his name until 20 years after his daughter Minnie's death, and then be divided between her heirs. Her brother's heirs were not included.

Today, owners of the remaining land include the four children of Charles and Hedwig previously quoted, and their cousins — Mary Jane Showers, Ernie Showers, and Mrs. Martha Showers Backus.

In addition to Admiral Donald Showers' many years of distinguished service in the U.S. Navy in WW II and 26 years thereafter, his nephew, Paul Cooper, Portia Cooper's son, served in the South Pacific in the Vietnam War period.

THE McLAUGHLIN-HATCHER FARM OF LINN COUNTY

Settled 1864

Ireland made another contribution to Iowa and more specifically to Linn County when that country sent Bernard and Hannah McLaughlin to America in 1854.

Their journey to Iowa was a round-about way. Shortly after their 1848 marriage, they went to Scotland where "Barney", as Bernard was best known, worked in mines until they emigrated to America. They first came to Philadelphia where there was railroad work. Next it was to Iowa in 1854 where more railroad work was in prospect at Anamosa, but failed to materialize.

Nevertheless, the McLaughlins soon became an integral part of the community and their church. In fact, Barney turned the first sod for building an Anamosa Catholic Church. In the meantime, five more children were added to the two sons previously born in Scotland.

In 1864, attention and talent turned to farming. Forty acres were bought for $1.25 an acre to establish a homestead in Buffalo Township in Linn County. From time to time, additional 40 acre increments were added to the farm until it totaled 160 acres. The original stone home on the farm was used for Catholic services many years.

The present farm owner is Cecilia McLaughlin Hatcher, a great granddaughter of the original farm owners. She now lives in Anamosa not so very far from where the farm is located on Prairieburg Road.

In a form Mrs. Hatcher filled out for the Iowa Department of Agriculture in its search for Iowa's oldest farms, she lists B.I. McLaughlin, the youngest of her great grandparents' family, as her grandfather, but does not indicate whether he was the farm owner or not, although it is to be assumed he was owner or partial owner.

In a separate Linn County publication, Simon McLaughlin, Mrs. Hatcher's great uncle, is listed as a farmer and harness shop operator. The same publication lists Glen McLaughlin, Mrs. Hatcher's father, as the owner

Stone home built on McLaughlin farm in 1872, where Catholic services for farm neighbors were held many years.

of the farm before she gained possession.

Mrs. Hatcher's grandfather was Overseer of Highway Township Trustee, and school board director. Her father, Glen McLaughlin was a WW I veteran, City Attorney, County Attorney, American Legion Post Commander, seventy year Knights of Columbus member, football team manager, Red Cross Chairman, Chamber of Commerce President, and with his wife, the former Dorothy Ludley, served in many community projects.

Dorothy and Glen had two daughters, Cecilia and Catherine.

Cecilia married John Hatcher. They had four children — Sharon, Thomas, David and Mary.

Catherine married Larry Rogge. Their children are Gabrielle, Steven, Jennifer, and Julie.

The farm now totals 177 acres and produces corn and soybeans.

THE SCHMIDT-VAN HAMME-BLOMME FARM OF IOWA COUNTY

Settled 1864

By the year 1860, a total of 106,081 foreigners from 28 different countries of the world had crossed the oceans to settle in Iowa. Of that number, more than one-third were German immigrants, by far the largest number of any single country.

It was known that more than 38,000 Germans had come to Iowa by the end of 1860, most of whom had settled on farms. Just how many had come by the year 1864, we do not know exactly, but it most certainly was over 40,000.

One of them to come to Iowa that year was Charles Schmidt, who came from Lepp Datmott, Germany, in the "Old Country" to Iowa County to buy 160 acres from the government for $1.25 an acre. There, he established a homestead, cleared land, planted crops, and raised a family. He was the great grandfather of Duane J. Blomme, the present owner of what is now 200 acres.

One of Charles Schmidt's daughters married Theophiel Van Hamme, who was Duane Blomme's grandfather, and who kept the farm going successfully by virtue of his foreign work ethic. The Van Hamme family also included a daughter. She married Lawrence Blomme and became Duane's mother.

Actually, Charles Schmidt was a blacksmith over in Germany before coming to Iowa, and although the "smithing" trade often came in handy while establishing an Iowa County farm, he became a good farmer as did all of his fellow Germans, and was able to help instill "good farming" in the three generations that have followed.

The corn and soybean crops on Blomme farm in recent years are proof of that.

WARD-FARLEY FARM OF ALLAMAKEE COUNTY

Settled 1864

Paul and Mary Ellen Farley of Allamakee County are the owners of a 520 acre farm that wasn't anywhere near that large when it was bought by a great grandfather on Paul's mother's side on November 8, 1864.

He was John Ward who was born in Ireland and had come to America before the Civil War in which he served with distinction as an officer. After his discharge in 1864, he and his wife, Mary, bought 80 acres with a mortgage on it for $287.

On January 1, 1870, M.B. Hendrick, the County Auditor, acknowledged full payment and certification of the mortgage.

During his early years as a farmer, the Irish immigrant cleared land and grew corn, wheat, oats, and hay. Livestock came later.

Nor did it take long for John Ward to become an integral part of the community. A post office was set up in the Ward house, and John served as postmaster. He was also the Township's Justice of the Peace, and in winter months was the teacher in the nearby rural school.

Members of the present family on the farm still have the post office door John Ward used so many years ago with its postal slot in it.

John bought additional land from time to time until his acreage finally totaled 420 acres.

One of John's sons, William Ward, and his wife, Annie, became the second owners. They had a daughter, Catherine, who married Charles Farley. Catherine and Charles were the next to own the farm, which had increased in size considerably.

In the meantime, a larger, more comfortable home was built, and a barn was put up for larger livestock herds.

Current owners are Paul and Mary Ellen Farley, who moved onto the farm in 1958 and bought it in 1967. It now totals 520 acres, and presently corn, oats, and hay make up the cropping program.

No additional information was provided on dates of ownership by the various generations of Wards and Farleys, or of family members.

THE WESSEL FARM OF CLAYTON COUNTY

Settled 1864

Virgil Wessel, father of Walter Wessel, the present owner of the Wessel farm in Clayton County, has provided meaningful information to help understand the family's background. He has drawn a chart showing that this feature must start in Germany in the year 1800.

In that "Turn Of The Century" year, H.B. Wessel, whose first name might very well have been "Heinrich", was born in Hanover, Germany. In March of 1832, he married Anna Elsebein Hartbecken, who was seven years his junior.

In August, 1833, their first child, Henry Herman Wessel, was born in his young parents' home in Hanover. At age 29, he married Katherine Caroline Datisman over in Germany, but the newlyweds did not stay in their native country very long. They had learned of the freedoms and opportunities in America and of farmland available in Iowa, so they boarded a ship and came to Clayton County, where they bought some of that land in 1864.

This is how Virgil Wessel tells the story of what happened after the young German immigrants reached Iowa:

"The Wessel homestead in Mallory Township in Clayton County was purchased by Henry Herman Wessel from Michael and Margaret Carrigan on January 6, 1864. The tract consisted of 40 acres. On May 15, 1866, he added to the original 40 acres by purchasing adjoining land with his brother, Bernard. Then on February 9, 1887, Henry and his wife, Katherine, purchased the one-half interest held by his brother Bernard and his wife."

Virgil Wessel then continues by saying, "On July 1, 1916, Roy Wessel, son of the Henry Wessels, purchased the farm from his parents. The property had been increased to 190 acres — quite a jump from the original 40 his father had first acquired."

Roy had married Helen Keck in 1912 and they had a family which included a son they named Virgil Merril. Virgil is the family spokesman who provided us with all this information.

Virgil was born in 1924, and married Doris Hansen in 1946. They bought the farm in 1947, less than a year after their marriage. Their family also included a son, named Walter William born in 1954. Walter purchased the farm from Virgil and Doris in 1986, thus becoming the fourth generation in the Wessel family to own what continues to be a 190 acre tract.

For most of the 132 years of its existence, the farm has been concentrating on dairying and continues to do so under Walter's ownership, along with growing the traditional field crops and raising some beef cattle.

Walter married Judy Mormann in 1980 and they have two sons — Brent William and Jason Noah. The sons are both now in their mid-teens and both are helping their father operate the dairy and the field work.

Brent and Jason are now the fifth generation to live on the Wessel farm.

AN ACKNOWLEDGMENT OF A PIONEER AGRICULTURAL BENEFACTOR:
JOHN DEERE

Although this is a book primarily designed as an Iowa Sesquicentennial salute to the state's pioneer farm families and their descendants, it would not be complete without acknowledging a person who is regarded as early American Agriculture's greatest benefactor.

He is John Deere, inventor of the steel plow and founder of the world's largest, and leading, farm implement manufacturing firm.

It is appropriate that, before turning to the trials and triumphs of Iowa's oldest farm families and their farms, a section be devoted to the fascinating story of this man, and his company, that had so much to do with opening the nation's farm frontier more than 150 years ago.

John Deere was born in Rutland, Vermont, in 1804. His parents moved the family farther north to Middlebury so he grew up near the Green Mountain State's National Forest.

It was in Middlebury that John became a blacksmith's apprentice when he was only seventeen. A fast learner, he fully mastered the trade under the tutelage of a Revolutionary War officer, Captain Benjamin Lawrence.

In 1825, when John was just 21, he became a journeyman blacksmith and soon gained recognition for the excellent work he was doing and for his ingenuity. His highly polished hay forks and the shovels and spades he was making were in special demand.

However, after close to 12 years of success as a blacksmith, business conditions in Vermont suddenly deteriorated. Many residents of the Green Mountain State left for the Midwest, then America's frontier. The future began to look gloomy for the ambitious young "smith" in Vermont. Letters from friends who had emigrated to Illinois convinced him there were "greener pastures" for him on the frontier.

Accordingly, he sold his "smithy" in Middlebury in 1836, bundled up his special tools, withdrew a small amount from the family's savings, kissed his wife and bade her and the children a temporary good-bye, and started west. The trip was made by canal, lake boat, and stagecoach and took several weeks. Finally, John reached Grand Detour, a small Illinois village where several Vermonters had settled, including a long-time friend, Leonard Andrus.

Andrus and others were delighted to have a blacksmith come to their community. There were horses and oxen to be shod, plows to be repaired, chains and devices to be made, and much else to be done. In fact, the day after his arrival, Deere set up a forge and was in business the next day.

Much of his first work was on plows the Easterners had brought with them and with which they were terribly dissatisfied. Back East they had worked well in light, sandy soil, but here in Illinois, the rich black loam just kept sticking on the shares and the wrought iron, or wood, moldboards. While plowing, they would have to stop every 15 or 20 feet to scrap off the gummy soil. Many farmers were so distressed, they were ready to give up. The new blacksmith kept hearing one sad tale after another and soon decided something needed to be done.

John started to put his creative mind to work and convinced himself that a plow with a highly polished, properly curved, moldboard might do the trick. That winter, he found an old, discarded steel saw blade. He took it to the shop, and with the help of a large log, his forge and anvil, was able to get the proper curvature on the steel blade and shape it into a moldboard. He also attached it to a white oak beam.

Early in the spring of 1837, he took it to the nearby Crandall farm, borrowed a horse to pull his new creation, and to his delight found it "scoured" nicely as it turned the soil into neat furrows. Few modifications would be necessary, and those were quickly made when he got the plow back in the shop.

Showing the new plow.

Naturally, there was other work to be done, but John managed to make two more similar plows that year. Then, when he offered to demonstrate one of them, most of the neighboring farmers gathered around. As he proceeded, they watched in disbelief as he turned neat furrows without once stopping to scrape clumps of soil off the moldboard. To those farmers, that was the "Moment of Truth". John Deere had found the answer to their dilemma, and word spread fast that their plowing problems might soon be over.

Elated with his early success, John sent for his wife and family in Vermont to come and join him in Illinois. They came soon thereafter, and the reunited family moved into a home not far from the blacksmith shop.

Several more "self-polishing" plows, as they were being called, were made in 1838, and one Iowa farmer heard about them. He was Herman Shaff, who had bought land in Clinton County the year before and had also encountered plowing problems. Shaff went some 40 miles to the Grand Detour blacksmith shop, met John Deere, and managed to get one of his plows. Shaff took it back across the Mississippi and found it worked so well that some neighbors begged him to let them use it at night. He let them do so with the understanding it would always be back for his use during the day. This incident is further detailed in the first feature found in the first section of this book.

The Clinton County farmer found his plow in such demand that he went back to John Deere in 1840 to get a second "self-polisher". Both plows have been preserved by members of the Shaff family and are now on display at their 159 year old farm.

All told, John Deere made ten such plows in 1839; and then, after installing a second anvil in the shop and hiring extra help, made and sold 40 of the steel plows in 1840.

By now, John Deere's name was on the lips of most prairie land farmers. His creation of a plow that would scour was a Godsend to those who could obtain one. All were reasonably priced, but demand continued to exceed supply.

Moreover, every plow seemed to carry an unwritten guarantee. From the very beginning, John Deere vowed, "I will never put my name on a plow that does not have in it the best that is in me." Add to that his penchant to continually strive to improve the design and performance of all his tools.

However successful John Deere had been, there were also problems to be overcome. The American-made steel he was using did not measure up to his rigid standard, and the supply was often inadequate. So, in 1843, he ordered an importation of British steel from England. It was costly and difficult to transport 40 miles by wagon from the river port where it arrived, but it made for a better finished plow.

Another problem was that in a small town like Grand Detour, banks were not equipped to meet some of the growing financial and credit needs. Transportation also continued to be a major concern.

Yet the demand for the steel plows continued to increase.

By 1846, the year Iowa gained statehood, about a thousand plows were produced. By 1847, Deere had made arrangements with a Pittsburgh firm to secure American-made rolled steel. It was at this point that John Deere felt obliged to consider moving his operation from Grand Detour to Moline, Illinois, where water power and river transportation were available. Plans for the construction of the Moline plant then began.

The phenomenal demand for the John Deere steel plows continued to increase. Meanwhile, the 1848 delivery of U.S. made steel to a port near the new factory's back door gave the new plant the additional impetus it needed that year. Within a few months, production increased to 1600 plows. Within ten years, up to 10,000 John Deere plows were being made annually at the new Moline plant.

By the early 1850s, treaties made with Indians had almost all been made throughout the nation, and the native Americans had all moved farther west, or onto reservations. Thus, almost all land in Iowa and other Corn Belt states was open for settlement, and pioneer families had moved in. However, to break the prairie sod, they needed a plow that would turn the rich earth, and the John Deere steel plow was the instrument that could, and did, do just that.

So successful was the plow manufacturing enterprise that by 1848, John Deere felt the time had come to bring his son, Charles Deere, into the company. As the business continued to grow, a son-in-law, Stephen Velie, also joined the firm in 1853.

It was also a time to begin branching out so the introduction of a steel-shoveled cultivator was added to the plow-making firm. While this added another dimension to the John Deere works, it was only the beginning of a farm machinery manufacturing empire that John Deere himself could never have imagined.

Both Charles Deere and Stephen Velie were shrewd business men. By 1868, they had a major hand in the incorporation of the firm under the name, Deere & Company. John Deere, himself, was named President. His son, Charles, became Vice Present and General manager, and Stephen Velie was named Secretary.

Although none of the three officers could possibly have envisioned it at the time of the 1868 incorporation, that is the move that marked the beginning of what is now the world's largest agricultural implement manufacturer.

Proof of Deere & Company's domination of farm machinery is seen in the manufacturing plants established throughout the world. They are found in Germany, France, Holland, Spain, and England in Europe, Brazil and Argentina in South America, as well as in South Africa, and in Canada and Mexico, as well as the United States.

In addition, sales branches are located in Australia, Italy, Germany, France, England, South Africa, Argentina, and Canada, plus five major U.S. cities.

Today, the Company founded in 1868 does business in 160 countries around the globe and employs more than 34,000 persons.

Not only is Deere & Company the world leader in agricultural equipment, but it is also a leading supplier of construction and industrial equipment, and is the major North American supplier of forestry tools and machines.

Moreover, Deere & Company offers this nation's broadest lines of lawn mowing tractors and other outdoor power products for homeowners, commercial lawn and ground care markets, and for parks.

In addition, Deere & Company offers countless engines and other power train products to original equipment manufacturers.

The Company also has parts distributors everywhere, along with export sales branches, credit offices, insurance groups

and lines, and health care arrangements for its 34,000 employees.

In 1995, the last year for which total figures are available, Deere & Company earned $706 million in total sales and had revenues of $10.3 billion.

Small wonder then, that what the Vermont blacksmith started 159 years ago has become the symbol of success in the world of farm machines and in many other areas.

It must be added that just as John Deere and the firm he established so long ago has gone through almost incomprehensible change, so has American Agriculture.

When the clang of hammers was first being heard in the Grand Detour blacksmith shop, more than 90% of the nation's population lived on farms and worked hard to produce enough food to sustain their own families and to also provide for the less than 10% who were city dwellers.

Today, 98% of the U.S. population lives in cities and towns, but thanks in part to Deere & Company, the 2% on farms and ranches provide an abundance of food for all of urban America and millions upon millions of tons of additional food is exported to nations across the sea.

John Deere and the crude steel plow he pounded out back in 1837 had a lot to do with that remarkable phenomenon.

Deere Engine Works, Waterloo, Iowa.

John Deere 7200.

John Deere 5300.

John Deere 9500

John Deere 8770.

IOWA STATE FAIR BLUE RIBBON FOUNDATION

Bringing the Fairgrounds into the 21st Century

This Article is Sponsored by John Deere

For over 140 years, the Iowa State Fair has been the premier showcase for Iowa's products and people. But after years of neglect, its home, the 400-acre Fairgrounds listed on the National Register of historic places, was becoming a less than first-class facility. In response to this situation, the Iowa State Fair Board established the Iowa State Fair Blue Ribbon Foundation in 1993. This non-profit entity was then charged with the mission of conducting a major capital campaign for the renovation and preservation of the Fairgrounds - with a vision for the future.

Since its inception, the Blue Ribbon Foundation has been successfully securing individual contributions, state appropriations, in-kind services, and corporate, federal and state grants. The first two-year campaign, *Treasure Our Fair*, was based on a contingency pledge by Pioneer Hi-Bred International, Inc. Pioneer made a $500,000 commitment to the Foundation, provided $6 million was raised within two years. Deere & Company was the first company to respond to this campaign, with a gift of $500,000; a major boost to the Foundation's future achievements. After succeeding with this two-year campaign, the Blue Ribbon Foundation launched a new $7 million campaign, *Rebuilding the Dream.*

The Blue Ribbon Foundation's goal is to reach $30 million by the year 2000. Achieving this goal will not come without hard work. The Foundation staff puts in many hours researching individuals, corporations and other foundations for major capital contributions and grants, as well as, managing the day-to-day activity of 13,000+ constituents who support the Foundation. Constituents contribute through fund-raising programs such as Fan Fair, the Brick Program, Trees for the Fair, Have A Seat, and the Iowa State Fair Tax Check-off.

Special events are another popular avenue of fund raising. Throughout the year, the Foundation exhibits at the Iowa Beef Expo, the World Pork Expo, Iowa Heritage Expo, and the Association of Iowa Fairs Convention. In addition, the Foundation sponsors an annual May Fair auction event that draws over 150 people and raises over $15,000. Other Iowa organizations frequently sponsor events to benefit the work of the Foundation. Staff members work hand in hand with these organizations to provide promotional materials and act as support staff.

A new and exciting project for the Blue Ribbon Foundation is the sale of a limited edition, commemorative John Deere 4440 toy tractor. It commemorates John Deere as the official tractor of the Iowa State Fair and marks Iowa's Sesquicentennial year, 1996. This tractor adds to the many other items that the Foundation sells to not only promote the Fair, but raise additional funds. These items include everything from t-shirts and caps to note cards and coffee mugs. Staff members coordinate volunteers to work at booths during the State Fair to sell the merchandise.

However, as great progress continues each year, the Foundation continually stresses the fact that we cannot forget that we must finish what we started. Further improvements to the buildings and the grounds need to be completed in order to project our Fair into the 21st Century. Once the improvements are finished, the Foundation will establish an endowment for the Fairgrounds, so that she will always be provided for in the future years.

For more information about the campaign for the renovation of the Iowa State Fairgrounds, please write or call:

Iowa State Fair Blue Ribbon Foundation
601 Locust, Suite 900
Des Moines, Iowa 50309
515/245-3730.

SOME NECESSARY AND IMPORTANT EXPLANATIONS

From the very outset of this book, the author has been deeply concerned about securing names and addresses of members of Sesquicentennial and other pioneer Iowa farms held in the same family for so many years.

When the Sesquicentennial Commission announced its search for Iowa's oldest farms in the state's nine crop districts, and arranged for questionnaires to serve as applications for such recognition, 397 families with pioneer ancestors applied.

This was done early in the Sesquicentennial year. Deadline for application was February 16, so all applications sent to the Iowa Department of Agriculture and Land Stewardship could be processed in time for the March 15 Sesquicentennial Farm Family Awards meeting. Winners of the nine Iowa Crop Districts were announced and honored by Secretary of Agriculture Dale Cochran on that date. Summaries of those winning farms are found in the first section of this book.

Names and addresses of the 397 applicants were made available to the author. A letter telling of plans for this book, along with a more comprehensive questionnaire, was sent to everyone. More than 75% returned the questionnaire, some with pictures and additional information.

All the farms that were established in 1834 through 1864, and who returned the questionnaire, have been summarized in volume one. All those whose farms were founded 1865 through 1896, and who responded to the questionnaire submitted will be reported in a second book.

Unfortunately, not all Sesquicentennial pioneer farms in Iowa were included in the 397 farms reported to the Department of Agriculture by February 16, 1996.

However, full recognition of those farm owners, their full addresses, the year their farm was established, and the county in which their farm is located, is seen on the following pages. To each of them go hearty congratulations for the contributions they and their ancestors have made to Iowa's rich agricultural heritage.

CEDAR COUNTY

Five H Farm Partnership
5205 Nursery Rd.
Cedar Rapids
1837

Palmer, Richard B.
1557 Old Muscatine Road
Tipton
1841

Svoboda, Alberta J. Clifton
398 Badger Rd.
Mechanicsville
1841

CLAYTON COUNTY

Grave, Richard E. & Diane M.
(Bierbaum)
27182 Hwy 52
Guttenberg
1846

Palas, Jerel & Lynn
14057 Spook Cave Rd
McGregor
1841

Phelps, Vivian
RR 1
Colesburg
1841

Uriell, Edward
27119 Holly Ave.
Elkader
1845

DAVIS COUNTY

Kruse, Charles R. & Verda A.
RR
Pulaski
1820

DES MOINES COUNTY

Brown, Robert J. & Debra A.
18502 Golden Rd
Yarmouth
1840

Ekstrand, Maude
2825 Henry
Des Moines Ave.
Danville
1839

Hedges, Frank C.
24727 Highway 99
Oakville
1838

Murphy, Mrs. Kenneth H.
4675 - 155th Ave.
Burlington
1838

Murrell, Eric F. & Mary B.
13085 S. Prairie Grove Rd.
West Burlington
1839

Seymour Estate
Russell-Velda Seymour
20303 - 110th St.
Danville
1839

Sharar, Robert W.
7246 - 235th St.
Mediapolis
1844

Swank, Elaine & Paul
25021 Highway 99
Oakville
1838

Taeger, Lawrence H. & Dorothy A.
14848 Flint Bottom Rd.
West Burlington
1841

Thomas, Ray F. & Mary E.
16382 - 210th St.
Mediapolis
1839

Wright, Robert M.
22345 - 170th St.
New London
1841

DUBUQUE COUNTY

Kluesner, Bernard & Inez
18688 Highway 136
New Vienna
1846

Molony, Donald J., James M. & Kathleen
979 Molony Rd
Bernard
1840

FREMONT COUNTY

Rasmussen, Elizabeth Anne
RR
Bartlett
1846

HENRY COUNTY

Corell, Jo Ann (Maxwell)
RR 4
Mt. Pleasant
1838

Ekstrand, David C. & Virginia L.
2825 Henry
Des Moines Ave.
Danville
1841

Parrott, Ruth E.
300th St. - Sec. 12
Danville
1845

Patterson, Dwight
2448 - 105th St.
Winfield
1838

Vorhies, Stanley K. & Mary E.
RR
Lockridge
1840

JACKSON COUNTY

Ernst, M. Anthony & Rita
35791 - 308th St.
Bellevue
1845

Henneberry, Richard
28598 - 9th Ave.
Bernard
1845

Lubben, John S. & Arla
6989 - 50th Ave.
Baldwin
1837

McKenna, Robert
28308 - 46th Ave.
Bernard
1840

Reed, Ross C.
18834 - 442nd Ave.
Bellevue
1845

Reed, Gordon D. & Marie E.
18900 - 442nd Ave.
Bellevue
1845

Zirkelbach, Ralph R. &
Elizabeth (Wilson) Zirkelbach
RR
Maquoketa
1845

JEFFERSON COUNTY

Craff, LeRoy Andrew
1453 Germanville Rd.
Brighton
1841

JOHNSON COUNTY

Bailey, Thomas Jay & Jacqueline Ann
3173 - 560th St. SW
Riverside
1839

Hendershot, Frederick J.
2209 Hendershot Rd.
North Liberty
1843

Miller, Laurance H.
4789 - 210th St. NE
Solonb
1845

Wertz, Robert Lynn
9252 Calkins Ave. SW
Kalona
1846

Wieland, Lester &
Josephine (Heitzman)
5655 Naples Ave. SW
Iowa City
1846

JONES COUNTY

McLaughlin, William L.
20702 County Road D62
Monticello
1846

KEOKUK COUNTY

Wonderlich, Neoma & Charles
Norma Gene & Robert
PO Box 134
Ollie
1846

LEE COUNTY

Foecke, Adrian J. & Winifred
1400 Highway 218
West Point
1840

Houston, Gerald
3228 - 159th St.
Fort Madison
1838

Kinyoun, Darlene Schoene
RR 2
West Point
1840

Marsh, Verne Eugene
1681 - 330th Ave.
Fort Madison
1839

Schoene, Ivan James
2351 - 218th St.
West Point
1840

LINN COUNTY

Burge, Vernon E.
510 Spring Creek Rd.
Mt. Vernon
1839

Moore, Richard A. & Barbara B.,
Jean Moore
1281 W. Mt. Vernon Rd.
Mt. Vernon
1842

Oxley, Myron B. & John R.
2266 Oxley Road
Marion
1842

Railsback, Daisy D.
4596 Bear Creek Rd.
Palo
1844

Stodola, Charles Albert
3299 Lewis Bottoms Rd.
Palo
1846

Swanson, Mary L.
1330 W. Mt. V ernon Rd.
Mt. Vernon
1842

LOUISA COUNTY

Bar M Farms Inc. • Marie C. Bartenhagen
10708 "I" Ave.
Wapello
1840

Clark, Hazel Jeanette
14873 "O" Ave.
Columbus Jct.
1842

Creswell, John Stanley
RR
Wapello
1840

Jolly, Gwendolyn M. & Frank
15172 - 25th St.
Morning Sun
1842

Newell, Thomas Herbert
15868 "O" Ave.
Columbus Junction
1841

Ryan, Wayne E. & Mary Ann Drake
14438 County Rd. G
Wapello
1846

MADISON COUNTY

Cutshall, Robert W. & Judy A.
2626 - 110th St.
Van Meter
1843

MAHASKA COUNTY

Baker, Ivan J. & Alice L.
RR
What Cheer
1843

Powell, Lois
2341 - 340th St.
Eddyville
1846

Wanders, Gary & Iana
1290 Elba Ave.
Pella
1845

MUSCATINE COUNTY

Petrucelli, Jean Barkley;
Lelah F. Townsley & Marian Hyland
RR
Letts
1841

POTTAWATTAMIE CO.

Bostwick, Glenn E.
28246 - 152nd St.
Honey Creek
1846

SCOTT COUNTY

Freund, Carol M.
8945 - 140th St.
Blue Grass
1838

Gillmor, Vada, Evelyn,
Mary Ann & Allen
27025 Allens Grove Rd.
Donahue
1846

VAN BUREN COUNTY

Clark, Eugene Morris
RR 1
Stockport
1845

Hootman, Lester & Erma
RR 1, Box 169
Douds
1846

McIntosh, James Duffield
RR
Keosauqua
1838

Zeitler, James C.
RR
Douds
1843

WASHINGTON COUNTY

Brinning, Donald J. & Mercedes M.
1395 - 275th St.
Brighton
1843

Brinning, David L.
1460 - 275th St.
Brighton
1843

Colthurst, George R.
3216 Old White Way
Ainsworth
1843

Huston Farms, Inc.,Huston, Thomas H.
3334- 325th St.
Crawfordsville
1840

Morgan, Craig E. & Sarah M.
3056 Birch Avenue
Richland
1839